"*Loving by Leading* is a must volume for every parent and parent-to-be, written to sit beside their favorite reading chair and not just adorn a bookshelf. Designed to be read and referenced frequently, it is the best guide to successful child rearing I've encountered in my more than 40 years as a Pediatrician. As it moves parents to a leading and loving relationship with their children it also provides abundant advice on problem solving. Consulting the book feels much like a face-to-face visit with your child's physician. It's warm and familiar, never preachy, or authoritarian (well defined in the book and something a parent shouldn't be). *Loving by Leading* is a parenting book I'll strongly recommend, as I do now, and for years to come."

—**Joseph R. Zanga, MD, FAAP, FCP**
Past Pediatric Department Chair, Loyola Chicago Stritch
School of Medicine and Assistant Dean,
Brody School of Medicine, East Carolina University
Former President, American Academy of Pediatrics
Former President, American College of Pediatricians

"In a day when much parenting advice restricts what parents should do, Dr. Den Trumbull uses his 30 years of pediatric experience to expand the options for 21st-century parents, clarifying how and when to use each tool in the parent's toolbox to *lead* their child to develop their own character and competence. It all starts with foundations of a positive parent-child relationship and appropriate sleep, nutrition, and exercise. Dr. Trumbull's approach to discipline balances instruction, affirmation, and correction, appropriately preferring the first two, but using negative consequences when needed to train age-appropriate self-control. His approach will help parents of young children develop an authoritative style that will pay off big time in the teenage years and beyond. Conveniently, the book's design allows parents to pick and choose the guidance that best fits their particular child and situation from Dr. Trumbull's detailed advice acquired from years of experience as a parent and a pediatrician."

—**Robert E. Larzelere, PhD**
Endowed Professor of Parenting
Oklahoma State University

"As a life-long educator with almost four decades of experience teaching and leading students and families, I have observed many parenting philosophies, styles and strategies. I have concluded that common sense parenting is not very common. The vast majority of today's parents want to parent well, yet lack the fundamental knowledge and timeless wisdom that equips and empowers them to be effective. Dr. Den Trumbull has written a clear and practical guidebook that anyone desiring to be a better parent will find enlightening and instructive. *Loving by Leading* should be on every parent's nightstand or bookshelf as a primary reference when parenting questions and challenges arise. Thank you, Dr. Trumbull, for encouraging parents to 'prepare the child for the path, not the path for the child.'"

—**Bill McGee,** Head of School
Legacy Christian Academy
Frisco, Texas
Contributing author, *Building a Better School*

LOVING BY

A Parent's Guide to Raising Healthy and Responsible Children

LEADING

Jim & Beth,
The book comes a bit too
late for Clarie and Anne,
but you will recognize much
of the advice within.
Blessings to Forresters!

Den A. Trumbull, M.D.

Psalm 127:3

DT

IMPORTANT DISCLAIMER:

> The information in this book is intended to assist parents in making informed decisions about the rearing of their children. It is not intended to be a substitute for consultation with a physician concerning a child's health or behavior. The ultimate decisions concerning the healthcare of your child should be between you and your child's physician. You are strongly encouraged to follow his or her advice.

The Library of Congress has cataloged the softcover and ebook as follows:

Control Number: 2018909896
Softcover ISBN: 978-1-7326598-1-0
eBook ISBN: 978-1-7326598-0-3

Cover design and interior graphics by Amy Harmon at AmyHarmonDesign.com
Interior design and typeset by Katherine Lloyd at TheDESKonline.com
Editing by Tim Grissom

To my wife and best friend, Nancy, whose loving
encouragement, patient support and honest advice
spurred me on to the completion of this book.

And to my dear children, Allison, Amy,
Julie, Den, and Kelly, who have taught me much
and blessed me even more.

CONTENTS

ACKNOWLEDGMENTS

I have been blessed with trusted individuals around me to give helpful advice and feedback in writing this book. The process has tested the patience of some more than others, for this journey has been slow and tedious. Nonetheless, my "consultants," especially my family, have been faithful through it all.

There are many folks to thank for their support during the writing of this book. First, to my dear wife, Nancy, and our children who sacrificed time away from Dad on many occasions, and endured my opinion-seeking questions *ad nauseum*. And then Paula, my sister-in-law, who applied my advice to the rearing of her young children and was candid enough to share with me what worked and what didn't, and then offer suggestions in how to do it better. I am grateful to the mothers of our two grandchildren (our daughters, Allison and Amy), who gave me real-time feedback as they followed the advice of this book. And also to Amy for the hours of tireless dedication to this book using her graphic design skills to create the cover and the many diagrams and tables within. To my colleagues, Drs. Tom Benton, Joseph Zanga, Jane Anderson, and Rebecca Huizen, who critiqued earlier versions of the manuscript and offered invaluable edits and advice. I am grateful to the mothers from whom I sought opinions, namely Danellen DeHuff, Carla Genin, and Ruth Givens. Finally, I am grateful to the many devoted parents in my practice who have trusted me with the care of their children and made me feel like a member of their families. We have learned much together.

INTRODUCTION

Without a doubt, the most enjoyable and satisfying aspect of my work as a pediatrician is counseling new parents in the care of their precious newborns. I tell them, "There is no such thing as a 'dumb question.' If it is on your mind, *ask it*." This is important because there is so much information out there on parenting. Sources once were limited to relatives, particularly grandparents. Now, there is an abundance of sources, including the Internet, social media, an endless supply of parenting books, and advice from friends who can't resist telling their stories. While the support is appreciated, the messages to these young parents can be conflicting and confusing. So, I tell them to ask whatever is on their minds.

In writing this book, my desire is to answer your questions as well, and to provide you with reliable advice on the rearing of your child. I do not claim to have all the answers, or even the only answers, to questions you may have or challenges you will encounter. But with over thirty years of pediatric practice, the wonderful experience of rearing five children alongside my dedicated wife, Nancy, and the knowledge gained from years of studying parenting literature, I have advice to offer you—advice that may allow you an easier and more productive path than I experienced as a parent. Advice that has been time-tested. Advice that can benefit your children as you *lead* them to become healthy, responsible, happy adults.

This book is a product of over thirty years of contemplating the challenges of child rearing. It began in the nineties with my participation in the national debate over the use of punishment with child discipline, progressed to a focus on the benefits of sleep training, and then culminated in the deeper investigation of authoritative parenting—the most optimal, research-proven style of parenting. Through it all, I have realized that the most successful parents *lead* their children to healthy and responsible living rather than *follow* them in pursuit of happiness.

You may ask, "Why lead?" Lead because children do not naturally know what is best for them, their health, or their interaction with others. Here are a few areas in life where children need guidance:

- Sleep: As early as the first year of life, infants need their parents to help them be good sleepers, teaching them when to sleep and how to achieve deep sleep.
- Nutrition: As early as the second year of life, children need their parents to guide them in healthy eating, avoiding the tendency to just offer them whatever they are willing to eat.
- Exercise: As early as toddlerhood, children need a gentle push to be active and self-entertaining, because the temptation to stay indoors and play with electronic devices will intensify as they grow.
- Behavior: As early as the second year of life, toddlers need their parents' leadership to know what proper behavior is and the importance of denying their selfish tendency to please themselves.
- Encouragement: As early as the first days of life, newborns need their parents to show that they love them with encouraging words, facial expressions, and physical hugs and kisses.

Parents need to love their children by leading them, which will build the invaluable parent-child relationship that ultimately determines the effectiveness of all future parenting efforts. At times this will require sacrificial leadership, where parents must deny their own desires and comfort for the sake of their child.

This book is my call to action for all parents: *Lead* your child to good health and high character. In doing so, you will produce a genuinely happy child, who is comfortable with himself, confident in his talents, compassionate toward others, and ultimately competent in his vocation.

How to Use This Book

Loving by Leading is a practical manual of opportunities for you to lead your child. It is not intended to be a comprehensive compendium addressing every aspect of parenting. Also, the methods and solutions offered are not absolutely required to have success with your child, nor are they the only way to achieve success. They may be modified and customized to fit your unique child and family setting.

This book is uniquely divided into two parts.

- Part One (chapters 1–9) explores why children need their parents to lead them.

- Part Two (chapters 10–21) offers parents practical suggestions in how to lead. This section is divided by the particular areas of parenting—sleep, nutrition, exercise, behavior, and encouragement—and is then further divided by the age of the child.

For example, if two-year-old Johnny seems to be throwing a tantrum every hour of his waking day, you can reference the first section to understand why he is behaving this way. Then turn to the Behavior section in Part Two to discover how to lead him to better behavior and self-control. You can also use the Topical Table of Contents at the end of this book (page 273) to search for specific topics and subtopics.

The focus of this book is on the first ten years of your child's life, especially birth to five years, which is a formative time of life. My intention is to help you build a basic and effective style of parenting that will allow you to reach your child's heart—the core of his emotions, motivations, values, and personality—and to build his character and competency. While your child is young, if you train him to sleep better, eat better, play better, work better, cooperate better, and to do all with a loving respect for you as his parent, then later, during his school-age and teenage years, he will be more teachable and receptive to your instruction. If this foundation of health and respect is ignored when your child is young, then it will be harder to lead him toward acquiring a mature heart later.

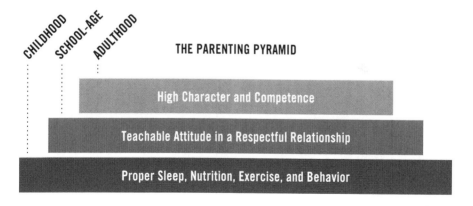

It is my hope that this book will serve as a helpful resource for you as your child grows and matures. And if you are picking this book up for the first time with an older child, the advice can still be very useful. It is never too late to begin leading your child to good health and high character. So, enjoy the journey of parenting your child. It can be one of the most rewarding experiences of your life!

For more details and discussion of parenting, visit LovingbyLeading.com. Research supporting the theme of this book can be found on this website.

Part One

LOVING BY LEADING YOUR CHILD: WHY?

Chapter 1

WHO'S LEADING?

At two years of age, Colton was a cyclone of energy and chaos. For the first six months he had been an easy-going child, cooing, smiling, and sleeping well. But then he began waking in the night for no apparent reason and rarely took a nap during the day. His blissfulness turned to crankiness as he fought sleep at every turn. Not knowing what to do, his parents resorted to giving him whatever he wanted, just to keep the peace.

Colton's behavior grew worse after his first birthday, and he began having tantrums at home, in restaurants, and at the grocery store. His parents were often paralyzed by his protests. The only relief came when they gave in to his demands—a snack between meals, getting out of bed when he didn't want to sleep, throwing food from the table if he didn't like what was offered, and playing with cell phones when he wouldn't settle down in public. But the relief was always and only momentary; it was just a matter of time until the next tantrum. The evenings brought no respite, with battles over bedtime leading to late nights and eventual success—on Colton's terms, sleeping in his parents' bed rather than his. Nestled restlessly between them, Colton would often wake in the night making requests for food or drink followed by cranky negotiations to get him back to bed. His parents were exhausted!

What had gone wrong? Did Colton have a sleep dysfunction, a behavioral disorder, or some other issue that required medical attention?

Many parents can identify with the desperation Colton's parents felt and have the same longing to find answers. In my experience, the primary problem behind this all-too-common scenario is an incorrect perception of child-rearing and a lack of leadership by the parents.

What has happened, and why?

The general approach to raising children has changed significantly over the past half-century. With modernization and the development of technology, American families have become more productive and more efficient in their work. Initially, these advancements came with the promise that families would have more time to spend with one another. Ironically, the opposite has occurred. Because we can accomplish more with our time, we attempt more. This has led to hectic lives for parents who are actually spending less time with their children than ever before. Additionally, the very technology that has allowed these advancements has become a major distraction. Increased screen time, for children and adults, is fracturing our relationships.

Social scientists have further complicated parenting by proclaiming that children do not need comprehensive leadership from their parents as once believed. According to this way of thinking, children will eventually chart the best course for their lives if left to their own persuasions. Today, it is commonly accepted that children only need freedom to be themselves, express themselves, and to learn by exploring. Couple this belief with busyness and distraction, and you have a recipe for a whole new approach to parenting: children lead, parents follow.

This is where we currently stand as a culture, and the emerging results of this approach are proving disastrous for both children and their parents.

In his book, *The Collapse of Parenting*, Dr. Leonard Sax describes the situation this way:

> Many parents are afraid of seeming too dictatorial, and end up abdicating their authority rather than taking a stand with their own children. If kids refuse to eat anything green and demand pizza instead, some parents give in, inadvertently raising children who are more likely to become obese. If children are given smartphones and allowed to spend the bulk of their free time texting, playing video games, and surfing the Internet, they become increasingly reliant on peers and the media for guidance on how to live, rather than looking to their parents. And if they won't sit still in class or listen to adults, they're often prescribed medication, a quick fix that actually undermines their self-control. In short, parents are failing to prioritize the parent-child relationship above all other relationships. The

result is children who have no absolute standard of right and wrong, who lack discipline, and who look to their peers and the Internet for direction, instead of looking to their parents.[1]

Children, such as Colton, desperately need guidance from their parents, and they generally want it, even if it sometimes causes a battle of wills. To indulge children by letting them make all the decisions puts them in a position of leadership that they are not equipped to handle. Most children do not know what is best for them and, when given the opportunity, will make unhealthy choices based on selfish intentions. The ideal goal of parenting is character building and good health; these can only come when parents lead and children follow.

By *leading* your child to better life habits, you are not only improving his health, but more importantly you are equipping him to learn self-control and to be more thoughtful in his actions and choices. This results in skills that are foundational to success in life.

For example, when parents lead a toddler to becoming a better sleeper and eater, the toddler will find it easier to control his impulses. A well-rested child is more receptive to his parents' efforts to teach him respect and submission to authority. When a child learns to submit to his parents' loving leadership, less conflict occurs, harmony prevails, and the parent-child relationship is greatly enhanced. Everyone in the family benefits when you *lead* rather than *follow* your child. (The technical term for this style of parenting is *authoritative* parenting, which we will take a closer look at in the coming chapters.)

Some will rightly point out that allowing a child to participate in some decision-making can build competence and confidence. However, when this is introduced too early or allowed too often, it can create anxiety in the heart of the child. For example, two-year-olds need clear guidance in their daily wardrobe selection, foods served, amount of television watched, and designated bedtime. Their participation can be occasionally allowed and even encouraged, but when constantly called upon to make choices beyond their capacity, they often become apprehensive and fearful of failure.

Parents need a confident understanding of *how* to lead their children at the various stages of development. In the following chapters, I will attempt to provide this understanding by looking at the styles of parenting, the nature of the child, and the need for discipline. Then, by age group, we will look at practical ways you can lead your child.

Why are some parents reluctant to lead?

If leadership in parenting is so important and rewarding, why don't more parents take this approach to child rearing? Good question. Here are some possible reasons.

1. Misled by the Parenting Media. Authoritative parenting has lost its appeal. Parents are being increasingly convinced that children do not need authoritative direction in their lives. They have been led to believe they are helping their child by taking a permissive approach and giving the child unlimited freedoms.

2. Paralyzed by uncertainty. Parents are just not sure what is best for their children, or are uncertain how to guide and correct, so they adopt a follow-the-child approach by default. In many ways, this seems to be the more efficient approach in the moment.

3. Seeking to be friends too early. It is natural for parents to desire a harmonious friendship with their child, but a respectful parent-child relationship must come first. Young children are afflicted with self-centeredness and in desperate need of their parent's guidance to develop healthy social skills. Parents must assume an authoritative role when their children are young, and allow the role to change as the child matures. This process cannot be rushed, however. Affirm and correct a child while he is young, and your relationship with him will grow into a healthy respectful friendship later in life. Resist letting your desire to please your child govern your relationship.

4. Thinking their role is to be "happiness fairies." True happiness cannot be accomplished by simply meeting a child's every demand. This is a difficult concept for young parents to grasp. Because children don't always *want* what they *need*, or *need* what they *want*, parental wisdom must come in play. Making the call to deny a child his desires—and enduring the protest—is a small price to pay for the long-term benefits he will enjoy.

5. Desiring to avoid conflict with their child. Every parent wants to maintain a peaceful, pleasant relationship with their children. However, when this desire causes them to ignore the child's need for discipline and leadership, the parent will often resort to compromise and excessive, unreasonable negotiation with the child. This approach of postponing correction inevitably leads to parental outbursts and child exasperation. Conflict avoidance is a short-term solution that leads to a long-term problem.

6. Hoping someone else will train their child. In the hurriedness of life, many parents hope that the daycare or sitter will do the dirty work of child discipline for them, when in fact only the parent has the true authority and influence to correct and lead.

7. Too busy to invest the time needed. Life's many distractions are tempting. Even after a full day at work, there are many things competing for our attention: social events, child activities, church gatherings, social media, or simply recreational screen time. Productive parenting requires the intentional investment of contemplation and time. Don't let the demands of life distract you from this important task. Invest now, and enjoy the fruit of your efforts later. Delay, and you will likely see less fruit and more heartache.

Perhaps you can identify to some degree with one or more of these reasons. I have listed these not to create guilt, but to help you recognize any obstacles and then help you focus on overcoming them.

To that end, I add this note: While a good outcome with your children cannot be guaranteed if you lead well, a bad outcome is much more likely if you don't.

Chapter 2

YOUR PARENTING APPROACH

Parenting is the most significant undertaking of a person's life; daunting when contemplated, yet doable on a day-by-day basis. It is the classic long-term investment; risk now, reward later. It is a venture marked by personal sacrifice and eventual fulfillment. Parenting brings both setbacks and successes. You will make mistakes and adjustments along the way, but don't be discouraged. Parenting can be the most fulfilling task of your life when viewed with the importance it deserves. So, let's consider the commitment you will need in order to parent well, by establishing some goals and reviewing some common parenting styles.

Your Commitment

Successful parenting requires a high level of commitment to your child and to the discipline process, especially in the early years. This responsibility must be taken on intentionally; it won't just happen. With the overwhelming demands of life, it is tempting to treat your parenting efforts as just one more thing you must do. However, for the best results, you must give it consistent attention and careful planning. Raising children is a high calling. Unlike other temporal endeavors in life, the results of your parenting efforts will have long-lasting, even eternal, consequences.

With the long term significance of parenting in view, let me introduce you to four forms of commitment you will need.

Be ready to invest.

Have you heard someone say, "I am dreading my child's teenage years"? This is usually said because there is an expectation of unreasonable and rebellious behavior during that time. But I want you to know that it doesn't have to be that way. The teen years can be wonderful for you and your child. How? By investing more in the early years. Postponing this investment until your child is older will result in more work later, and possibly a poorer outcome.

The following graph depicts the benefits of early investment in your parenting.

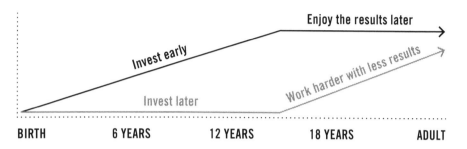

| BIRTH | 6 YEARS | 12 YEARS | 18 YEARS | ADULT |

Be willing to sacrifice.

Parenting is a life-altering, inconvenient, long-term commitment holding hope of great reward. It will bring limitations to your leisure and recreation time, and will alter your budget. It might even require postponement of some career goals. At times it will disturb your personal peace and can result in temporary conflict. These inevitable sacrifices are necessary to accomplish responsible, loving parenting with your child. While these are short on fun at the time, your reward will be a healthier child and healthier relationship with him in the long run.

Be the leader.

As mentioned earlier, parents should *lead* and children should follow. Here are just a few of the ways in which your children need your leadership:

- Lead them to healthy sleeping habits.
- Lead them to healthy eating habits.
- Lead them to safe behaviors.
- Lead them to self-control.
- Lead them to respect others.
- Lead them to proper behavior.
- Lead them to high character.

- Lead them to industriousness and productivity.
- Lead them to true contentment.

Be persistent and patient.

With the parenting of most children, results do not come quickly or easily. You will experience setbacks and have to make adjustments. Your child may resist; his young mind cannot always take in the good that you are doing for him. Beware of discouragement and of the temptation to relax your standards. Stay focused and be strong. In the moment of conflict your child will not understand the long-term benefits of your discipline, but down the road he will be thankful for your leadership. Consider the wisdom of the writer of the book of Hebrews:

> No discipline seems pleasant at the time, but painful. Later on, however, it produces a harvest of righteousness and peace for those who have been trained by it.[1]

Your Parenting Style

All parents assume a particular style of parenting, whether they realize it or not. This happens either intentionally or by default. Your style will be influenced by several factors, including:

- How your parents raised you
- The desires of your spouse and how he or she was raised
- Your observation of other parents or mentors
- The subtle parenting messages you receive from the culture and the media
- Input from friends and family
- Information from parenting resources you read or view

Your style will also be influenced by your personality, including your strengths and your weaknesses. It will be affected by the personalities and temperaments of your children. It may even change with the number of children you have. Many factors will be at work in shaping your parenting style. For this reason, I encourage you to be as intentional as possible in developing your style.

Let me now introduce you to what I believe is the optimal parenting style.

What does research tell us?

There is no shortage of opinions and advice on parenting. The bookstore shelves are full of books written by parenting "experts" who speak with confidence about how to raise a healthy child. How does one decide which are the best voices to listen to?

The most objective and least opinionated approach to discovering the optimal parenting style is to explore the parenting research. The best design for a research project is prospective and longitudinal, where children and parents are observed over a long period of time and data is collected along the way. Lower quality designs rely upon questioning adults about their childhood experiences rather than observing. When a search of the scientific literature focuses on high quality, prospective, longitudinal research, the decades-long work of psychologist Diana Baumrind, PhD emerges as pre-eminent.[2] Her studies led to the categorization of parenting into three basic styles: authoritarian, authoritative, and permissive. Researcher E.E. Maccoby later added a fourth parenting style: uninvolved.[3]

Additionally, Baumrind identified two fundamental factors that were applied differently by the parents in each of the parenting style groups:

- *Demandingness*: The parents' control of the child's behavior, their expectations of the child, and their degree of monitoring the child.
- *Responsiveness*: The parents' support and encouragement of the child, their warmth in relationship, their communication with the child, and the degree to which they foster individuality.

Here is a summary of how the four parenting styles compared.

Authoritarian

These parents were high in demandingness and low in responsiveness. They were harsh in their demands, more controlling, more restrictive, less inclined to explain, more punitive, detached, less warm, and expressed more anger when children disobeyed.

Permissive

These parents were low in demandingness and high in responsiveness. They were markedly less controlling, minimally demanding, freely granting of the child's demands, uninvolved with the child, and warmer than authoritarian parents. They did not feel in control of their child's behavior. They were affirming and accepting, and indifferent toward the child's impulses and actions.

Uninvolved

These parents were low in demandingness and in responsiveness. They made few demands of the child and were mostly unresponsive. They met the child's basic needs, but were otherwise detached from the child's life. In extreme cases, parents were neglectful of the child. They did not require mature behavior and were very lenient.

Authoritative

These parents were high in demandingness and in responsiveness. They employed a combination of firm control and positive encouragement of a child's independence. They affirmed the child's qualities, yet set standards for future conduct. They made reasonable demands of their children and promoted respect for authority. They were more consistent with the discipline.

Baumrind's findings are not surprising, and clearly point to the most effective parenting style. Which one was the best?

- Not Authoritarian parents—They are highly demanding but not responsive, rearing children who are uncertain, withdrawn, unemotional, and angry.
- Not Permissive parents—They are responsive but not demanding, rearing children who are unproductive and disruptive.
- The winner is Authoritative parents—They are both highly demanding and highly responsive, rearing children who are more socially responsible, more achievement oriented, friendlier toward peers, and more cooperative with adults.

The most successful parenting style, the authoritative style, used a balance of positive encouragement and high behavioral control. *Positive encouragement* includes an approach that is warm, affirming, rational, and receptive toward the child. *High behavioral control* consists of firm discipline and supervision of the child by the parent. Authoritative parents direct the child in a rational, intentional manner. They encourage verbal give-and-take from the child, they share the reason behind their directives, they value expressive attributes of the child, and yet they exert firm control over the child's behavior. Their use of control is often combined with reasoning.

A fifth parenting style has gained popularity in recent years: *Attachment* parenting. This approach focuses on nurturing the child and building a strong bond between parent (especially mother) and child. These parents emphasize co-sleeping with the child for the first few years, "baby wearing" whenever possible, breastfeeding until two to four years of age, and avoiding all sleep training. While this does build a strong bond with the child, it comes at a price. The downside to this approach is more difficulty getting the child on a sleeping or eating schedule, less ability for the child to self-soothe, parental fatigue due to lack of sleep, and less intimacy between parents due to co-sleeping. Although intended to build security, this style tends to create dependency of the child upon the parent and place undue strain upon the marriage, which is counterproductive for the family.

Control and Power Exertion

Critics of the authoritative style have argued that firm control over a child by a parent teaches the child that strength is what's most important in life and that it is proper for the strongest to force his will upon the weakest, negatively referred to as "might makes right." These critics, however, overlook the fact that power is commonly exerted and necessary in routine childcare. For example: two-year-old Sally insists on running from her mom in the parking lot, so a firm hand grip from mom is needed to stop the dangerous behavior; eighteen-month-old Michael refuses to sit in his car seat, so mom must force him to sit and be buckled in for safety; four-year-old Merritt refuses to sit still while being vaccinated, so her mother and the nurse restrain her to prevent injury from the needle.

Control over a child is necessary at times to ensure safety, health, and, yes, proper behavior. Classic child rearing studies have shown that some degree of power assertion[4] and firm control[5,6] is essential for optimal child rearing. When power is exerted in the context of love and for the child's benefit, he will not perceive it as bullying or demeaning. The issue is not whether parents will use power in childrearing, but *how* they will use it and why.

How to Control Behavior

If behavioral control is this important, then it follows that a parent should learn what the most effective measures are to achieve healthy control. In her study, Baumrind noticed each group attempted to control behavior in different ways and for different reasons.

- *Authoritarian*: Used extremely high control by love-withdrawal (shaming), fear, and often used physical punishment. Offered very little encouragement. Results: Poor
- *Permissive*: Used little control relying upon love-withdrawal, ridicule, guilt provocation, little reasoning, and rarely used physical punishment. Offered little encouragement. Results: Poor
- *Authoritative*: Used a balance of control and encouragement relying upon reason, power, and reinforcement. Used less love-withdrawal and fear/guilt provocation than Authoritarian. Used physical punishment (ordinary spanking) more often than Permissive and less than Authoritarian. Employed a higher ratio of positive to negative reinforcement than Authoritarian. Used a balance of control and encouragement. Results: Optimal.

A Balanced Approach is Best

To summarize, the best research indicates that the healthiest parenting style balances firm behavioral control with encouragement. One without the other is counterproductive. In the coming chapters we will explore why these are necessary and how to accomplish a balance.

BEHAVORIAL CONTROL	Authoritative Parenting: A Balanced Approach	ENCOURAGEMENT

Uniqueness of Styles

Now that we have looked at parenting styles, let's take a brief look at the distinct contributions each parent brings to the implementation of parenting. The mother and the father play unique roles in the rearing of their child. Just as procreation of a child requires both, the optimal development of that child requires the involvement of both. Not only does each parent uniquely contribute to the care of the child, they each model for that child the unique characteristics of that sex.

Can children turn out well when reared in a home without their biological mother and/or father? Yes. Children are amazingly resilient and can prevail despite disruptions in family structure, including death of a parent, divorce, remarriage, or unwed birth. But contrary to some contemporary claims that family structure does not matter, research "clearly reveals that children appear most apt to succeed well as adults—on multiple counts and across a variety of domains—when they spend their entire childhood with their married mother and father, and especially when the parents remain married to the present day."[7]

Mothers and fathers parent differently and each makes unique contributions to the overall development of their child.[8] Mother-love and father-love are qualitatively different. Mothers are typically more nurturing, expressive, and unconditional in their love for their children. Fathers, by contrast, often parent with certain expectations of achievement. Research reveals that parenting is most effective when it is both highly expressive and highly demanding.[9]

Differences are also reflected in the way mothers and fathers use touch with their children. Mothers frequently soothe, calm, and comfort with touch. Fathers, on the other hand, are more likely to use touch to stimulate or excite their children during play. As fathers engage in rough and tumble play, they take on a teaching role like that of a coach. Roughhousing between fathers and sons in the younger years is associated with the development of greater self-control in adolescence.

Healthy diversity is also observed in parental approaches to discipline. "The disciplinary approaches of fathers tend toward firmness, relying on rules and principles. The approach of mothers tends toward more responsiveness, involving more bargaining, more adjustment toward the child's mood and context, and is more often based on an intuitive understanding of the child's needs and emotions of the moment."[10] Consequently, being reared by a mother and a father helps sons and daughters moderate their own gender-linked inclinations. Boys generally embrace reason over emotion, rules over relationships, risk-taking over caution, and standards over compassion. Girls generally place greater emphasis on emotional ties, relationships, caution, and compassion. Over time, parents demonstrate to their children the value of opposing tendencies.

Father Tendencies

- Fathers play with more spontaneity.
- Fathers allow children to explore and take risks by supervising rather than intervening in their play.[10]

- Fathers teach children how to interact with others and how to control themselves when they feel their needs aren't being met.
- Girls who enjoy a close relationship with their father, delay first sexual activity.[11,12]
- Fathers provide a sense of security.
- Fathers help children develop healthy independence by giving adolescents a sense of reliability.[13]
- Fathers discipline less frequently but more predictably, meaning that children are more likely to comply.[14]
- Fathers have an influence over children in steering them away from sex and drugs.
- Fathers empower their children, giving them the impetus to go out to explore the world, to meet new people and to take chances.

Mother Tendencies

- Mothers have an empathetic, emotionally healthy relationship with the child and have open communication.
- Mothers help children feel connected and wanted.
- Mothers play by emphasizing interaction, predictability, and joint problem solving.[15]
- Mothers provide crucial direction to fathers on childcare tasks.[16]
- Mothers impose limits and discipline more frequently, but with greater flexibility.[17]
- Mothers help their children develop empathy by helping them understand the emotions of others as well as their own.[18]
- Mothers provide an important role in getting children to connect to extended family and their peers.[19]

To summarize, the most successful parenting style takes a balanced approach to encouragement and behavioral control, and each parent plays a unique role in this style.

We are now ready to examine why your child so desperately needs your leadership, as we look in the next chapter at the nature of a child.

Chapter 3

UNDERSTANDING YOUR CHILD

Now that we have given some thought to the commitment, goals, and styles of parenting, let's take a close look at a child's nature. Much of your success or failure in childrearing will be built upon your relationship with your child. This relationship requires understanding why your child does what he does and how to influence him. While every child has a unique personality (temperament), there are some basic forces at play affecting a child's behavior. From birth, the personality is an emerging result of both internal and external forces. Internally, the child will struggle with his basic human nature, which is restrained by the conscience. Externally, the child's parents and his environment will play a formative role in influencing his conscience and developing personality. Therefore, it is helpful to understand these dynamics as you build your relationship with your child.

Many parenting experts today advise parents to acquiesce to their child by letting him "discover life" through granting his requests with gracious obliging, allowing almost unlimited exploration, and sheltering him from all disappointment. They would argue that children are just small adults, and that all they need to behave properly is a series of explanations and pleas. This approach can be very appealing to parents because it assumes the best of the child, seems to be the path of least resistance, and appears to require the least amount of training and planning. There is a problem, however. The basic nature of a child is to be self-centered and to lack self-discipline. An approach of negotiation and leniency fails to acknowledge this basic nature and actually feeds a child's tendency to please self, often at the expense of others.

Let's now look more closely at the internal forces that drive your child to do what he does.

The Nature of a Child

Babies are cute and cuddly, especially as newborns. They are dependent and appear so innocent. All seems well at the mid-year point when they smile and coo in response to every smiling face. Then, as they begin crawling and eventually walking, they are even more fascinating to watch. But something seems to change when they enter that second year. Toddlers become more self-assertive and independent, protesting when their desires conflict with ours. Suddenly, they refuse to stop running when we say, "Stop!" They begin to resist and rebel (e.g., refuse to sit in the car seat, fight diaper changes, contest teeth brushing, and throw food from the high chair). "What happened to my innocent baby?" you may ask. The fact is, he was never totally innocent, just less able to express his self-centered desires.

Understanding the nature of a child is fundamental to how you will approach the rearing of your child. Will you be directive (active) or just facilitative (passive)? Will you lead him or follow his lead? Here are two opposing views about the nature of a child.

Children are born innocent.

For centuries, philosophers have claimed that children are born innocent. John Locke described this concept in his 1690 publication, *Essay Concerning Human Understanding*, where he said at birth the mind of every individual is a "blank tablet" to be written upon by environment and experience. This implies that children are born neutral and it is for society to make its imprint and determine the character of the child. They are essentially pure and innocent as newborns and any deterioration in character is a result of negative influences from parents or their environment. With this belief, a parent must be a facilitator who meets the child's basic physical and emotional needs and, more importantly, who shields the child from any and all disappointment in his young life. Discipline is neither a priority nor even a need with this approach. Appeasement, conflict avoidance, and even submission to the child's lead are the objectives of the parent who holds to this belief.

Example: A toddler throws a temper tantrum because his mother ends his outside play to come in for supper. This theory would blame the mother for being too abrupt, or for not asking the child if he wanted to come inside, or perhaps for not bringing the meal outside to accommodate the child. The protest is essentially the fault of the mother.

Children are born self-centered.

Years of psychological research and the practical experience of parenting tell us that children are not born innocent or others-conscious, but rather are self-centered and focused on their own physical needs and satisfaction. Infants truly believe the world revolves around them and exists to meet their every desire. This innate drive seeks indulgence and resists a parent's efforts to tame these desires. Holding to this concept, a parent must actively direct a child toward acceptable, civil behavior and away from his anti-social, self-aggrandizing tendencies. Discipline is needed to teach a child self-control and consideration for others.

Example: A toddler bites or hits his older brother for not giving up a toy he wants, even though the toddler has plenty of his own toys and the one he wants belongs to his brother. According to this theory, the toddler's behavior may in part be due to his parent's inadequate correction, but primarily is due to his own selfishness and deserves correction.

With maturity, even an undisciplined child, to some degree, will embrace the benefits of cooperation with his parents and his peers. This cooperation will begin to somewhat temper his focus on self, and foster a desire to get along with others. An internal struggle, however, will naturally ensue between the child's innate desire to please himself and his developing urge to please his parents and others. It is the outcome of this internal struggle that fundamentally determines the character of an individual.

Therefore, the role of discipline is to lead a child from being a *self-centered* child to being a *self-disciplined* adult. Will your child live *foolishly* by impulsively pleasing himself, or live *wisely* by displaying self-control over his natural impulses and being considerate of others?

Comparisons of the Untrained and Trained Child	
Foolish Child (Poor judgment)	*Wise Child (Good judgment)*
Self-centered	Self-controlled
Selfish	Generous
Demands that desires be met	Delays gratification
Rudeness to gain more attention	Respectfulness
Disrespect for authority	Obedience
Tantrums/violence when desires are challenged	Self-control
Laziness driven by self-pleasure	Industriousness

Foolish Child (Poor judgment)	Wise Child (Good judgment)
Dishonesty for personal gain	Honesty
Unreliable because of self-pursuits	Reliable
Low achievement in vocation	High achievement
Prideful	Humble

The traits in the left column come naturally, in varying degrees, to the young child while those in the right column do not. So, how does a parent lead a child into acquiring these favorable traits? The answer? First, by *controlling* the behavior, and then by *persuading* the child's heart—not simply by focusing on behavior. As a child matures, parents must focus on the heart (the motive behind the behavior). Behavior, good or bad, flows from the heart. To require good behavior without persuading a child to *want* to behave correctly is to teach hypocrisy. So, how does a parent take a naturally self-centered infant or toddler and persuade him to want to obey? Let's explore the answer.

> *To require good behavior without persuading a child to want to behave correctly is to teach hypocrisy.*

A Child's Will

A child's will is his natural drive to attain his desires, which by nature is bent toward pleasing himself. The strength and persistence of the will varies from child to child, and even from sibling to sibling. Every child has the ability to choose how he expresses his will. A parent's goal should not be to *break* the child's will, but rather to *train* it and channel it in a responsible and productive direction. If properly trained, a child's will can become his closest ally and source of confidence in daily living. If untrained or broken, a child's will can become his greatest enemy and handicap throughout life.

Parents must be careful to guide their child's drive or will. In the discipline process, after clear instruction has been given, the child exercises his will to either obey or disobey. Parents then use a combination of encouragement (affirmation) and correction to train his will. He can then choose to obey and be rewarded with approval, or he can choose to disobey and suffer the consequences. If the affirmation is pleasant enough or the correction is unpleasant enough, the child will eventually come to accept his parent's point and comply. Exactly when this surrender occurs will depend upon the internal struggle between a child's desire to please self and the desire to please his parent. The magnitude of this battle varies from child to child and depends upon the strength of his will and the degree of persistence to get his way. This means that the intensity and persistence of a parent's efforts must vary with each child. With time (longer for some and shorter for others) and with a loving approach from his parents, a child will come to realize the true benefits of discipline and will adopt their choices as his own. This process is called *internalization*, the molding of a child's heart to *want* to properly control his behavior.

At this point, you may be wondering, *but what about the strong willed child*? The term "strong willed" is often used to describe the relentlessly disobedient child. However, the term is really too vague to accurately determine how to handle a particular child's actions. If by "strong" you actually mean "persistent," then you are describing most young children. Persistence that leads to disobedient behavior may be caused by either determination or defiance. *Determination* is the personality quality of persistence that, if properly channeled, can be very positive and productive. Conversely, *defiance* is a heart issue, and comes from a selfish desire to rebel against a parent's directive. While disobedient behavior is always wrong and deserving of correction, how to correct should be determined by the source of the disobedience. Is it a matter of determination or defiance? An example of each may help.

Determination: When asked by his mother, Billy resists putting up his LEGO® blocks because he wants to complete what he's building.

Correction: Billy's mother commends him for his determination ("I am pleased that you are working so hard to finish building the figure"), but he is again told to stop and put them up. Also, she tells Billy that next time she will give him a five-minute warning so he can prepare to stop on time.

Defiance: When told by his mother to share his LEGO set with his sister, Brady refuses and yells at them both.

Correction: Brady mother takes his toys away and she sends him to time-out. She later explains that he will not be allowed to play with his LEGO blocks for the rest of the day, and if he wants to play with them again tomorrow, he must share a few pieces with his sister.

Both children could be considered "strong-willed" (persistent), but a parent's proper approach will depend upon the source of that persistence—determination or defiance.

A Child's Conscience

Every person has a conscience. *Conscience* is defined as "the inner sense of what is right or wrong in one's conduct or motives, impelling one toward right action."[1] It is a warning system that alerts us to wrong and confirms what is right. It is the moral compass by which we are guided. This internal sense of right and wrong exists as early as infancy, demonstrated by an infant's expression of empathy for a crying baby or for a sad face. It is, however, merely at seed level in infancy, but when properly nurtured, it can become a powerful force for good to moderate a child's self-centered nature. The conscience counters the child's nature, reminding him that he is not alone and he must be considerate of others around him. With proper training, the conscience persuades a child to resist selfish temptation and to pursue a life of high moral and social character.

How then does a parent train and develop the conscience to eventually guide a child toward noble living? This occurs through three basic types of interaction:

1. **Behavioral control** is the earliest influence a parent has over a young child. By correcting improper behavior, the parent identifies to the child wrong behavior, and by allowing proper behavior, teaches what is right.
2. **Reasoning** (dialogue and explanation) becomes operational as a child matures, in informing and convincing a child's understanding of right and wrong.
3. **Modeling** of proper behavior by the parents is essential in convincing a child at any age what is right.

Developmental theory indicates that young children acquire a moral sense of right and wrong through punishment and reward. They will obey and yield to authority to avoid punishment. Therefore, if a toddler's aggressive behavior is properly controlled and corrected by the parent, he comes to understand the wrongness of it. On the contrary, if wrong and disrespectful behavior is ignored, his conscience is desensitized and he is led to believe that cruelty toward others may not be so bad, especially when it even helps him get what he wants. Research shows that the more a person defies his internal moral code, the easier it is to defy it with the next opportunity. For example, when a person repeatedly tells lies, there is a "gradual escalation of self-serving dishonesty," and detectable changes can even be seen on MRI images of the brain.[2]

Actions Speak Louder than Words

When adults in a research study were asked, "What did your parents do to teach you good values and good character?" their answers were varied. Some mentioned their parent's love, their high expectations, their firm discipline, and their wisdom. But, the most common answer was, "My parents set a good example."[3] It is a daunting realization for young parents that the results of their parenting efforts are mostly determined by their modeling. Actions do speak louder than words, especially with children. On the other hand, no parent is perfect, but even foul-ups can bring a positive result. When parents honestly confess their wrongdoing to their children, they repair the relationship and also set a good example for their children to follow when they do wrong.

When parents model the same moral standards they are requiring of their child, the conscience grows stronger. However, parental hypocrisy undermines the conscience and its internal influence upon the child is weakened. For instance, if violence between parents is modeled in the home, a child will likely adopt this same behavior as a means of problem solving, even though his conscience may have initially caused him to feel some guilt. The "conscience seed" must be fertilized, watered, and pruned as it grows in order to assure its fruitful development. This is accomplished through the discipline process in the presence of a loving relationship and through the observation of healthy parental role models.

Discipline and *disciple* both originate from the same Latin word root, *discipulus*. Discipline, therefore, can be viewed as a parent's effort to make a disciple of his child. How is a disciple made? Through instruction and modeling from the teacher.

	CONSCIENCE BUILDERS		CONSCIENCE BUSTERS
HEALTHY MODELING	✓ always telling the truth ✓ being patient and accepting of others ✓ treating your spouse with respect	**UNHEALTHY MODELING**	✗ asking your child to tell a "white lie" for your convenience ✗ being highly critical of others behind their backs ✗ mistreating your spouse verbally and/or physically
APPLYING DISCIPLINE	✓ controlling your child's impulsive, selfish behavior ✓ correcting your child's bullying behavior towards others ✓ teaching your child to politely respect others' property	**LACK OF DISCIPLINE**	✗ ignoring and not correcting your child's impulsiveness ✗ ignoring your child's mistreatment of others ✗ allowing your child to grab or play with others' things without asking

Persuading the Heart

You might be surprised to realize that persuading a child to behave does not begin with reasoning with him or trying to talk him into obedience. Children under three years of age are very difficult to persuade through talk. They are not mentally mature enough to realize the benefits of obedience simply through reason. Their internal drive to please themselves often overrides even the most persuasive talk from a parent. Research has shown that attempting to use reasoning *alone* with a young child can actually be counterproductive and encourage more disobedience.[4] Children under six years of age will initially require a combination of reasoning (brief explanation) and punishment to be persuaded, and then, as submission and compliance are achieved, reasoning and discussion will become more effective.

Persuasion is accomplished through the discipline process, and begins with behavioral control. When a child is *required* to obey in the early years (external control), the desire to obey is *acquired* by the child in his later years (internalization).

YOUNGER AGE		OLDER AGE
Behavior Focus: Obedience is *required*	·····················>	Heart Focus: Obedience is *aquired*

When the "requiring" comes from a loving, nurturing parent in a consistent manner, the "acquiring" is more likely to follow. In others words, it is the discipline that *requires* the young child to behave that will eventually persuade the heart and conscience of the older child to *want* to behave.

Training the Behavior of the Younger Child

Lead your child to healthy sleep habits.
Lead your child to nutritious eating.
Lead your child to safe behavior.
Lead your child to proper behavior.

Teaching the Heart of the Older Child

Lead your child to self-control and respect for others.
Lead your child to high character.
Lead your child to humble confidence.
Lead your child to industriousness and a productive life.

Submission and Obedience

The teaching of submission, the yielding of one's will to authority, is a basic principle for successful parenting and ultimately for character building. Today, however, submission is not a highly valued virtue in society. Independence and self-determination are revered as superior character traits, even in children, and submission and obedience have been regarded as signs of weakness and inferiority. Children are often considered to be "little adults" and assumed to have the accompanying wisdom.

Unfortunately, under this misguided premise, children lose. When the foolishness of a child (lack of sound judgment) is unrestrained, and submission to the parents is not required, the child is led to believe he has authority and wisdom equal to that of his parents. From this mindset comes pride, arrogance, and stubbornness. If unchecked, the un-submissive child enters primary school with an inability to accept instruction due to his scorn for authority, and eventually becomes an adult lacking wisdom (sound judgment), boldly displaying foolishness, and still scorning all authorities in his life. You may even know a few of these adults who have never grown up.

Heartfelt obedience cannot be acquired by a child without him first submitting to wise teaching and authority. Submission is about taming and directing a child's will, not breaking it. That is, training it to listen to authoritative voices. The un-submitting, prideful child says, "I am always right and you are wrong." Behind this attitude is an inconsiderate desire to satisfy self with foolish, even reckless, determination. By contrast, the submissive child feels the desire to please self as well, but develops a realization of the benefits of delaying self-gratification and of obeying the authoritative voices in his life. When children are required to submit in their younger years, they eventually see the rewards (individually and socially) of being obedient and others-conscious, and gradually adopt this character quality for themselves. Additionally, the submissive child is more teachable and will reap benefits as a more productive individual in life's endeavors.

This process of teaching submission and obedience must begin early, for it will be increasingly more difficult to teach as the child gets older. Retraining a child to replace misbehavior with correct behavior is much harder than training correct behavior in the beginning. If a young child is not taught to respect the authoritative position of his parents, then it will be much harder to convince him later that his judgment is not superior to that of his teachers, employers, or any other authoritative figure in his life.

The concept of submission does not completely relieve a child of his voice or opinion. Even though submission should be consistently required in the early months of life, an "appeal process" can be introduced with a responsible child at about four years of age. He can be taught to request an appeal of his parent's directive or command if he has *new* information to bring to his parent's attention that may influence the directive. Teach the child to first state his understanding of your request: "I know you want me to do . . . because . . ." Then he may make his appeal: "May I make an appeal to change your decision?" While this option may not work with all children or in all situations, parents should consider this for those children who are respectfully submissive.

Young Children Need Limits

Although not always apparent, children need and even want boundaries. Like the guardrails on a bridge, boundaries enforced by parents bring needed security to a child's journey through life. Behavioral limitations protect a child from environmental dangers and help mold socially acceptable behavior. Early in life, especially the first three years, parents will need to maintain more structure in their child's day and have more control over their child's behavior (external control). As he matures and learns to submit to his parent's directives and behaves more responsibly (internalization), the child can be granted more freedoms.

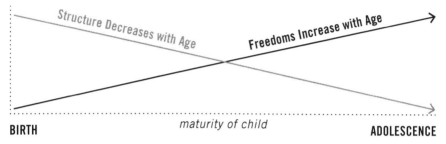

BIRTH   *maturity of child*   ADOLESCENCE

For the more compliant child, freedoms come sooner. For the more defiant child, freedoms are delayed as the parent maintains tighter behavioral control to teach responsibility. This balance of behavioral control and freedoms must not be rushed. If freedoms are granted before a child is ready the discipline process is impaired.

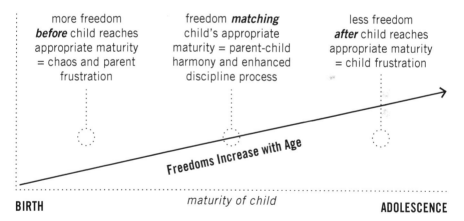

BIRTH   *maturity of child*   ADOLESCENCE

A child can become frustrated when he is given behavioral freedoms or privileges before he is ready. This arises from the child's inability to handle the privilege and from the parent's eventual need to revoke the privilege. In this mistaken process, parents compromise their position of authority with their child, as well as their child's trust in their judgment.

Unfortunately, many parenting experts today recommend that parents treat their children as little adults and use minimal external control of their behavior. They recommend early empowerment of the child. This results in poor internalization of standards and poor development of the child's conscience. Consider this example:

Two-year-old Haley's mom eagerly allows her to make her own decisions in the course of a day. She is often given the choice of various food options at dinner, or what clothes from her entire dresser drawer she would like to wear. She's even asked if she is ready to stop watching a movie and go to bed. But Haley is too young for the privilege of making such choices. These are decisions that a parent should be making, only allowing her to occasionally choose when her behavior and attitude have been good and have earned this (limited) freedom.

In summary, children, as adorable and lovable as they can be, are born with a natural drive (will) to please self. Their nature can be positively influenced by their conscience, which is primarily shaped by discipline from their parents. This discipline progressively takes the form of behavioral control, reasoning, and modeling by the parent. Teaching a child submission to authority is the first step in developing a teachable child. Children need limits in their lives and they thrive when the limits are reasonable and lovingly enforced.

Chapter 4

YOUR PARENTING GOALS

Before beginning a project, you are more likely to succeed if you have a goal in mind and a plan to reach it. Parenting is no different. So, now that we have contemplated your parenting style, let's identify your general and specific parenting goals.

General Goals

In the beginning, every parent has grand hopes and expectations for their child. Will she be a doctor, lawyer, accomplished musician, star athlete, beloved teacher, or successful entrepreneur? The sky is the limit when our children are infants—according to our dreams for them—and we are willing to do whatever it takes to give them the best chance to succeed. But, as the busyness of life takes over, fatigue sets in, and the challenges of parenting grow, even the noblest ambitions can fade. The demands of life can blur a parent's goals for a child and tempt them to take the easier route with childrearing.

Here, then, are some common goals adopted by parents (some intentional, some by default), along with the traps and temptations that often short-circuit these goals.

Entertain or Equip?

It is commonly believed that the primary goal in raising children is simply to make them happy. This approach involves seeking ways to indulge the child and guard her from all forms of disappointment (see "Disappointment" in chapter 9). Conflict and correction are avoided due to the unrest they often cause. By meeting or even exceeding the child's every wish, the parent feels good about their childrearing efforts. For these parents, every day is a quest to pacify and find new ways to entertain their child and, thereby, keep the peace.

While making our children happy can be very satisfying to us, to make this a goal of parenting is actually shortsighted. This approach can create narcissistic tendencies in a child as it appeals to her natural self-centeredness. Contrast this approach with parents whose desire is to equip their child with character and wisdom to meet life's challenges, the long view. Although the "equipping" parents also desire to have a happy child, they realize that disappointment and conflict are inevitable in life. Their goal is to teach their child how to deal with life's disappointments and how to overcome failures, not just avoid them. In persuading the child toward proper behavior and self-control, these parents do not shy away from correction when necessary, because they see character development as the primary goal of parenting.

Your Reputation or Your Child's Heart?

For other parents, the goal is to have well-behaved children who look good in public and are a compliment to themselves. Their children are trophies on display. For these parents, the child's heart and motivation are not as important as her behavior. These parents overlook the discipline their child's heart needs and instead focus only on externals. It is their reputation that is at stake in parenting, not their child's character or conscience.

When parents have the child's best interest in mind, they focus on developing her heart (the reason behind her behavior), not just her actions. They are willing to sacrifice their personal schedules and pleasures to spend one-on-one time with their child. They are willing to endure the embarrassment of a child's outburst in public in order to teach her the folly of her misbehavior. They are willing to be inconvenienced by leaving a public setting in order to administer immediate correction when necessary. These parents make the effort to instill in their child high standards, and model the same standards in their own lives.

Companionship or Character?

For still other parents, the objective is to be their child's best friend. Although it is natural to desire this relationship, pushing for it too early in your child's life can be ill fated. As I will address in chapter 7 ("The Discipline Process"), children are emotionally and mentally immature, in need of guidance and leadership from you, their authority figure. This teacher-student relationship is very different from an equal status friendship you may have with a peer. Seeking a friendship relationship too early in your child's life will sabotage the process of discipline. High-quality friendship with your child can only be accomplished through years of character development. It is only later in life that you can relax your oversight and be a best friend to your child.

Specific Goals

In identifying the specific goals for parenting, we need to examine two primary components of child development: character and competence.[1] *Character* can be defined as the aspect related to accountability, control of impulses, and persistence in the face of obstacles. Researcher Diana Baumrind describes it more specifically: "Character consists of positive and cultivated habits of social responsibility, moral commitment, and self-discipline that provide the internal structure of conscience, regulating inner thoughts and volitions."[2] A child's character is shaped by interaction with his parents, other personal contacts, and his environment. As will be explained later, parents use the discipline process to help the child reach desirable character qualities, including:

- Self-control
- Honesty
- Patience
- Trustworthiness
- Humility

Competence can be defined as the acquired capability to obtain one's desired (appropriate) personal and social goals in life. Optimal competence in a person balances independence, individuality, and self-serving achievement with social interaction such as service to others and connectedness. A child's natural tendency is to serve self at the expense of others. Parents use the discipline process to help the child reach optimal competence, including:

- Respect for others
- Kindness
- Respect for authority
- Industriousness

- Confidence
- Sense of humor

So, a parent's real goals are not centered on good behavior but on *genuine* behavior. Good behavior can consist of temporary performances to please a parent in order to selfishly obtain a reward. Genuine behavior, however, will flow from a child's heart that is rightly oriented and considerate of others. This is the kind of behavior that is lasting. Therefore, healthy discipline seeks to persuade the heart to *want* to behave. This approach to parenting focuses on inner development rather than outward performance.

Focus on developing your child's heart,
and proper behavior will follow.

Let's take a closer look at a few common, yet significant, displays of a child's character and competence.

Self-Control

One of the greatest gifts you can give your child is to teach her self-control. Just how important is it that a child learns self-control, and how soon should a parent pursue it with a child? The answer: self-control is critical to success in life, and the sooner a child develops it, the better. Research finds that children who demonstrate self-control by three years of age will become the healthiest, wealthiest, and most successful adults.[3,4] Conversely, those who demonstrate the least self-control by the same age are more likely to eventually drop out of school, break the law, and struggle financially. One report described it this way:

> Early self-control has a profound and lasting effect on one's life in adulthood. A 32-year longitudinal study indicated that possessing self-control in childhood (defined as two to ten years of age) predicts physical health, substance dependence, personal finances, and criminal-offending outcomes in adulthood.[5] Moreover, in that study, the effects of children's self-control were separated from the effects of intelligence, social class, and mistakes that were made when the children were adolescents. Similarly, there is evidence that

individuals who have strong self-control in early childhood are more successful in school and are more likely to have successful careers and harmonious family relationships in adulthood. Furthermore, numerous studies have confirmed that self-control at an early age has positive effects on preschool and middle-childhood academic, social, and emotional ability, as well as on the development of conscience. Moreover, self-control can also alleviate behavior, academic, and emotional problems.[6]

Self-control begins early in life as self-regulation, which is the process of regulating one's reaction to experiences with people, the environment, and various sensory encounters (noises, pain, etc.). Childhood is a fertile period for developing this regulation or impulse control, and parents can play a formative role. Once passed, this opportunity cannot be recovered, and the effort required to retrain is far greater than that to initially train.

Self-regulation starts with healthy nurturing during infancy, where a baby's needs are promptly met and affection is generously shown, leading to a stable sense of security. It is then, upon this loving foundation, that parents can teach their child to be self-controlled by *leading* the child. Some of the first challenges come in infancy with protests over naptime, diaper changes, and crawling restrictions. Then for the toddler, impulses needing some degree of control include haphazardly running, curiously touching, boldly grabbing, and erratically screaming. As parents confidently and lovingly lead a child to accept their directives, the child comes to submit his will to theirs and eventually finds reward and security in being self-controlled.

A parent's control *over* a child in the early years eventually leads to self-control *by* the child in later years. Early on, this process produces some degree of conflict between the parent and child, but later on it yields respectful and loving harmony in the relationship. Sadly, parents who seek to overindulge their young child and avoid all conflict will never experience the harmony that could have been theirs during the school-aged and adolescent years.

You may ask, "How does a parent teach self-control?" The answer: by leading your child early on. Teach your child healthy sleep habits, healthy eating habits, and limitations to their blossoming, impulsive behavior. This is accomplished through the discipline process, which will take various forms depending upon your child's personality and level of maturity.

When behavioral control is *required* in toddlerhood and preschool years, self-control is more likely to be *acquired* in the school-aged years.

PARENT REQUIRES
behavioral control from **younger** child ⟶ **OBEDIENCE** ⟶ **CHILD ACQUIRES** self-control as **older** child

Specific opportunities to teach self-control:

- Have high, but reasonable expectations for behavior. (*Instruction,* Chapter 7)
- Teach healthy sleep habits with sleep training. (Chapter 12)
- Properly manage temper tantrums and whining. (Chapter 8)
- Teach impulse control. (Chapters 8 and 15)
- Teach proper conflict resolution. (Chapters 8 and 15)
- Require good behavior at mealtime. (Chapter 6)
- Teach respect and kindness for others. (Chapter 3)
- Allow for disappointments. (Chapter 9)
- Model self-control in your family relationships. (Chapter 3)

Whether your child is an infant, toddler, or a school-ager, make teaching self-control a priority. Typically, results will not come quickly, but be persistent for your child's sake. Remember, the research shows that more self-control leads to greater success and happiness in life.

Patience and Delayed Gratification

Patience is a character quality that is often overlooked and even intentionally ignored by many parents. In our self-indulgent world, delayed gratification is an almost foreign concept that is considered of little value. Immediate gratification, which fosters impatience, is more the norm as children are overly indulged in two common areas: material items and entertainment.

Material Items: We parents get great pleasure in seeing our child's excitement when receiving a desired toy or surprise gift. We love to celebrate with them and even explore with them the facets of the new toy. When we are overly indulgent, however, our child actually suffers. If children are routinely given whatever they want, they become self-focused, overly expectant, and easily discontented. They don't become more satisfied as you may expect; they actually become insatiable children who are never satisfied. It is healthier for a child to long for, wait for, and especially work and save for a desired item. After all, this is the reality of adult life. So, even if you are independently wealthy, prepare your child to live with less and to be content. Don't deny your child the enormous benefits of delayed gratification; it will prepare him for the real world.

Entertainment: Entertainment and visual/auditory stimulation are very gratifying to our senses. Children today learn this early and even develop a craving for it. With the many forms of electronic stimulation available to a child, they are almost never without it. Consider two-year-old Sam running errands with his mother. Upon waking, Sam eats his breakfast bar in front of the TV while mom is getting dressed. He protests when mom turns the TV off, but is pacified when she promises to play his favorite movie in the car. When they arrive at the grocery store, mom opens the cartoon app on her smartphone and hands it to Sam as they stroll through the store. Once back at home Sam goes to the playroom and opens the tablet to play a game. Now Sam has certainly had a stimulating morning, but what has not been stimulated? His physical body. Playing in the backyard is no match for the allure of screen time entertainment inside. And Sam's mom has denied him an appreciation for quietness, the opportunity to practice patience, and the stimulation of his creativity that comes with playing with blocks or toy trucks.

While it is often easier and more pleasing for us to just gratify our children's craving for entertainment and things, resist this temptation. Let them be bored at times so they can learn how to entertain themselves. Teach them patience and contentment by guiding them toward more active, creative play and teaching them to appreciate what they have. In time, your children will be more grateful with the smaller things in life, less demanding, easier to be with, more content, and even happier. Train them to wait. Later, they just may thank you for it.

Industriousness: The Source of Confidence

Want to develop your child's confidence? Then teach him the value of work and industriousness. It may seem ironic, but real confidence is a byproduct of accomplishments, not of attempts. Success and accomplishments come from hard work. On the contrary, when children are falsely rewarded for any and every attempt, and made to believe success comes easy, they eventually see the fakery in this approach, especially when they see their peers surpassing them. For example: The little leaguer who regularly practices in the batting cage will improve his hitting and earn a position on the starting roster. Contrast this with the child whose father is the assistant coach and appoints his son to bat leadoff, despite his below average ability. Eventually, the unpracticed, privileged child will become discouraged as he realizes his own failures and sees his teammates excelling.

Another byproduct of an industrious work ethic is generosity and the desire to serve others. Giving flows more naturally from a working heart than it does from a "getting" heart. If a child is constantly served by his parents and others, he will tend to be more self-indulgent. This child comes to expect others to meet his needs and wants, rather than expecting to earn his own keep. Generosity doesn't naturally flow from a narcissistic heart.

Warning: In the adult world today, work is considered an activity to be dreaded and avoided at all costs, and entertainment is the golden egg. This may seem natural since no one longs for hard work, but the acceptance of work as normal is an important concept for our children. We will subtly teach our children to avoid all work if they rarely see us work (and when they do, we are complaining about it), if we don't affirm them when they work hard, or if we revere play above all pursuits. Teach your child a proper balance between work and play.

Chores

The desire to work does not come naturally to most children. However, young children generally want to be involved in family life and are pleased when given some responsibilities around the home. Chores are a good way to begin teaching the value of work to your children, and, once successfully implemented, can lighten your own workload. Children also feel a greater sense of worth and of being needed when they are contributing to the family.

Consider Michael as an example. He seemed to be doing well and working hard at college, but when he came home during the summers, he was unmotivated and aimless. He slept late each day and kept a messy room. When his mom prompted him about getting a job or even helping around the house, his answer was always no, citing the need to rest from the school year and to spend more time with his friends. She would relent, but it bothered her that he was so lazy. Michael's dad would angrily complain that he wasn't working, but Michael was unmoved by his words. What Michael's parents failed to realize was that they had missed a key opportunity during his younger years for teaching the value of work and developing in him the pride and satisfaction of contributing to the family. Little did they know that they were creating this lazy monster by overindulging him without requiring any effort from him. Retraining him now will require much more effort than if they had taught him the value of work when he was younger.

How then do we teach our children the healthy value of work? By our actions and our teaching.

Your Actions

Are you modeling an industrious work ethic? Today's generation has enjoyed many benefits of modern technology and general prosperity. The greatest of these might be an easier, less physically strenuous lifestyle than that of previous generations. Unfortunately, with this benefit has come a degree of general inactivity and even laziness among adults. Many of the home duties, once performed by our grandparents' generation, are now performed for us by service industries. We buy our food at the store, sometimes even online, instead of growing it or hunting it. We purchase houses and furnishings rather than building them ourselves. For many, the home is cleaned and the lawn cut by hired workers. As a result, our children rarely see us physically work, and their help around the house is rarely needed as it was for children in the past.

When parents are inactive, their children generally adopt an inactive lifestyle. A solution to this is for you to begin working more around your home and enlisting your children's help. Consider cleaning your own homes to some degree. Cut your own lawn and have your child assist with the yard work. Show your child how pleased you are when he completes his work and applaud him for being a productive member of the family team.

Your Teaching

Be intentional about teaching your child the positive value of work and physical labor. The earliest opportunity to do this is with the institution of household chores. Chores are required duties that the child must perform on a periodic basis. These may be as often as daily or as infrequent as monthly. The tasks should be simple and easy at first, but as your child matures, the expectation of quantity and quality of her work should grow. This is an opportunity to teach your child to take pride in her work and to see it to completion. Personal satisfaction will come as you genuinely praise her for work well done. It is equally important that you point out work that is poorly or incompletely done and require that it be completed to your satisfaction. Remember that you are teaching work habits that will follow your child into her adult years.

Getting Started with Chores

Start young. Begin as early as three years of age by encouraging your child to help you with household chores, such as gathering dirty clothes for washing, feeding the pet, or setting the table. These are intended to inspire your little one to feel she is a needed member of the family.

Offer praise often. Your approval is your child's greatest reward.

Don't insist on perfection. You can insist on completion without demanding perfection. Gauge your expectations by your child's developmental level. Don't expect performance beyond her ability.

Be specific. Develop a list indicating the chore, the frequency, and a box to check when completed. Post it on the refrigerator for all to see.

Motivate with positive and negative consequences. Reward your child with words such as, "You make me so proud of you," or with an allowance. Negative consequences for not completing a chore may come in the form of displaying your disappointment, briefly removing a toy, reducing screen time, or withholding some portion of their allowance.

For a complete list of specific chores to be instituted at specific ages, see chapter 17, Industriousness.

Allowance

Paying an allowance is the common practice of giving a set amount of money on a regular basis to children for their own use. It may be framed as payment for work performed in the home, or it may be given as a "stipend" to cover the expense of certain items in your child's daily life. I prefer the latter approach where the allowance is not directly tied to the required chores. However, if your child's performance during the week has been significantly lacking, partial or no allowance may occasionally be an appropriate consequence.

Using the allowance as a stipend gives your child early opportunities to manage her money. We taught our children to divide the allowance into three categories: giving (10%), savings, and spending. Allowances were paid on Saturdays so that our children could divide the funds accordingly, and offer the giving portion as their offering in church on Sunday. The other two portions of the allowance were placed in separate containers labeled *Spending* and *Saving*.

An often overlooked but essential ingredient of a successful allowance system is a child's *need* for income. This is accomplished by requiring that certain types of items be purchased by the child with the "spending" portion of her allowance. These categories broaden as the child grows. Without this ingredient, your child will never have a true need for the allowance money; and we found with our children that "Where there is no need, there is no desire." Allowance money is more highly valued and additional opportunities to earn extra money are more eagerly sought if money is needed for certain purchases. The book of Proverbs states this concept well: "The appetite of laborers works for them; their hunger drives them on" (Proverbs 16:26 NIV).

For a list of suggested items or events by age that should be funded from the child's own spending money, see chapter 17, Industriousness.

One final point about allowance: Don't be overly generous with the amount you pay your child each week. Choose an amount that is low enough to require some degree of saving to reach the purchase level for toys your child may want to buy. Remember, *without a need* for toys, there will be *little or no incentive* to earn and save money. Over indulgence is a killer of industriousness with children.

Also, monitor and even restrict the amount of money and toys that grandparents may give your child. It's perfectly reasonable to ask that they please limit their generosity if you think it is excessive. If they resist, respectfully stand firm, remembering that your child's character development is your responsibility, not theirs.

Chapter 5

YOUR HOME

I t has been said that the home is a child's first church, first school, first business, and first government. Home is where a child first learns about life, work, law, and morality. Noah Webster, author of the first exhaustive English dictionary, wrote:

> In the family are formed the elements of civil government; the family discipline is the model of all social order; . . . the respect for the law and the magistrate begins in the respect for parents, for their injunctions, their authority, and their instruction. ...Families are the nurseries of good and bad citizens. The parent who neglects to restrain and govern his child, or who, by his example, corrupts him, is the enemy of the community to which he belongs; the parent who instructs his child in good principles, and subjects him to correct discipline, is the guardian angel of his child, and the best benefactor of society.[1]

The home is where it all begins for the child. Instruction, discipline, nurturing, and modeling by the parents all come together to mold and make the child what he is, and how he will function in society.

When the home setting is optimized, your parenting efforts are much more likely to succeed. This may at times mean "going against the flow." I want to challenge you to resist the temptation to manage your home like everyone else does. The status quo is not necessarily the best for your family. While it will often be difficult to go against the cultural flow and make the unpopular decisions, the results will have life-long positive effects for your child and your family.

Your Marriage and Family

The family unit fundamentally begins not with the children, but with the parents' marriage. The health of the family is directly related to the health of the parent's marriage. This relationship should be nurtured as the highest priority within the family.

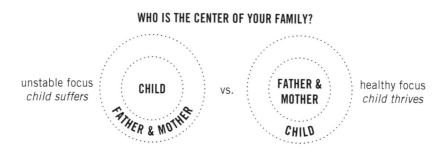

WHO IS THE CENTER OF YOUR FAMILY?

unstable focus
child suffers

CHILD

FATHER & MOTHER

vs.

FATHER & MOTHER

CHILD

healthy focus
child thrives

A child's general health (emotional, physical, and spiritual) often mirrors the health of his parents' relationship. When the marriage suffers, the family unit and the child suffer. One of the most common reasons for a child's misbehavior is instability in the marriage. If parents are modeling disrespectful behavior toward one another, it should not be surprising when their children behave disrespectfully toward family members and others. When parents model and display love for each other, the children feel more secure and free to do the same. Invest in your marriage and your child will benefit. Here are a few basic suggestions.

- Spend time alone with your spouse, from minutes to weekends. Mark the times on your schedule and make them a priority.
- Communicate daily. Nurture the relationship by talking often. Commit to turning off the devices and talking in the evenings, especially after the children go to bed.
- Don't let your children dominate the moment when the family is together. It's okay to ask them to play alone while the two of you catch up.
- Speak positively about your spouse when with your children. By "building each other up" in your children's eyes, their impression of you and your marriage, and marriage overall, is strengthened. Doing this also strengthens your spouse's relationship with the children. Keep your arguments private. Resist the temptation to compete with each other for your child's favor.

- Work on the problem areas in your marriage. Read books, talk with mentors, and seek counseling when necessary. Don't ignore, postpone or allow layers of bitterness to build.

A Strong Family

A strong family is critical to the healthy development of your child. The family is your child's team and you and your spouse are the coaches, managers, and cheerleaders. Building this team will require strategy, practice, investment of time, and protection from outside influences. Furthermore, your family's connectedness will play a crucial role, that is your child's closeness to you and his perception of being loved and desired by you. Research has shown that family connectedness is an important factor in keeping teens from engaging in anti-social or high-risk behaviors such as juvenile delinquency, violence, substance abuse, and sexual activity.[2]

Here are some high points to consider in building your team.

- Consistently spend time together. Have "family only" time regularly.
- Encourage and verbalize support for each another. "We are the Smiths and we stick together."
- Create family traditions.
- Develop and protect the "family table" experience at mealtimes.
- Enjoy life together: Play games together at home, take walks, sing, and take field trips. This requires intentional scheduling to accomplish.
- Be a leader to your child. Every team needs a strong, dedicated coach.
- Applaud each child's contribution to the family.
- Seek to have order in your family life. In the pre-technology days it was easier for this just to happen, but today there are many distractions competing for your family's time and attention. Be intentional.
- Nurture your relationship with your child. It has been said, "Rules without a relationship leads to rebellion." Your child must see and feel your love for him. As you discipline, he must know that you have his best interest in mind (more on the parent-child relationship in chapter 7.)

- Take family vacations. These don't need to be expensive or elaborate. Visit out-of-town relatives. Tent camp at state parks. Make a commitment to regularly get away together, even if it is just for a weekend.

Order in the Home

Order is foundational to our universe. It is evident all around us. The sun's rising and setting can be predicted to the millisecond. A tree's budding and its dormancy are as reliable as the predictable seasons in which they occur. The dependability of gravity requires that the ripe fruit on a tree will always fall down, never up. A healthy seed provided with sun and proper nutrients will always produce. There is a predictable pattern to nature upon which all of life depends.

The human body functions with order as well. Our heart beats at a regular rate to pump oxygen-rich blood to the organs of our body. Each organ has a precise and orderly function that must be reliably carried out for the good of the whole. When this order is disrupted by disease, the body suffers.

We, as adults, depend upon order and routine in our daily lives for survival and productivity. Routine frees our minds to explore higher ideas. Getting up in the morning, brushing our teeth, showering, and getting dressed require little active thought. Order and routine are good.

Children need order as well, and with it comes improved health, confidence, and security. Order, however, does not come naturally to a child or even to a household. It requires intentional, proactive planning from parents, and then, once established, regular reevaluation and adjustment. Order does not mean assuming a rigid schedule; actually, flexibility is a must. It means regularly taking inventory of your family's days and taking control of the schedule rather than letting it take control of you. It means saying no to certain activities or events that are disrupting to the family. And it means saying yes to periods of quietness and idleness in the day when children are napping or playing. It means being intentional about minimizing distractions and outside interferences. In summary, order in the home requires a family to slow down and not let life evolve into chaos.

Here are some ways to create and maintain order in the life of your child and your family.

- Make family meals a priority. Eating supper together has many benefits, as detailed in the next chapter.
- Limit family and personal screen time as detailed in the next section.
- Schedule regular "down time" for the family in order to rest, play, read, or just talk.
- Establish an evening routine. Eat, go for a walk, bathe, read, and then to bed.
- Limit extracurricular activities to one per child per season. Multiple child activities can be exhausting to the child and family.
- Limit your extracurricular activities. Parents need to commit to being at home with their children, especially in the evenings. This may mean postponing a hobby until your children are older.
- Be a good example. Limit your distractions in the presence of your children. Be available to your children and commit to catching up on computer work or your social media after the children go to sleep at night or during their naps.

Among the benefits of order in the home: Children in families with regular routines such as eating meals together are less likely to become obese and more likely to be mentally and emotionally healthy.

The Digital Influences on Your Child and Family

Electronic devices have made life today very different from that of our parents and especially their parents. While offering many advantages to our everyday life, these devices have ushered in risks for the family that our parents could never imagine. For children, as well as adults, electronic attractions and distractions abound: television viewing (often available in every room of the home), movie watching (on devices big and small, fixed and mobile), exploring the vast world of the Internet (by tablet, computer, or smartphone), app gaming, video gaming, computing (at home, at work, and during travel), and more. Digital devices are here to stay, so our obligation must be to set parameters for our children and for ourselves to allow for wise usage.

Negative Effects of Excessive Screen Time

Want to improve your child's chances of being self-controlled, patient, and attentive in school? Of course you do. Then, avoid the early exposure to screened digital devices.

Screen time (television, tablet, computer, video game, and smartphone) can be harmful to your child. The early and frequent use of smartphones and tablets can interfere with healthy brain development. Video gaming can be powerfully addictive to the teenager, especially males. The frequent use of social media by teens can lead to anxiety, depression, and general discontentment. Addiction to pornography among adolescents and young adults is skyrocketing due to easy access on the Internet and mobile devices.

Here are some potentially negative effects of excessive or premature exposure to screen time.

- Decreases creativity. The allure of video entertainment replaces the challenge of original creativity. The child has less time for self-directed daydreaming and creative thinking.
- Interferes with conversation skills. The screen devices become the center of attention and reduce face-to-face interactions with family and friends.
- Discourages reading.[3] Reading requires much more thinking than watching television. Reading improves a youngster's vocabulary. Early exposure to television or tablets reduces reading tendencies at later ages.
- Disrupts sleep. Television watching, tablet entertainment, and video gaming in the evenings tend to push bedtime later. A television in the bedroom is closely linked to poor quality sleep and actual insomnia of teenagers.[4,5] Screens (large and small) in the bedroom are associated with less sleep and poorer quality sleep.
- Reduces school performance. Excessive screen time interferes with study, reading, and thinking time. If children do not get enough sleep, they will not be alert enough to learn well in school.
- Lowers ability to pay attention.[6,7] In one study, the exposure to television at early ages was directly associated with reduced attention in class for seven-year-olds. The high-energy mental stimulation from video watching makes concentration in a seemingly dull classroom very difficult by comparison.
- Encourages a sedentary lifestyle and low achievement. Excessive entertainment from the screens encourages toddlers to be sedentary and to prefer effortless leisure activities, which fosters low achievement in school and homework.

- Displaces time for active forms of recreation. Screen time promotes a sedentary lifestyle and takes away time for participating in sports, music, art, or other activities.
- Increases likelihood of obesity.[8] Excessive screen time leads to less exercise and less calorie burning, and is also associated with more snacking and junk food consumption. A sedentary lifestyle as a child follows many into adulthood.
- Interferes with learning self-control. Using screen time as a distraction or reward to get children to behave in situations where they should be learning self-control aids the parent in the moment, but harms the child in the long run. This can also lead children to seek distractions when confronted with mental, cognitive challenges, such as occurs in the classroom.
- Encourages a demand for material possessions. The frequent exposure to commercials provokes children to pressure their parents to buy the toys they've seen advertised.
- Increases fearfulness. Television exposes children to interpersonal violence and worrisome adult matters that are beyond their level of maturity to emotionally handle. Unlimited exposure to the Internet is unhealthy for the same reasons.
- Increase violence and antisocial behavior as an adult.[9,10] Viewing excessive violence can numb the sympathy that a child normally feels toward victims. Young children can be more aggressive in their play after playing violent video games or seeing violent television programming.

Managing Screen Time

Take control of your family's devices before they take control of your family. Have a plan for their usage and review it with the family regularly.

Win your child's trust. Invest in your relationship. Make it clear that it is your child's heart and your relationship with him that is most important. Therefore, if the use of a digital device is harming either of these, it will be taken away. If your children know you have their best interest in mind, they are more likely to submit to your leadership.

Slow down and seek to keep life simple for the children, especially when they are young. This will be hard with all the digital temptations surrounding you. Keep the screens turned off most of the time. Encourage reading and active play. Be available to your children and create opportunities for conversation.

Don't be intimidated. You may feel overwhelmed by the complexity of digital devices and the peer pressure your child is under to use them. But take action. If you don't monitor their use, no one will. Your child needs your oversight, especially during adolescence. The unlimited content on the Internet and the overpowering pressures of social media will overwhelm your child without your guidance.

Accept your responsibility of being the parent. This means you have authority over all digital devices used by your child, even when your intervention appears to invade his privacy. You also have the right and responsibility to occasionally review the content of your child's devices.

Use of a digital device is a privilege, not a right. This privilege must be earned by your child through responsible behavior, just as it can be lost through irresponsibility.

Don't underestimate the negative content these devices can bring into your child's life. Examples include: Uncensored texting with peers, lewd pictures (sexting), derogatory comments, foul language, gossip, pornography, predatory adult exposure, and access to deplorable content on the Internet.

Don't assume your child is immune. Temptation is a powerful force to cause your child to do things she would not have dreamed. Block the digital temptations. Your child needs your guidance and oversight from the cradle to college, and probably beyond.

Actions for the Family

Don't allow digital devices in bedrooms. The bedroom should be a screen-free sanctuary in order to promote the highest quality sleep. Screens (tablets, phones, and TV) in bedrooms are associated with insomnia and poor quality sleep. Only allow computer use in the living areas of the home where monitoring is possible.

Designate other screen-free zones in the home. In addition to the bedroom, consider making the dining area screen-free as well. Eating is a prime time for conversation.

Designate screen-free times. No device usage during mealtime, during family time, during homework, while in the cars (except on long trips), and one hour prior to bedtime. No video or app game playing on school day evenings and limit it to one to two hours on a weekend day.

Set device curfews. All mobile devices will be turned off at ____ and placed in the kitchen for charging overnight and possible review by parents.

Actions for Younger Children

Limit your child's exposure or use of screened devices. Avoid intentional exposure to screens before the age of two years, with the exception of occasional video chatting with a distant loved one. There is no firm evidence of any benefits of television viewing for children under two years. After two, allow limited time (one hour or less) of quality programming on the family TV or playing quality apps on a family tablet. Ideally, watch the TV or play the games with your child.

Suggested Time Limits on Total Recreational Screen Time

Child's Age	Limit on a Weekday*	Limit on a Weekend day	Device**
Less than 2 years	*Avoid all intentional viewing*	*Avoid all intentional viewing*	*All devices*
2–6 years	½–1 hour	½–1 hour	All devices
6–12 years	½ hour	1–2 hours	All devices
12 years or older	½–1 hour	1–3 hours	All devices

* These weekday limits assume school attendance for at least a half-day after age six.
** Devices include television, computer, tablet, smartphone, and video consoles.

Encourage outside play as an alternative to screen time. Screen-free, active play is healthier for the mind and the body. Consider linking screen time allowance to outside play and/or to the completion of chores.

Avoid (at least limit) using a phone or tablet as a distraction for your young child. While it is tempting to give a mobile device to a toddler when calmness is desired (restaurant, church service, waiting room), it does not teach or train self-control and often does the opposite. Outbursts commonly follow the turning off of the device, and next time your child will likely protest until you give the device again. Instead, prepare for outings by bringing coloring books, toy cars, dolls, or books for your young child. If your phone is never an option, it will not be requested.

Co-view TV programs and co-play tablet games with your children. This allows for monitoring and explanation of content.

Activate parental protection or filters on all Wi-Fi devices. Turn on filters and limits on all devices that access Wi-Fi, including video game consoles.

Be Internet cautious. The Internet can be a useful resource for the family, but it can also be a source of dark, degrading material for a child. Consider the following measures to protect your child.

1. Allow computer use only in the common areas of the home where monitoring is possible; not in a child's bedroom.
2. Program your family computer Internet browser to block pop-ups.
3. Turn on parental control settings on tablets and smartphones.
4. Install an Internet filter/monitor program. This is easy to install and inexpensive for multiple computers in the same household. These programs allow a parent to monitor and even limit a child's access to certain Internet content.

Actions for School-aged Children

Limit screen time on school day evenings. Limit TV and free screen time to 30—60 minutes on school nights to allow time for outside play, homework, and to be in bed on time. No video or tablet gaming on school day evenings.

Avoid screen time just before bedtime. Avoid screen time within one hour of bedtime. Both the light from the devices and the stimulation from watching the programs interfere with a child's ability to fall asleep.

Restrict video console or tablet gaming to weekends only, and then one to two hours a day. Delay video console gaming until eight years of age or later. It can be quite addictive, especially with boys. Avoid violent games; encourage educational or sports games. Review and even play every game you allow on the device. Prohibit online group play, or monitor it very closely.

Delay ownership of devices. Wait until the following ages (or later) to allow personal possession of the device: tablet—10 years; cell phone—13 years; smartphone—15 years. Delay giving your child a cell phone until there is genuine need, such as communication when away from home which is more likely in middle school.

Talk to your child about device use. Let him know that you are trusting him to use it responsibly. Here are some suggested rules.

- The device use is a privilege, not a right. If the privilege is abused, the device will be taken away.
- As your parents, we have the right to monitor the phone, and this will mean giving up the phone occasionally to us for review.
- You are not to load any apps on the phone without our permission.
- Limit game playing; it can be addictive and very wasteful of your time.
- Enjoy this device. You have earned it.

Manage the apps on the phone. Set up parental controls on your child's devices to restrict the downloading of apps. Periodically review the apps on your child's phone. Consult websites like CommonSenseMedia.org for reviews about age-appropriate apps, games, and programs to guide you.

Monitor the devices. Periodically (not every day) request to see your child's device to review its content and history. Ask that your child not delete history records on the device. Strongly consider installing tracking software and browser restrictions on the phone.

Manage any social media allowed. Delay your child's enrollment in social media as long as possible, but no earlier than 13 years of age. If your teen uses social networks, here are some guidelines:

- Open your own account and "follow" your child. View your child's page weekly.
- Know your child's user name and password to monitor his account. Warn your child about creating duplicate secret accounts.
- Review the privacy settings on the social site account and set it to the strictest settings for a young teen.

Teach your child to be wise and polite online. Be sure they are aware of the potential dangers and reinforce some safety measures, including:

- Don't share private or personal information (i.e., date of birth, social security number, address, and personal photos).
- Don't chat or text with anyone your parents don't know or have not approved.
- No chat rooms.
- Don't be rude or bully others. Respect the privacy of others. Don't participate in gossip.
- Once you send a post or picture, the whole world sees it and it cannot be reversed.

- Don't let it steal your time and energy.
- Be on guard for discontentment. Posts are not always as perfect as they appear.

Turn off phones and tablets at bedtime and have your child bring them to a central location in the home for charging overnight. This also provides you an opportunity to review the activity on these devices.

Avoid phone use or texting during homework.

Monitor your child's school-issued computer. If your child is issued a computer from the school and brings it home to use, talk with administration about the installed Internet filter and its limitations. Periodically review the computer history.

Be selective about the movies watched. Going to the movie theater is a popular form of recreation for youth. Movies, however, can subtly influence a child's mind and morals. Don't allow your child to go to a movie simply because it is popular. First, read about it on a dependable movie review website such as MovieGuide.org, PluggedIn.com, or CommonSenseMedia.org. If a movie has a lot of violence, sex, or bad language, talk with your child about why it is best not to see it. Be a trend-setter and hold high standards. Your child will eventually appreciate you for it.

Actions for Parents

Your children are watching. Be a good model. Use your devices responsibly.

Keep your phone in your pocket or purse during idle times with your child. Talk with your child instead.

When driving with children in the car, don't use your phone; talk to your children instead.

Have restrictions about any use of your phone by your children, especially toddlers.

Put your phone down. Make eye contact during conversations with your child. Show interest for what she has to say. Ask for the same respect from her as well.

Designate screen-free times for yourself. In order to give the family your undivided attention, commit to no screen usage on weekdays from 5 p.m. until the children go to bed.

Limit your own social media browsing to times when children are not present. Be on guard for its influences upon you, particularly creating discontentment.

Daycare or Home Care: What is Best for Your Child?

One of the most important decisions parents will make is where and by whom their child will be reared. Will she be placed in a daycare or will she remain at home? Thirty years ago, when I first started practicing, I would occasionally be asked by a mother, "Is it okay if I work outside the home and place my baby in daycare?" Today the question is reversed: "Doctor, I am thinking about quitting my job and staying home with my child. Is that okay for my baby? Will she be socially deprived if I do?" Now, at the risk of offending some parents, I must truthfully answer this question. For a child, the answer to that question is simple: "There's no place like home." Care given by a parent within the home is always superior to a commercial alternative, especially in the early years when parent-child attachment is so critical. (See chapter 7 *Relationship* for the details) The nurture of a child by her parents, especially her mother, at home far outweighs any perceived benefit of social-ization in a daycare. This is especially true in the first three years of a child's life, according to research.[11]

For many moms, working outside the home and placing the baby in a daycare is a necessity, and for others it is a choice. If a choice, then parents must weigh the pros and cons for themselves, the child, and the household. If a necessity, then parents need to make the best selection of daycare options. Let's take a closer look.

Factors to Consider

Advantages of home care by a parent include:

- Greater nurturing from a parent
- Greater opportunity for parent-child attachment and bonding
- Less exposure to infectious diseases and their sequela (ear tubes, etc.)
- Calmer setting
- Less competition for caregiver's (parent's) attention
- Better sleep/nap quality
- Better and more consistent supervision of the child's discipline
- Greater control of influences on behavior and thought

Disadvantages of daycare or frequent childcare outside the home include:

- More exposure of child to infection and more medical visits
- More separation of parent and child with poorer bonding

- Less control of the child's care and instruction
- Less control of child's discipline
- Potentially more behavioral problems at a later age. Research reveals that toddlers and preschoolers who spend long hours each week at daycare exhibit more behavioral problems in kindergarten.[12,13]
- More sleep deprivation due to poorer quality of sleep/naps
- Potentially over-stimulating environment

The appeal of daycare ultimately hinges on increased household income and parental career advancement. The advantages may include:

- Higher economic standard of living
- Greater opportunity for household economic growth
- Greater career advancement for each parent
- More earning potential to fund private education for the child

Therefore, in deciding whether to work outside the home, be sure to consider *all* the costs involved. After factoring in these costs, you may find yourself working for much less than expected.

- Transportation: additional car, gas, maintenance, auto insurance
- Clothing/uniform: costs of purchasing and cleaning wardrobe
- Food: eating out for lunch, more dining out for family, and if working prohibits breastfeeding, formula costs (can run $1100–$1600 in a child's first year)
- Childcare costs and accessories required
- Medical: more child and family illness, more doctor visits, medicines, use of sick days
- Lifestyle: More hurried lifestyle for entire family

Socialization has been an argument in favor of daycare, but this can be accomplished with at-home care through peer interaction at church, gyms, with neighbors, and with organized play groups. A popular option for the stay-at-home arrangement that gives a child more opportunity to socialize and a parent a break from childcare is a half-day Mom's Day Out or pre-school program. These are usually sponsored by local churches or community centers and provide care four to five hours a day. My simple formula for the use of these programs is:

Preschool or Mom's Day Out Program	
Age	Duration
18 months to 36 months	1–2 half-days a week
3-year-olds	2 half-days a week
4-year-olds	3 half-days a week
5-year-olds	Kindergarten (3 to 5 days a week)

Choosing the Best Daycare Setting

When daycare is necessary, consider the following options in how you structure your baby's care.

- Care by a relative. In general, care given at home by mother or father is the ideal, but care by a relative in a home is better than care from multiple caregivers in a commercial daycare.
- Care by a non-relative. Care given in the child's home by a nanny, trusted friend or neighbor can be more nurturing option, where the child receives undivided attention.
- Homecare. Daycare in a home is better, in general, than a commercial daycare setting. Homecare has fewer children, which usually means less exposure to infection, better one-on-one care, less frenzied environment, better napping, etc. This setting may require more scrutiny by the parent since it may not be as rigorously regulated. Use the Evaluation Checklist on page 59 to assess.
- Delay by age. If possible, delay daycare until after one to three years of age. There is evidence that infants who enter daycare under 12 months have less secure attachment to their mothers than those who enter later.[14] Also, the younger an infant gets certain infections (RSV, ear infections, etc.), the greater the chance of subsequent health issues, such as wheezing episodes or the need for ear tubes.
- Delay by season. If possible, delay your infant's entrance into daycare until after the winter months to avoid the respiratory illnesses that prevail during that time.
- Limit time. Limit your child's weekly attendance at daycare, if possible. Half-day attendance is better than full day. Fewer days each week is also better. Perhaps a relative or friend could regularly keep the baby some days each week.

- Quality. Seek the highest quality childcare within your budget. Use the Evaluation Checklist below to assess the facility and the caregivers. In one large research study, "children in higher quality non-maternal child care had somewhat better language and cognitive development during the first 4½ years of life."[3]

Child Care Evaluation Checklist

In your search for the best daycare setting for your child, make one or more personal visits to the facility to observe the care given the children. Use the checklist below to evaluate and compare the features of each facility.

Facilities

1. Are the center/home and all equipment clean and well maintained?
2. Is there plenty of space for the number of children present to play and for toddlers and infants to crawl?
3. Is there a fenced outdoor play area free of dangers such as hard surfaces and rocks, high climbers, tall slides, and unprotected swings?
4. Is there a variety of safe toys appropriate for each age? Are there art and music activities and supplies?
5. Are there designated beds or mattresses to sleep on? Is there a designated sleep (quiet) area large enough for all children during naptime?
6. Do all children have a place for their own belongings?
7. Is there a sufficient number of adult caregivers present at all times? (One adult per 3–4 infants; one adult per 4–5 toddlers; and one adult per 6–9 preschoolers)
8. Does the staff appear to enjoy caring for the children?
9. What is the turnover rate of staff members?

Health & Safety

1. Are there an adequate number of smoke detectors and a fire extinguisher?
2. Are there electrical outlet covers, safe places for cleaning fluids, and medicines and other childproofing measures?
3. Is there always a caregiver present who has recent first-aid and CPR training?

4. Is there an area where ill children can receive care until parents pick them up?
5. Do caregivers wash hands after each child's visit to the toilet or diaper change and before preparing food?
6. Are there written policies about care of ill children? Ask to see them.
7. Will the caregivers give prescribed medications to children?
8. What kind of food and snacks are provided?

Care Plan

1. Is there a written plan for play and learning activities?
2. Is television viewing limited to short periods and child-appropriate programs?
3. Is there a written policy concerning discipline?
4. Do the caregivers meet regularly with parents?
5. Are substitute caregivers, who know the child, available when the primary care givers are absent?

Summary

1. Is your first reaction to the program good?
2. Do the children in the program appear happy?
3. Are all the costs spelled out and available upon request?

If you choose to use daycare, the search for the best daycare for your child is an endeavor worthy of your time and effort. Not only will working parents rest easier, but their child will benefit from the right daycare setting.

Tips for the Stay-at-Home Parent

Staying at home can be a challenge in that the parent must learn to stay engaged with the children on their level and manage their naps and other care. There are many resources available to help the stay-at-home parent be equipped and balanced in childcare responsibilities. Here are a few tips:

- Take a parenting course (such as Love & Logic; loveandlogic.com) with your spouse to give you tools to parent your child well. Basic discipline starts in your child's first year.
- Schedule time out for yourself. Trade a couple hours of childcare with another stay-at-home parent or utilize a Mom's Day Out. See the chart on page 58 for suggested times.

- Get involved with a community of stay-at-home parents, such as a playgroup or Bible study, to give yourself a weekly time to be with other adults and your kids time to play with others.
- Try to have some degree of a weekly routine so that you and your children know what to expect and can get into a rhythm, such as laundry on Mondays, shopping on Tuesdays, or playgroup on Wednesdays.
- Keep nap/rest time a priority and at the same time each day. This gives the child a chance to rest and you a chance to rest or work on your own projects each day. Even older children can benefit from a rest time each day and can be trained to stay in their rooms and play quietly or look at books for an hour or two.
- Keep up communication with your spouse so you both can have time with the kids and you can have breaks for yourself. For example, you could ask your spouse to spend time with the kids when he/she gets home from work so you can cook dinner or take 15 minutes by yourself.

Tips for the Working Mom[15]

- Don't try to be Super Mom. Share the workload with your husband.
- Delegate the household duties to your children as they get older. In other words, institute chores, as we discussed in chapter 4.
- Plan and perhaps prepare meals a week in advance.
- Consider hiring a housekeeper once every week or two.
- Investigate the possibility of working from home, at least part of the week.
- Sleep training for infants as described in chapter 12 can work even though someone else may be caring for your child during the day. (See details in that chapter.)
- Try to carefully select caregivers who will have similar standards and routines for your children while you are away.
- Breastfeeding is still possible, but will require some breast milk pumping while at work. Consider meeting with a lactation consultant prior to returning to work to discuss strategies to help you be successful.
- Try not to impose a hurried mentality on your children. For example, if you need to leave with your little ones early in the morning,

get ready the night before, and allow plenty of time in the morning so it will not be a stressful time for you both.

- Even on days when you work, prioritize trying to give your child some undistracted quality time. On your days off, focus on parenting and relationship building with your children, even if it means saying "no" to other activities.

As I said at the start of this section, this will be one of the most important decisions you will make for your child. It will be a tough decision for some. My intention in writing this chapter is not to make working parents feel guilty. I fully realize the fact that many families have no choice but for both parents to work. My goal is to help you make an *informed* decision. Without all the facts, this is not possible. You can now take into consideration all the facts as you make the best decision for your child and family.

Chapter 6

FIRST THINGS FIRST

Hopefully you have been inspired by the previous chapters to devote your best efforts in parenting your child. Foundational to the success of your efforts will be to meet your child's basic physical needs which will provide your child the best possibility of thriving. So, your attention to this chapter is essential before moving forward. As a matter of fact, if your efforts at parenting begin to fail, you should return to the basics detailed in this chapter to begin diagnosing the problem.

At every stage of life, these needs will have significant influence upon your child. Neglect of any one of these can lead to poor behavior and attitudes that are even resistant to adjustments in your use of discipline methods.

Your Child's Basic Needs

The importance of your attention to your child's basic needs—sleep, nutrition, and exercise—cannot be overemphasized. At every stage of life, these needs will have significant influence upon your child. Neglect of any one of these can lead to poor behavior and attitudes that are even resistant to adjustments in your use of discipline methods. Sleep deprivation, poor diet, and inactivity can negatively affect a child's body, mind, and emotions. It is to these basic needs that I always suggest parents look *first* when troubleshooting problem behaviors, especially with toddlers. Let's take a brief look at each of these now and a more detailed look in the age-specific chapters that follow.

Basic Need #1: SLEEP

One of the greatest gifts you can give your young child is healthy sleep habits through training and enforcement. The sooner these habits are established in a child's life, the easier the process and the more likely they are to continue into the teenage years. Actually, training a child to sleep is a parent's first opportunity to lead the child to good health. Infants, toddlers, preschoolers, and even adolescents need their parents' training, guidance, and oversight to achieve and maintain healthy sleep habits. Without leadership from parents, a child's sleep typically deteriorates as he ages, becoming erratic, shallow, and too brief, and yet his need for sleep remains constant throughout childhood. It is not enough to attend to this matter during infancy or toddlerhood and then let up. It is worthy of continuing oversight through adolescence.

Good Sleep is Essential

Research indicates that when children sleep the recommended number of hours a day on a regular basis, they have better health, including improved attention, behavior, learning, memory, emotional regulation, quality of life, and physical health. Poor sleeping habits and insufficient sleep can lead to myriad problems. For example:

Infants & Toddlers

- Irritability
- Emotional and behavioral problems
- Parental fatigue from nighttime waking
- Poor sleep habits at later ages
- Overeating and higher risk of obesity

School-agers

- Inattention in school
- Poor grade performance
- Emotional liability
- Behavioral problems[1]
- Obesity

Adolescents

- Inattention in school
- Lower grade performance

- Poor executive brain function and poor decision making
- Difficulty waking up
- Tardiness
- Depression
- Anxiety
- Chronic headaches and/or abdominal pain
- Obesity
- Daytime drowsiness, leading to unsafe driving

The Anatomy of Sleep

Since sleep is so important, it is useful to understand the stages and cycles of sleep that we all experience. Scientists have discovered that children and adults experience multiple sleep cycles throughout the night.[2] Each cycle lasts about 50 minutes in infants and increases to 90–110 minutes in adults. Each cycle consists of five basic stages. Stages one through four are non-REM sleep (Rapid Eye Movements), followed by REM sleep.

Stage 1 is light sleep where we drift in and out of sleep and can be awakened easily. In this stage, the eyes move slowly and muscle activity slows. About 2–5% of an adult's night is spent in this stage. During this stage, which lasts one to ten minutes, you may experience hypnic jerks or nap jerks, and may even have a sensation of falling.

In Stage 2, your body begins to prepare for deeper sleep, as the body temperature begins to drop and the heart rate slows. Your muscles relax and you begin to enter deep sleep. It becomes harder to wake you. This stage, which lasts about 20 minutes per cycle, makes up the greatest portion of the night (50%) for an adult in an average night.

Stages 3 and 4 together are known as deep sleep. Breathing and heart rate become very slow and regular. In this stage, which lasts 30–45 minutes per cycle in an adult, it is very difficult to awaken the person. A child in this stage can be picked up, clothes changed, and returned to bed without waking. This stage of sleep is considered the most restful. It is during this stage that a person may experience sleepwalking, night terrors, talking during sleep, and bedwetting. These behaviors tend to occur during the transitions between non-REM and REM sleep. The amount of deep sleep is highest in early childhood (50%), drops during adolescence, and eventually declines to 3–5% in elderly individuals. This is an important stage for healthy growth and development.

REM sleep, also known as dream sleep, is the final stage of a standard sleep cycle. During this stage, the eyes move rapidly in all directions, all muscles in the body are paralyzed, and brain waves are very active—as active as when awake. This is an active stage of dreaming. It usually lasts about 10 minutes per cycle and starts about 90 minutes after falling asleep. This stage represents about 20–25% of an adult's typical night. Newborns, however, spend 50% of their night in REM sleep, suggesting that this is also an essential stage in their development.

Knowing these sleep stages can help you understand what to expect of your child's sleep and how it changes as he grows.

Sleep Cycles

Adults and children experience the stages of sleep in a series of cycles throughout the night. Each cycle ends in a short period of awakening from sleep called an *arousal*, before returning to the next sleep cycle. For young children, these shorts arousals occur every 60–90 minutes (up to ten times a night), followed by a return to sleep. It is important to note that for children who never learn to fall asleep by themselves, these ordinarily brief arousals can turn into all-out, sudden, and prolonged awakenings of agitation requiring parental help to return to sleep.

Another interesting point about sleep cycles is that as the night progresses REM sleep occupies a larger portion of the cycle. Most of the non-REM sleep occurs in the first third of the night, and most of the REM sleep occurs in the last third. So, sleep behaviors associated with deep non-REM sleep (sleepwalking, night terrors) are more likely to occur earlier in the night, and those associated with active REM sleep (nightmares) happen later in the night. Surprisingly, sleep deprivation causes more REM sleep (dream sleep), which can lead to more intense and vivid dreaming, including nightmares.

Sleep Needed

A child's need for sleep varies with age, and may also be affected by her energy level and temperament. There is, however, a minimum amount of sleep that every child needs. If chronically deprived of proper sleep, many children can become numb to their needs, adapt, and appear to be fine. Parents of these children will often claim that their child just "doesn't need much sleep," when in fact it is because the child has not been taught healthy sleep habits. Sooner or later this child's sleep deprivation will lead to emotional or physical problems. Regardless the age of your child, there is no substitute for getting sufficient sleep each night.

All children need their parents' guidance at each stage of life. In infancy, some degree of sleep training (as described in chapter 12) is needed to learn how to sleep deeply and uninterrupted through the night. In toddlerhood, healthy sleeping requires close attention to designated naptimes and bedtime. For the school-ager, it involves teaching after-school time management to achieve a designated bedtime on a consistent basis. For teens, it requires parents monitoring their teen's lifestyle and offering advice (and even restrictions) in order to achieve sufficient rest.

Assuming a 6–6:30 wake up time, these are my recommended target bedtimes for various ages, meaning the times you aim to achieve as often as possible:

Age	Bedtime
4 months to 6th grade	7–8 pm
7th to 9th grade	8–9 pm
10–12th grade	9–10 pm

HOW MUCH SLEEP DO YOU REALLY NEED?
Source: National Sleep Foundation

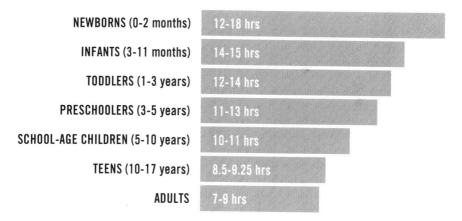

NEWBORNS (0-2 months)   12-18 hrs
INFANTS (3-11 months)   14-15 hrs
TODDLERS (1-3 years)   12-14 hrs
PRESCHOOLERS (3-5 years)   11-13 hrs
SCHOOL-AGE CHILDREN (5-10 years)   10-11 hrs
TEENS (10-17 years)   8.5-9.25 hrs
ADULTS   7-9 hrs

Achieving Good Sleep

From their first year to their eighteenth year, children need a parent's help with sleep in the form of providing (1) proper guidance and (2) the proper environment. Guidance initially involves training a child to sleep independently (falling asleep by themselves), and later involves overseeing a proper sleep schedule.

Here are some basic guidelines, given by age, for helping your children develop proper sleep habits.

1. Providing Guidance

Infancy

Train your baby to fall asleep unassisted (to self-soothe) at designated naptimes and bedtime in order to sleep deeper and longer. The details on how to accomplish this are discussed in chapter 12.

Toddlerhood

- Maintain consistent naptimes and bedtime.
- Avoid screen time within one hour of bedtime. No intentional screen time allowed before two years.
- Avoid eating or drinking prior to bedtime. A full tummy can interfere with good sleep.
- Dim the lights in the bedroom and don't allow any screened devices in the bedroom.
- Allow a transition object. Some children feel more secure if they have something to snuggle at bedtime, such as a stuffed animal or blanket.
- Develop a bedtime routine. Have a set time to begin your routine. Make the routine pleasant and relaxing. Example: Bathe, put on pajamas, brush teeth, read story, lie down together, sing a song, say prayers, and then leave the room while your child is still awake. Research shows that reading stories at bedtime (either parent or child reading) is associated with getting more sleep at night and having fewer sleep problems.
- Avoid "sleep associations" to fall asleep at bedtime, such as rocking, drinking, or video watching. A child who needs these at bedtime will need these in the middle of the night if she wakes.
- Teach independent sleep. In order for children to be able to sleep through the night, they must be able to fall asleep—alone and in their bed—at bedtime. So, leave the room while your child is relaxed, but still awake. Falling asleep independently leads to deeper, higher quality sleep and to more consistent sleep through the night.

School-age

- Strive to have a consistent bedtime. Limit extracurricular activities to one per season to avoid late nights.
- Encourage active outside play after school. This helps promote tiredness at bedtime.
- Limit screen time on school nights. No video or tablet gaming on school nights. No screen time within 45 minutes of bedtime. Screens stimulate the brain, masking your child's need for sleep.
- Maintain a consistent bedtime. I often hear from busy families with multiple children that they are too busy to achieve a consistent bedtime for their school-aged children. My advice is to limit extracurricular activities (no more than one activity per season) and to enforce a healthy bedtime on the nights when it is possible. Getting to bed on time two to three out of the five school nights a week is better than none. Too often, we let the exceptional nights (baseball game, gym practice) define the normal nights and the bedtime becomes consistently too late every night.

Adolescence

- Monitor and enforce a healthy bedtime. Your teen needs your oversight.
- Encourage an active lifestyle. Limit screen time after school.
- Avoid regular napping after school, since this will diminish sleepiness at a reasonable bedtime.
- Remove screens from bedroom at bedtime, including a laptop, tablet, or smartphone. Phones should be removed to charge in a common area of the home, like the kitchen.
- Avoid caffeine drinks any time after lunch. This is a stimulant that can interfere with sleep.
- Prohibit gaming on school nights.

2. Providing the Best Environment

Your child's bedroom should be a sanctuary for sleeping, free of distracting sounds or lights. Here are a few tips to creating a healthy environment for sleep.

- Banish electronics from the bedroom. Digital screens emit a type of light that stimulates the mind and interferes with healthy sleep.

From infancy to adolescence, your child's bedroom needs to be a screen-free sanctuary. Watching movies may appear to help your young child fall asleep, but the quality of this sleep is poor and shallow, and eventually insomnia will set in.

- Use black-out shades or curtains. Make the room as dark as possible after your child falls asleep. This includes small lights on baby monitors or alarm clocks; move them away from your child's bed. A nightlight may be desired while your child is going to sleep, but turn it off after he is asleep. A darkened room in the morning helps a baby sleep later.
- Use dim lighting in the evening. This stimulates secretion of the sleep hormone, melatonin, in the brain. One hour prior to bedtime, dim the lights in the bedroom. Have a small reading lamp to read to your young child and for your school-aged child to read to himself.
- Make the bedroom comfortable. Sleep comes easier in a cool room, or at least one where there is air movement (running a fan).
- Keep quiet or block the sounds. Encourage quietness outside the baby's room. If you have other young children making noise in the house, then a fan or soft sound machine in the room may be necessary to drown out the outside noises. Once your child is asleep and the house is quiet, turn off the sound machine before you go to bed.

Be patient and persistent. Success can be slow in coming with adjustments in sleep guidance and the sleep environment. Your persistence will pay off. Sleep training in particular takes time, especially if you are retraining your child. It can also cause some temporary emotional stress between the child and the parent. Keep in mind that once the training is completed, however, your child will experience wonderful confidence in himself and have more stamina for the next day.

Basic Need #2: NUTRITION

Your child's eating habits begin developing very early in life. How you manage mealtime with your children will have lasting consequences for them. While nutrition is fairly straightforward during infancy, toddlerhood can bring much uncertainty and frustration. It is during these trying days that the establishment of the "Family Table" can help guide you and your child toward harmony and good health. First, let's talk about eating responsibilities.

Eating Responsibilities

"I just can't *get* my child to eat anything!" This is a common declaration from parents of toddlers, even though the weight and height may be entirely normal for their age. What they really mean is the child eats very little at the dinner table and what she does eat is not the healthiest. To this I usually respond, "Did you know that it is not your responsibility to get your child to eat?" This is a revelation to many, but once realized it relieves the parents of tremendous pressure and guilt. Really, it is not a parent's responsibility! It is the child's responsibility to eat according to his needs. The parent's responsibility is only to offer healthy foods in a healthy setting. A normal child will never under-feed himself.

It's not the parents' responsibility to get their child to eat; it is only to provide healthy foods in a healthy setting.

The real question is, "Why is he not eating?" Here are some possibilities:

- He has no appetite due to excessive snacking prior to mealtime.
- He drank away his appetite with juices and milk, either just before or during mealtime.
- He is distracted by the television, family pet, or a parent's smartphone.
- He is in a habit of getting down and running around the dining area while the rest of the family eats at the table.
- He is waiting for the "filler foods" (mac-n-cheese, PB&J, chicken nuggets, dessert) that Mom or Dad always bring out at the end of the family meal.
- He's not hungry. Toddlers will have days when they eat very little.

Taking the "Family Table" approach to mealtime eliminates many of the pitfalls to eating which a parent may experience with toddlers or preschool children. Let's examine this concept and then I will offer some pointers on preserving your child's appetite.

The Family Table

Do you want your children to be healthier eaters, smarter, more accomplished in life, less prone to obesity, more obedient, more articulate, less likely to use drugs and alcohol, less sexually active as a teen, and more likely to embrace your values? Of course you do! According to research, eating together will help accomplish these.[3]

Over the past three decades, family time at the dinner table and family conversation in general have declined by more than 30%. Families with children under age 18 report having family dinners an average of only three to four times per week. A third of families with 11- to 18-year-olds eat one or two meals together a week at most. Only one fourth eat seven or more family meals per week.[4] The experience at the family table has also declined in quality with the increase in distractions, such as television watching, smartphone apps, text messaging, telephone conversation, and clean up from the meal preparation.[5] Barriers cited by parents to coming together for meals include too little time, child and adult schedule challenges, and food preparation. Nonetheless, most parents say they place a very high value on family meals, ranking them above every other activity (including vacations, playing together, and religious services) in helping them connect with their families and children. Most wish they had more family dinners.

Benefits of the Family Table

- More mealtimes at home is the single strongest predictor for the child earning better achievement scores and showing fewer behavioral problems. Mealtime is more powerful than time spent in school, studying, church, playing sports, or art activities.[6]
- More family talk occurs at mealtime than at any other activity, including playing with toys and storybook reading.
- Children ages 9–14 who have more regular dinners with their families have healthier dietary patterns, including more fruits and vegetables, less saturated and trans fat, fewer fried foods and sodas, and more vitamins and other micronutrients.[7]
- Preschool-aged children exposed to the three household routines of (1) regularly eating the evening meal as a family, (2) obtaining adequate nighttime sleep, and (3) having limited screen-viewing time had a 40% lower prevalence of obesity than those exposed to none of these routines. These household routines may be promising targets for obesity-prevention efforts in early childhood.[8]
- Adolescents from homes where the family regularly eats meals together (more than five meals/week) have much lower likelihood

of disordered eating (weight control tactics of self-induced vomiting, laxative use, diet pills, fasting, eating very little food, using food substitutes, skipping meals, and smoking).[9]

- Teens who eat with the family eat more vegetables, fruits, and dairy products.
- Teens eating dinner with their families have fewer negative effects from online bullying. Mealtime can provide a release for teens and an opportunity to communicate their problems with family members.[10]
- Teens in families who eat together five times or more a week are one and a half times more likely to have an "excellent" relationship with their mother and father. Those teens with poor relationships with parents were four times more likely to use marijuana, two and a half times more likely to smoke cigarettes, and two times more likely to drink alcohol. [11]

Creating a Healthy Family Table

Practicing the Family Table will require intentional planning on your part. There will be resistance from your children but less if you begin at early ages. There will be work schedule and child activity conflicts along the way. There will be times when only one parent can be present at the meal; it is still worth practicing for the benefit of consistency for your child. The entertaining element of TV watching and desire to answer a text message will be difficult to resist. In the long run, these sacrifices will pay great dividends. Here are the basic elements of the Family Table.

- Make family meals a priority. Take some time to discuss with everyone in your family ways to make family meals possible. Schedules or meal times may need to be rearranged to make this happen. Try to have family meals at least three to five times a week.
- Turn off all electronic devices during mealtime. The dietary patterns of children from families in which television viewing is a normal part of meal routines include fewer fruits and vegetables and more pizzas, snack foods, and sodas than the dietary patterns of children from families in which television viewing and eating are separate activities.[12]
- Serve the same foods to everyone at the table. Avoid short-order cooking for children older than 18 months. Be a good example, eat your veggies!

- Serve a healthy variety of foods. Serve home-cooked foods as often as possible. However, even a fast-food meal purchased on the way home from work and served at the family table is better than no table time at all.
- Encourage pleasant conversation. Require that all talk be respectful and encouraging. Don't allow excessive silly talk that may lead to chaos at the table. Mealtime is not a time for rehashing the day's misbehaviors or failures. Research shows that a happier emotional atmosphere during meals allows preschoolers to make healthier food choices. For example:
  ▸ Make conversation by asking, "What was your high and low today?"
  ▸ Talk about your child's successes that day (good grade, helped others, assisted with house work, kind words to a sibling).
  ▸ After the meal, read through a book together over the course of several evenings.
  ▸ Do a family devotion; sing songs together.
- Refrain from discussing a child's poor eating habits at the table. Instead, once everyone is finished, require that your child take a few bites of any foods on the plate that she has avoided. This will increase the likelihood that they will like the food in the future.
- Require that everyone stay at the table until all have finished. While this can be the most difficult to enforce, it is key to the success of the family table. Teach this concept early and it will enrich mealtime for years to come. For the toddler, it may mean strapping him in the highchair and listening to prolonged periods of protest until he realizes that you are not going to give in. For the school-ager, it will mean consistent enforcement, even when your child's attitude is less than attractive and the pleas to leave the table are quite persuasive.

The Family Table eliminates a common dilemma encountered at the dinner table—The Picky Toddler. The scenario is all too common: After only five minutes at the family table, the toddler is throwing food and pitching a fit to get down and go play. What's a parent to do? Should he be given a different food he is known to like, or be allowed down, or made to stay with no change in food selection? By giving an alternate food, the parent is encouraging poor nutrition. By allowing him to leave the table, the parent is opening the door for manipulation upon his return, when he says he is hungry. Under the Family Table, the toddler must stay in his seat with no change in foods offered, and can only be dismissed after all have finished eating. If he sits in the highchair for the entire mealtime without eating, then the parent can know he is simply not hungry. No normal child will voluntarily starve himself. If given the opportunity (under these arrangements), he will eat according to his needs.

As the practice of the Family Table is continued through the adolescent years, healthy eating habits and enriched relationships among family members occur. Not only does healthy nutrition affect the body, it also positively affects the mind and the emotions, whereas hyperactivity, inattention, depression, and other behaviors have been linked to poor nutrition.

Preserve their Appetite for Mealtime

Any parent of young children knows that their appetite can be quite finicky and unpredictable. In many cases, however, parents are unknowingly hurting their child's appetite by allowing excessive snacking and drinking before and during the meal. Here are some tips to preserving your child's appetite:

First year

- Breastfeed as long as you can during infancy, even if it means offering formula supplementation when your breast milk supply is low.
- Delay starting any sweetened drink (including juices) until after two years of age, and even then only offer it on special occasions.
- Delay solid foods until five to six months of age.
- With the introduction of solid foods, offer vegetables before fruits, and once fruits have been introduced offer them less often than vegetables.
- Stop the bottle by 12 months and move to a sippy cup. Continuing a bottle beyond a year often results in a child drinking too much milk by drinking for pleasure rather than for need.

Second year

- Delay the introduction of juices or sweet drink until after two years of age; offer water instead. Once introduced, offer the drink on special occasions with your child sitting in a chair at the kitchen table. Allowing your child to drink it daily, or to carry a sippy cup of sweet drink throughout the day, will kill his appetite for healthy foods at mealtimes.

- At mealtimes, offer only milk or water to drink, not juice or sweet drink. Sweet drink during mealtimes makes the bland, healthier foods less attractive. Also, limit the amount of milk to one cupful (six to eight ounces), then offer water as desired by your child.
- If your child seems thirsty between meals, offer water in the sippy cup.
- Begin practicing the Family Table at 18 months.
- Teaching your child to stay in the highchair until everyone has finished eating will not be easy in the beginning. There will be protest and resistance. Once convinced that you will not change your mind on the matter, your child will patiently stay in his seat and satisfy his appetite with a greater variety of foods.

Third Year

- Limit snacking to healthy snacks at designated times, such as fruit, raw vegetables, cheese, peanut butter and crackers.
- Require that your child always ask permission before getting any food or drink from the pantry or refrigerator. Children need your oversight. This should be a rule that continues until adolescence.
- Don't stress over how much your child is eating. Remember: It's not your responsibility to get your child to eat, only to offer healthy foods at regular mealtimes. Practice the Family Table, and your child's health will flourish.

Basic Need #3: EXERCISE

A better term for this basic need is *activity level* because it can take many forms and is essential for good health.

There are many health benefits for your child from having an active lifestyle:

- Improves physical fitness
- Promotes creativity and imagination
- Lowers a child's stress level
- Improves behavior

- Improves attention span
- Improves immunity
- Builds confidence
- Improves emotions
- Reduces depressed feelings
- Improves sleep quality

With all these benefits, you might ask, what is a healthy amount of activity for our children? The Office of Disease Prevention and Health Promotion recommends children and adolescents ages 6–17 get one hour of physical activity a day.[13] This includes:

- Aerobic Activity: Most of the 60 or more minutes a day should be either moderate- or vigorous-intensity aerobic physical activity (such as running, dancing, or biking), and include vigorous-intensity physical activity at least three days a week.
- Muscle-Strengthening: As part of the 60 or more minutes of daily physical activity, include muscle-strengthening physical activity (such as climbing trees, using playground equipment, or lifting weights) on at least three days a week.
- Bone-Strengthening: As part of the 60 or more minutes of daily physical activity, include bone-strengthening physical activity (such as running or jumping rope) on at least three days a week.

Play: Active v. Passive

One of the earliest forms of exercise for young children comes in the form of active play. As we play with our children and teach them to play alone, they gain many benefits. Play encourages active living, helps a child develop language and social skills, teaches them conflict resolution, and encourages creativity and independence. Not all types of play, however, are the same; some are more beneficial than others. Let's take a look at two broad categories, active play and passive play.

Active play is an enjoyable or entertaining activity in which the child is a participant using his many senses, such as seeing, hearing, touching, smelling, and tasting. It is an activity that involves a child's entire body to accomplish. The term "active" does not necessarily mean running and jumping; a child can be actively looking at a book, turning the pages, or playing with a puzzle.

Passive play is an enjoyable or entertaining activity in which the child is only an observer with little to no engagement, using one or two senses. Examples include watching TV, playing with electronic screened devices, or riding on battery-powered toy vehicles.

The two types of play can be illustrated by contrasting a child playing a game on a phone app with playing the game in real life. With the phone, the game comes pre-loaded with preset mechanics, where the child uses repetitive finger movements to play the game. With real life, the child must physically create the game and its rules of engagement. Imagination and cognition are needed more than if the child simply follows the pre-programed game directions on an app. Also, children who engage in active play with peers learn social, interactive skills.

ACTIVE PLAY		PASSIVE PLAY
Child learns to push self and then peddle on a tricycle		Child rides in a battery powered riding toy car
Child plays with LEGO blocks	VS.	Child plays game on a tablet
Parent and child sit on the floor and play together		Parent and child watch TV together
Child plays soccer on a team		Child plays soccer video game

Children should do more active play than passive, especially in the preschool years. Passive play can be more attractive to a child (or an adult) for its immediate and persistent gratification. For this reason, parents must take the lead in pushing their child toward active play, and restricting exposure to screened devices. Another reason to limit passive electronic play is the addictive nature of the devices, and the moody behavior that commonly follows this type of play with young children.

Encouraging Children to be Active

Model Activity. When parents model an active lifestyle, children are much more likely to adopt one as well. One study revealed that the physical activity levels of mothers and their four-year-old preschoolers are directly associated; the more active the mother, the more active the preschooler.[14] It is not enough to tell our children to be active or go outside to play, we too must be active in our work and our play.

Limit Screen Time. The first step in accomplishing an active lifestyle with most families today is to turn off those screens. Today's children and teens are much more sedentary than their parents or grandparents were. The main difference is the attractiveness of staying inside the home which is largely due to electronic entertainment. Making inside living more boring than outside play should be your goal with children from preschool to adolescence.

For children, toddlers, and preschoolers, I recommend avoiding electronic toys and providing toys that encourage more creativity and hand play, such as books, mechanical toys (cars, trucks, boats), dolls, and LEGO blocks. Console video games should be avoided until eight years of age or later, and handheld devices only after four to five years of age. For school-aged children, I recommend limiting entertainment screen time to a half hour on school day nights and no video or app game playing on these nights. They should be encouraged to get outside and play for at least 30 minutes before starting their homework.

Get Outside. Encourage outside play. As a family, go on strolls, walks, games, hikes, bike rides, and jogs. School-age children should be encouraged to get outside and play for at least 30 minutes before starting their homework. Encourage your children to enroll in activities that require regular practice or participation, like playing sports, joining the school band, or joining the local scouts. If not involved in an organized activity, then taking a fast 30-minute walk each day will be a good substitute.

Chapter 7

THE DISCIPLINE PROCESS

As we established in chapter 3, character and competence don't just happen in the development of a child. A sustained process of guidance and training is necessary. This process is best termed *discipline*, and is defined as "training expected to produce a specific character or pattern of behavior, especially training that produces moral or mental improvement."[1] The purpose of discipline is to guide a child from being a self-centered infant to becoming a self-disciplined adult. Discipline involves three primary components: instruction, affirmation, and correction. These components are then applied within the parent-child relationship, which is foundational to the success of the discipline process. Without a quality relationship, even the proper application of the discipline components will fail to yield favorable results.

As important as the discipline process is, it must be accompanied by proper attention to the child's basic needs. When these needs (sleep, nutrition, and exercise) are met, as detailed in the previous chapter, the child is freed of many of the natural hindrances to compliant behavior, and is afforded the best opportunity to respond to parental discipline and to achieve self-control.

The Discipline Process

The discipline process can also be compared to the growth of a tree. The gardener plants the seed (child) in rich soil (parent-child relationship), where there is ample water and sunlight (basic needs). He then fertilizes the plant (affirmation) to enhance its growth. The seed blossoms into a sapling which will require support and guidance from a stake (instruction) to allow for upright growth. As it matures, the young tree will require some pruning (correction) to ensure its fruitful and directed growth.

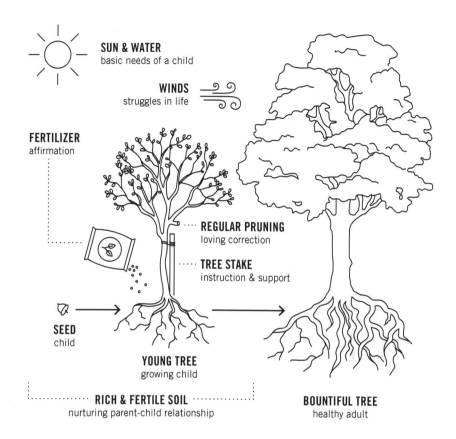

SUN & WATER
basic needs of a child

WINDS
struggles in life

FERTILIZER
affirmation

REGULAR PRUNING
loving correction

TREE STAKE
instruction & support

SEED
child

YOUNG TREE
growing child

RICH & FERTILE SOIL
nurturing parent-child relationship

BOUNTIFUL TREE
healthy adult

Perfect results are never guaranteed, for either gardeners or parents, yet a good outcome is more likely when the proper attention is given throughout the process. For example, if the soil (relationship) is not enriched or water and sunlight (child's basic needs) are lacking, the seed will grow poorly. Or, if there's too little pruning (correction) of the sapling, its sprawling branches will limit its stature and ultimately its production. Or, if there's too little fertilization (affirmation), the young tree barely grows and will yield little fruit. Just so, with a lack of discipline, a child will surely grow to be dysfunctional and weak.

Let's now consider how discipline works with children, starting with the foundation provided by the parent-child relationship.

Relationship

To repeat: the parent-child relationship is fundamental to the success of the discipline process. It provides the foundation upon which a child is instructed, affirmed and corrected. The relationship will greatly influence the child's interpretation of her parents' disciplinary actions and intentions. From birth, the relationship will develop and mature for better or for worse. Its health will be influenced by several factors and transitions within the relationship. Let's consider some of the factors that are within your control to enrich this relationship.

Being Available

The mother-baby relationship is the first for the baby and begins in the womb. A mother's brain is physically and chemically prepared during pregnancy by hormones released within her body to optimize her ability to give loving care to her newborn. The unborn baby likewise develops a unique attachment to its mother while in the womb by hearing her voice and through smell and taste of the amniotic fluid, which surrounds the baby. Research has clearly shown newborn's recognition of and preference for its mother's voice and mother's skin and breast milk.

After birth, the interaction and availability of the mother to the baby has emotional and physical benefits for both. With breastfeeding, the calming hormone, oxytocin, is released within the mother's body to aid her in tolerating the cry and sympathizing with the unrest of her newborn baby. This hormone, which aids in bonding, is released in greater levels as mother and baby physically interact after birth (i.e., eye contact, face-to-face interaction, feeding, and holding). The more a mother engages with her baby, the more oxytocin she produces, and the greater bonding—which benefits mother and child.

According to the research of psychiatrist John Bowlby, infants are born with an innate need to attach to one main figure.[2] While infants can attach to other figures later, there is a primary bond that is more important than any other, the mother. This primary relationship is the basis for forming all other relationships. It also lays the foundation for the development of self-concept and self-regulation. In her book, *Being There*, psychoanalyst Erica Komisar examines the research on mother-baby attachment.[3] She finds that "A mother's presence and attachment to her baby in the first three years of life are critical for the development of the social part of the baby's brain and for the ability of the baby to cope with stress." A baby's internal sense of security is largely controlled by the presence and sensitive care of its mother.

As a child grows, he seeks closeness to and maintains contact with a loving parent. If a child has a strong primary attachment to his parents from infancy on, then the relationship is enhanced and he is more likely to follow their lead. This, in turn, provides a child with the security to naturally break the bond and transition confidently into adult independence. There is no substitute for building a relationship and being available to your child from early childhood through adolescence.

Loving Unconditionally

The child must feel and know that her parents' love for her is unconditional. This will be her first source of self-worth. She must know that love is not based upon her performance, achievement, attractiveness, or even conduct. In the midst of disobedient behavior and the correction that follows, she must know that the foundation of her relationship with her parents is not threatened. This, of course, will stand in contrast to her relationship with peers and friends, which is often very conditional, especially in the teen years. Social media will tell teens that their self-worth is dependent upon how successful they are in achieving the "social norm," which of course changes by the day. This often leads to depression and anxiety. Security and inner peace are rarely found outside the family. They are more naturally tied to a secure and unconditional parent-child attachment that begins in infancy.

Leading Consistently and Compassionately

Today, more and more school-age children, especially teens, are feeling detached from their parents as they are drawn into attachments outside the family. The advent of digital technology is a culprit, increasingly driving a wedge between parents and children. Fewer and fewer children revere their parents as the primary source of wisdom in their life, and instead seek the advice of their peers via social media. The antidote to this contemporary relationship breakdown is to pursue the authoritative parenting style with your children, which balances loving affection with consistent enforcement of boundaries. As detailed in chapter 2, the authoritative parent seeks to establish a positive relationship by balancing responsiveness to the child with demandingness of the child.

Authoritative parents demonstrate *responsiveness* by:

- Displaying warmth and affection.
- Loving unconditionally.
- Seeking to understand the child's perspective.
- Praising good behavior and criticizing bad with sensitivity.

- Balancing their children's needs for protection and autonomy.
- Being involved in the child's life without excessive micromanaging.
- Encouraging independence and individuality with maturity.
- Being willing to use age-appropriate reason and discussion to obtain a child's compliance.

And yet concurrently they demonstrate *demandingness* by:

- Requiring mature behavior within the child's range of ability.
- Basing demands of the child on his attributes, abilities, and developmental level.
- Correcting and controlling behavior in a firm, yet goal-oriented manner.
- Accompanying their demands with explanations.
- Adding responsibilities and privileges as abilities are demonstrated.
- Monitoring the child's activities and knowing his whereabouts.

In other words, the parent-child relationship is built upon the parents' display of *affection* for the child and by their *actions* toward the child. Genuinely displaying love for the child in these two ways leads to a rich relationship, which is in turn conducive to proper behavior. Researcher Diana Baumrind describes the results this way: "Because authoritative parents are warm, responsive, and autonomy-supportive, their children are motivated to maintain family harmony by either complying with or responsibly dissenting to parent demands in an effort to change their parent's mind rather than by defiantly disobeying."[4]

In the discipline model, a parent's application of instruction, affirmation, and correction works to develop the parent-child relationship. In your child's early years of life, these components are defining the relationship, but later in life the relationship will actually determine the success of these components. When affirmation and correction are lovingly—yet firmly—applied early on, your child will perceive your intentions as being in his best interest and the relationship will thrive, making future discipline more productive. On the contrary, if your approach is heavy on correction and light on affirmation, your child will perceive your efforts as self-serving and not in his best interest. Furthermore, a heavy emphasis on power assertion and punishment has been shown to lead to higher levels of aggression and antisocial behavior. Equally harmful, if your discipline is all about affirmation with little to no correction, eventually your child will perceive your guidance as weak and without conviction. It is the customized balancing of the components of discipline that ultimately leads to successful development of a child. So, remember—

Rules without a relationship leads to rebellion,
and relationship without rules leads to chaos.

A healthy parent-child relationship is absolutely necessary for discipline to work.

Allowing Transition

Now that we have established the importance of the parent-child relationship, you might ask, "How does this relationship change with the age of my child?" As your child matures, your relationship will and must change for your child's benefit. In the early years, more structure will be necessary in your child's life, so the relationship will be more controlling and limiting. As he demonstrates more responsible behavior and more mature judgment, less control is needed, more reasoning is used, and more freedoms are granted. This change in the relationship is crucial to allow for your child's growth and development.

This change in the parent-child relationship is driven by the changing role of the parent. These transitioning roles are depicted in the following table, which is adapted from Bruce Johnston's material, *The Journey of Transition.*[5] The age range associated with each parenting role is approximate. Transition from one role to the next will depend upon your child's maturity and general compliance. If she is delayed in her maturity or resistant to your guidance, the current role will need to last longer and the transition will be slower than indicated.

THE CHANGING ROLE OF THE PARENT

child's age

0-12 MONTHS	1-5 YEARS	5-12 YEARS	12-21 YEARS	21+ YEARS
CAREGIVER	TEACHER	MONITOR	MENTOR	FRIEND
protect	teach	teach	advise	assist
provide	discipline	discipline	discipline	enjoy
train	control	persuade	monitor	encourage

Notice how your relationship with your child changes over time. Each role provides a foundation for the next. If you diligently carry out the duties of your current role, then transition to the next will be smoother. If you ignore the duties of any given role or if you refuse to transition to the next, your relationship with your child will suffer and his maturation will be jeopardized.

Each relationship phase has its unique responsibilities. The Caregiver phase is a time of provision, protection, and bonding. The Teacher phase is perhaps the most critical; it is during these years that a parent must teach proper behavior, require respect and cooperation, and correct misbehavior and rebellion. This stage can be quite intense and fatiguing. The process of discipline will occasionally bring unpleasant conflict to the parent-child relationship as the child's foolishness collides with the parent's direction. If the parent remains lovingly firm, the fruitful results of this discipline will soon emerge and the upcoming stages in the relationship will be much easier and more enjoyable. However, if discipline is ignored during these years and compromise dominates, conflict will inevitably increase as the child attempts to overrule the parent.

During the Monitor phase, the child should exhibit more "internal" self-control and therefore the parent can reduce the "external" control. More reasoning is used and much less physically assertive, corrective measures (like time-out or spanking) are needed. Parents must, however, continue to closely monitor the child's behavior. In the Mentor phase, the teen should be allowed more freedoms as responsible behavior and good judgment are demonstrated. If deserved, the reins must be loosened to allow the teen to experience some independence and to meet the challenges of individual decision-making.

For some parents, loosening the disciplinary reins is difficult. They sincerely feel that it is best for their child that they maintain tight control over her life, regardless of her level of maturity. But, when parents allow for the healthy progression of the parent-child relationship, they reach the final phase of Friend and find it to be rich and rewarding.

Our goal in parenting should be to slowly and surely work ourselves out of a job. This concept can be heart wrenching for those of us who love the job of parenting, but we must understand that to do otherwise is to hinder our child's success in life.

Instruction

Having established the foundational importance of the parent-child relationship to the discipline process, we next look at the first of three components of the process, namely *instruction*. Proper discipline must start with clear and appropriate instruction, which validates the other two components and reduces a child's exasperation. How can a child know what to do unless he is told? How can he be expected to behave unless he is first instructed in proper behavior? Through instruction, limits are set—and must be understood—in order to avoid the frustration of unknown, unclear, or unrealistic expectations.

Instruction must therefore be:

- *Simple and clear*—A child cannot be expected to behave properly without first being instructed how to behave. When misbehavior occurs, and before correction is meted out, ask yourself, *Have I been clear with my child about my expectations of his behavior?*
- *Age-appropriate*—Instructions must be clearly communicated in a language the child can understand. A parent's expectation for obedient behavior must not exceed the child's developmental ability to comply. For example, it would be unreasonable to expect an 18-month-old to sit still and quietly through a one-hour church service. However, it is reasonable to expect a six-year-old to do so.
- *Directing*—Your expectations for your child's behavior should be high, but reasonable. In others words, parents are not just to cope with their child's behavior; they are to direct it or lead it. This means understanding what can be expected of your child at his developmental level, and then instructing him in it. Your child needs your leadership to know what degree of self-control he is capable of. Low expectations yield low results. High yields high.
- *Expectant*—Instruct your child (from toddler to teenager) with confidence and expectation. Your child's perception of your expectations for her behavior will greatly influence her compliance. If you appear tentative and uncertain, she will ignore your instruction until you appear more serious or frustrated. If she believes you are serious about the directive (willing to back it up with correction) and are confident that she can do it, she is much more likely to obey. Be lovingly firm. For example: Asking, "Sally, are you ready to pick up your toys and go to bed?" is likely to fail. However, saying, "Sally, it's time to pick up your toys and get ready for bed. When I come back and see the toys put away, we can read a book together before bedtime," will prove successful.

- *Consistent*—Rules and their enforcement must not change with the whim of the parent or the setting. Consistency from a parent will produce security within the child, knowing that he can relax and enjoy his freedoms within his understood boundaries. Inconsistency creates anxiety, frustration, and even bitterness. A child will become exasperated when trying to please his parents' inconsistent enforcement of rules.

- *Modeled*—Live by the standards you set for your children. They are more likely to do what you *do* than what you *say*. As you instruct your child to be self-controlled, the same control should be present in your life. Our children learn patience and compassion for others as they see it demonstrated by us. If we expect our children to be industrious, they must see us working at home and in our professional setting. The best way to teach a child to genuinely apologize for wrongdoing is to seek his forgiveness when you have wronged him. A toddler is more likely to obey your directive to keep his room clean if you demonstrate order and neatness in your own living space. Don't promote a standard that you are not willing to keep yourself. Think about it, our children are watching:
  - how we treat each other as spouses
  - how we treat our guests and others outside our home
  - how we talk about others in our children's presence
  - whether we take moral stands on societal issues
  - whether we live by the standards we set for them, such as:
    - our use or overuse of digital media at the expense of conversations with others
    - our modesty or immodesty
    - the TV shows and movies we watch
    - the language we use, especially when frustrated
    - the music we listen to
    - the video gaming we enjoy

Affirmation

Second in the process of discipline is *affirmation*: applauding your children when they are behaving correctly. Affirming your child's behavior sends a strong message of approval and of your pleasure in him. You will be validating his decisions and actions. And, as a bonus, affirmation encourages him to repeat the behavior. It is a positive consequence or expression offered by the parent as a reward for proper behavior. Equally important, affirmation is an outward demonstration of your unfailing love for your child.

As we have learned, the most effective parenting style is the *Authoritative* style where there is a balance of affirmation and correction. One without the other leads to an imbalanced approach and poorer results. Affirmation is necessary for correction to work.

Parenting is a lot like coaching or teaching. Imagine a teacher who only corrects and never affirms, or a coach who constantly criticizes your performance and never commends you when you do well. You may have even experienced this with an employer who is overly critical. How motivated were you to follow his lead? Parenting is no different. Our children need affirmation before correction. They need to know that you believe they have the ability to excel.

Characteristics of Affirmation

Affirmation of your child must be characterized by the following:

Genuine

Affirmation must flow from a parent's heart of love and concern for the child's character development. It must never be used to simply manipulate desired behavior. It is equally wrong to voice unlimited praise for all behaviors, regardless of where they may fall on the spectrum of right and wrong. Children will pick up on insincere praise and will come to expect it, leading to narcissism and the craving for—or even the demand for—recognition.

Generous

It has been said that parents must "catch them being good." We need to look for opportunities to applaud our children. It is easy to be lulled into enjoying the harmony of good behavior, and only bark at our children when misbehavior occurs. Unfortunately, this approach encourages misbehavior as the child seeks to gain his parent's attention, which he naturally craves. Children deeply desire a parent's attention and affirmation, so behavior is generally better when the two are connected.

In general, your affirmation should exceed your correction.

Forgiving

Parents must keep "short accounts" with their children. Once an offense has been acknowledged and corrected, parents must forgive the child and restore the relationship. This means we don't hold past behaviors over our children's heads in the form of grudges. It does not mean we can't point out repeated offenses when they occur. It just means that we are to be the more mature party in the exchange, and therefore not allow our frustration to fracture our relationship.

Unconditionally Loving

In action and in word, your child must know that your love for him is not dependent upon his behavior or performance. This concept must be forefront in your mind whether correcting or affirming your child. Although misbehavior can be very frustrating, you must include in your correcting the reassurance of your love. Likewise, good behavior can make you proud as a parent, but your love for your child must not be linked to his performance.

How to Affirm

Here are some specific ways to affirm your children:

Talking and Listening

- Even during pregnancy, begin talking to your child. Think out loud as you go about the day with your young child. Respond to your baby's babble as a toddler, and then as she gets older, ask and answer her many questions.
- Have an "open door" policy in conversation with your child. Seek to be available.
- Commit to eating together as often as you can. Family mealtime is an ideal opportunity to engage your child in conversation. (Read more about the Family Table in chapter 6.)
- Put the phone down and make eye contact. When the opportunity for conversation arises, give your undivided attention. Show her your interest in what she has to say. Ask for the same respect from her.
- Ask questions, and resist commenting on her every word: teach as you go.

Commending Accomplishments

Applaud him as he reaches milestones in infancy. Commend him when he succeeds as a preschooler. Show him how proud you are of him and that you had confidence that he could do it as he matures.

Applaud your child's good behavior, and name the trait. When he shares, say "I am proud of you for being *generous*." When she tells the truth, say "I am proud of you for being *honest*." When he waits his turn to speak at the dinner table, say "I am proud of you for being *patient* while your brother was talking." By doing this, you identify the character traits you are trying to impress upon his heart.

Affirming Traits

Every child is unique, and each one has strengths and weaknesses. Seek to identify your child's strengths and then affirm them. Acknowledge his weaknesses as they become apparent and pledge to help him improve.

Be honest and don't affirm abilities that do not exist. Exaggerating a child's abilities can lead to unrealistic expectations and greater disappointment. It can also lead a child to have an inflated image of self.

Be patient and bear with your children. Don't expect perfection. Acknowledge their failures, but don't dwell on them. Lovingly correct, and offer grace (a pass on correction) when your child is truly remorseful about his misbehavior.

Staying Connected

Look for opportunities to do activities together. Spend one-on-one time with each of your children every day, even if only ten minutes. For example, read to your preschooler, build a craft together, play imaginary games, take walks together, go to the zoo, practice a sport in the backyard, coach your child's team, play an instrument together, and take a family vacation occasionally. Connect physically with hugs, wrestling, high fives, and pats on the back.

Correction

The third and final component of the discipline process, *correction*, is the hardest one to implement and the least enjoyable for either the child or the parent. It is, however, a crucial component and one that is ignored more and more by contemporary parenting experts. Because it is not a "feel-good" topic to discuss, correction is often glossed over in parenting manuals, magazines, and blogs. Ignoring it can derail a parent's entire disciplinary effort, though. Correction is more necessary in the early years when self-centeredness is at its peak, and then, if properly administered, is less necessary in later years.

Without proper correction, a child is led to believe that misbehavior is acceptable. Then, retraining of an older child, which is always more difficult than early childhood training, will be needed. This is complicated by the fact that it is usually someone other than the parents who must take on the task of retraining (teacher, coach, employer, or law enforcement). When, and how to apply correction can be challenging, and therefore I have dedicated the entire next chapter to its application.

Now, Let's Apply Discipline

What have we learned?

Scenario: You find your two-year-old drawing on the living room wall with a crayon. Here's how the discipline process would work.

Instruction

- Ask yourself, "Does she know better than to draw on the wall?"
  - ‣ If this is the first time she has done this, instruct her.
  - ‣ If this is the second time, correct her.
- Is she old enough to know better? Yes.
- Have I been consistent in enforcing this rule?
  - ‣ If no, instruct, and correct next time.
  - ‣ If yes, correct.

Affirmation

- Have I affirmed her in the past for not drawing on the wall?
  - ‣ If no, try to remember in the future. This will greatly encourage her. You still must correct her.
  - ‣ If yes, good. Correct her.

Correction

- Age-appropriate:
  - ‣ Logical consequences: take the crayons away for two days
  - ‣ Time-out for two minutes

- ‣ Spank: if milder measures have failed with other drawing offenses, or your child has a defiant attitude
- Instructive
  - ‣ Briefly reinstruct that crayons should be used on coloring books not on the walls.

Relationship

Tell her you love her and that you never enjoy punishing her, but if she misbehaves again, you will have to punish her again. Teach her to ask for your forgiveness: "Mom, will you forgive me?" Your answer: "Yes!" Then demonstrate your love with a hug and a smile. Acknowledge to her that your love for her is unconditional, and is not dependent upon her behavior.

All children need discipline (guidance). Some will require more effort to discipline than others. The process goes more smoothly, however, when you understand the factors involved. Maybe now, when you consider how to lead your child to proper behavior, you will think in terms of these components: Instruction, Affirmation, Correction, and Relationship. Giving proper attention to all four of these will improve your outcome with your child.

Now, let's turn our attention to the toughest component, correction.

Chapter 8

CORRECTING YOUR CHILD

Of the three components of the discipline process, Instruction, Affirmation, and Correction, none is more challenging to apply than Correction. For this reason, I have chosen to devote an entire chapter to it, including the methods of correction and various situations in which they are used.

When we think of correcting a child, most of us envision a quick, stern reprimand after which we move on with our day. I want to challenge you to take a closer, more thoughtful look at this very important component of discipline. When correction is properly used, the discipline process is much more effective; when misused, the problem behavior worsens and the parent-child relationship begins to unravel.

Defining Correction

Actions have consequences. This is an important principle for children to realize from an early age. Consequences may be positive (affirmation) or negative (punishment). With proper behavior, the resulting consequence will be positive and rewarding. With improper behavior, however, the consequences will be unpleasant in order to persuade a child to *want* to behave properly.

As early as infancy, a child is learning the connection between his actions and the consequences. It is the "If this, then that" principle at work. For example, two-year-old Ricky is told, "If you pick up your toys, then we will have time to read a story." Or, "If you throw your food, then I will take your plate away." Or, "If you can't play nicely with your brother, you will be separated for an hour."

Correction teaches a child that proper behavior (being obedient, kind to others, respectful, and truthful) is important and necessary. Without correction, a child is subtly taught that misbehavior is no big deal, which motivates even more self-centered behavior.

Conflict is sometimes necessary. Much of today's parenting advice is based upon a so-called "Positive Parenting" approach, where affirmation is exclusively used to shape a child's behavior and where correction of misbehavior using negative consequences (punishment) is forbidden. While this approach seems compassionate and has a "feel good" appeal, there is little evidence that it works, especially with more defiant or aggressive children.[1] Equally important, this is a serious disservice to the development of a child. Consequences, both positive and negative, are part of everyday life for children and adults. Consequences shape our conscience and our conduct. When we work hard, we are rewarded; when we are lazy, we fall behind. When we obey laws, we enjoy harmonious living; when we disobey, we suffer discord. When we are kind to others, we enjoy healthy relationships; when we are unkind, we suffer rejection.

To create a false world where all actions are rewarded indiscriminately and all consequences are positive is counterproductive to a child's development. If a young child is sheltered from all negative consequences, he will grow up to be either a narcissistic adult who thinks the world revolves around him, or an ill-equipped adult, unable to handle disappointment, and destined to mediocrity or failure. Ironically, the child who is sheltered from all disappointment in order to "build self-esteem" becomes the opposite of his parents' intentions with little self-confidence and little ability to overcome failure or defeat.

All parenting can be positive, but it starts with a parent-child relationship that says, "I love you and want the very best for you, and I am willing to suffer some temporary disharmony when your behavior requires correction." This is a balanced, positive parenting approach.

Punishment is needed. With this recent challenge to parents' use of punishment, let's briefly explore the history and evidence behind it. To punish means "to impose a penalty for a fault, offense, or violation." Parenting experts today commonly ignore or reject the use of punishment in behavioral management. Some of the most ardent opponents have suggested that all punishment be eliminated from the process of child discipline.[2] For instance, the American Academy of Pediatrics, in its misinformed *Guidelines for Effective Discipline* statement, recommends verbal reprimand as the *only* form of punishment available to the parents of young children, even relegating time-out to a form of extinction.[3] So, is punishment really necessary in childrearing?

The use of punishment in general has been a controversial topic for the past several decades. In the 1930s, psychologists B.F. Skinner and W.K. Estes dismissed punishment as a necessary component to effect lasting behavioral change and, instead, embraced positive reinforcement (reward) as the primary means. The basis for their conclusions was viewed with skepticism by their contemporaries, and in the following two decades, behavioral experiments validated this concern with significant research supporting the long-lasting effects of punishment on behavioral control. In the 1980s, after years of investigation, renowned research psychologist Gerald Patterson reported that the use of punishment was an essential component of successful discipline.[4] Patterson stated, "If I were allowed to select only one concept to use in training parents of antisocial children, I would teach them how to punish more effectively. It is the key to understanding familial aggression."

A parent's need for the use of punishment will vary. Parents of frequently defiant children will obviously use punishment more often than parents of more compliant children. Unfortunately, this correlation has led punishment opponents to claim that punishment *causes* aggressive behavior. However, Berkowitz and Patterson reported that variables *other than* punishment, such as nurturance, consistency, and proper instruction actually determine parental effectiveness.[4] The current debate about the use of punishment has been dubbed the "politicization of punishment," noting an unwarranted shift of emphasis away from the *effectiveness* of punishment toward the societal *ethics* of its use.[5]

Studies have also identified certain variables, such as timing, intensity, context, and consistency, which determine the effectiveness of punishment.[6] Furthermore, the shorter the delay between the act of disobedience and the resulting punishment, the more effective the punishment will be. The intensity of the punishment should be high enough to generate mild to moderate anxiety, but not so high that the child is panicked or terror-stricken. Punishment is most effective within the context of a warm, affectionate parent-child relationship and when used with consistency. Inconsistent, erratic discipline, whether overly firm or permissive, is associated with increased juvenile delinquency.

In summary, punishment is a needed and proven tool in the discipline process. It is only appropriate when a child is cognitively and willingly capable of defying a parent's directive. Innocent curiosity and developmentally driven exploration, which characterize most of infancy, are not grounds for punishment. After the first year, however, a toddler's increased mobility and curiosity tempt him to venture beyond a parent's directed limits. When repeat instruction and affirmation are unsuccessful in persuading a child's obedience, correction in the form of punishment is necessary to achieve behavioral control. The selection of punishment techniques is determined by a child's level of development, ranging from physical restraint and time-out for the toddler to grounding and privilege removal for the adolescent. Parents should always start with the mildest form of punishment or correction and then move to more unpleasant measures as needed.

Consistency Is Needed

Consistency is one of the hardest aspects of discipline for parents to achieve. With the exhausting pace of life and the relentless demands of parenting young children, it is tempting at times to overlook a child's offense for the sake of convenience. This, however, commonly leads parents to an emotional boiling point when they suddenly, even explosively, impose punishment without warning. This kind of inconsistent correction is often counterproductive as it leads to persistent misbehavior, child frustration, and a damaged parent-child relationship. Both *inconsistent* and *impulsive* correction can be harmful to your discipline efforts.

Inconsistent Correction

Did you know that children are gamblers? When we are inconsistent in our correction, they hold out for that one-in-ten chance that we will give in to their demands. This is the gambling principle where nine tries are worth one success, and ironically, it encourages the child to continue the improper behavior. Here are some examples.

- Three-year-old Sally asks, for the fifth time, if she can have some candy that she saw on a check-out display. You say no each time, but finally give in when the slow-moving line causes you irritation and her whining is grating on your last nerve.
- Two-year-old Marcus pitches a fit demanding mac-n-cheese when he doesn't find any foods he likes among the items served to the family at supper. You have told him he must always eat the foods put before him, but tonight, after a long day at the office, you give in.

- Three-year-old Michael comes out of his room for the fourth time protesting bedtime, and tonight you relent and let him watch TV with you in the den for a half hour more.
- Before entering the grocery store you review with two-year-old Anna the rules for how to behave while shopping, but no sooner than ten minutes in you break the rules and allow her to get out of the shopping cart because she's been screaming to get down. You know you should leave the cart in the aisle and return to the car to deal with this rebellious outburst, but on this day you are in a big hurry and let it slide.
- Five-year-old David's screen time is used up for the morning and you ask him to turn off the TV. He whines and complains that his friends get to watch TV "all the time." You give in and let him watch another hour, because you are working on a project and are enjoying the freedom from interruptions.

Impulsive Correction

When obvious misbehavior is ignored and tolerated, it gives the child the false impression that the behavior is acceptable. It also causes growing frustration for the parent who is hoping the misbehavior will just go away. Exasperation sets in when the child is impulsively (and often angrily) punished because the parent's tolerance has reached a boiling point. This *reactive* type of parenting is never effective and often damaging to the parent-child relationship.

For example, 18-month-old Robby has entertained the family for months by throwing food from his highchair to the dog; then one day, in a restaurant, Dad abruptly scolds him for pitching his roll at the waitress.

Take the long view and deal with behavioral issues consistently, even when inconvenient.

We've all been inconsistent at times, and that's okay—as long as it is not our standard approach to parenting. Yes, it is tempting to take these easier routes, but keep in mind that these short-term solutions often lead to long-term problems. So, take the long view and deal with behavioral issues consistently, even when inconvenient. Be *proactive*. Have a plan of discipline and deal with the behavior when it occurs. If you take the time to endure the short-term conflict that will come with correcting your child, you and your child will enjoy the long-term benefits of improved compliance and an enriched relationship.

How to Correct

What does proper correction look like? What is its purpose, how should it be applied, and how do we choose the right method of correction for our child in each situation? Let's answer these basic questions by examining various aspects of correction. As you read, ask yourself, "How am I doing with my child and how can I improve my approach?" If you feel some guilt as you read, don't be discouraged. We can all use some improvement. In fact, I tell parents in my practice that childrearing is a life-long adventure of studying our children and studying ourselves.

Instructive

There are two steps to instructive correction, showing the child what to *stop* doing and then showing him what to *start* doing instead.

Stop doing: First, teach your child that his behavior or attitude is inappropriate and unacceptable. Offer a brief explanation to help him understand why and to persuade him to not repeat the behavior. Keep in mind, you do not have to convince him to agree with you, but if he does with an expression of apology, commend him.

Start doing: Second, teach him the proper "replacement" behavior or attitude. This involves instructing your child in the correct action or showing him the correct tone of voice. Then, have him rehearse it at that moment. Here are a few examples.

- When a child speaks disrespectfully to a parent, the parent stops the child and says, "Let's say that again the right way."
- When a two-year-old is whining in a high-pitched voice, asking for a cracker, the mother interrupts, saying, "That is a whiny voice. I don't hear you when you whine. Let's try again with the right voice." With a calm tone to her voice, the mother then demonstrates, "Mommy, may I please have a cracker?"

- When a toddler slaps, the parent firmly replies, "No slap!" and then takes the child's hand and shows him how to touch gently, saying, "Gentle, gentle" with a smile.

The bad behavior must be replaced with proper behavior.

Constructive

Correction must be constructive and not bitter, spiteful, or unforgiving.

Your words and motive—A parent's motive for correction must always be the child's best interest, and not retaliation. Proper correction is intended to teach and edify, not shame. Yes, it can be very frustrating when a child repeatedly disobeys or misbehaves. And some children may require repeated correction or punishment for the same behavior. Parents, however, must continually remind themselves that the correction is not revenge for the inconvenience this misbehavior is causing, but an effort to teach and train the child to respect and obey for his own good.

Your tone—Yelling never helps. While you may occasionally need to raise your voice in order to gain your child's attention, continued yelling will damage your relationship and will ultimately reduce his respect for you. In the words of Solomon, the wisest man who ever lived, "A gentle answer turns away wrath, but a harsh word stirs up anger" (Proverbs 15:1). When your child harshly responds to you in a disrespectful tone of voice, rather than yelling back and being drawn into a verbal battle, calmly reply with your correction. You'll be surprised how well it works.

Your speed—Speak clearly, slowly, calmly, and briefly. Issuing a battery of "machine gun" criticisms will likely be ignored or seen as an attack. A further benefit is that you will be modeling to your child the proper way to communicate.

Persuasive

We must not forget that the goal of our correction is to instruct our child's mind and to persuade his heart. Children must see and sense this from us, and not feel that the punishment is retaliation for defying our authority or for causing us inconvenience. When we control our emotions and correct in a loving manner, our children are more likely to listen and be persuaded to obey. Also, as we will discuss later, the correction is more persuasive if the method chosen fits the offense. For example, taking the toys away from a toddler who refuses to stop playing and get ready for bed may be more effective than a spanking.

Selective

You have heard it said about disciplining a child, "Choose your battles." At the risk of sounding a bit permissive, I agree with this advice. For some children, misbehavior will be infrequent and deserving of correction every time. For more contrary children, however, misbehavior can be almost constant, and the need for correction will seem exhausting. In such a setting, the parent-child relationship is prone to suffer, as the tone in the home is continuously negative and the parent finds few opportunities to affirm the child. It is in these settings where the parent must be selective in punishment for the sake of the relationship, and do so without giving the false impression of endorsing the uncorrected misbehaviors. There is good evidence that preserving the parent-child relationship will have a greater positive impact upon a child's eventual compliance than delivering a constant barrage of corrections for every act of disobedience.

I encourage parents to choose two or three behaviors that you want to correct. Strategize about how you are going to approach each behavior. Discuss how you will instruct your child and then how to affirm and correct the behavior. Then, sit down with your child at a calm moment and review the rules and consequences. Finally, be consistent in your implementation of this focused plan.

Correct

Correct correctly. Interestingly, studies have shown that when parents of aggressive children are unable to control their misbehavior, it is more often due to improper usage, rather than inadequate knowledge of correction techniques. As with any procedure, the best results come when it is administered correctly. Therefore, I encourage you to study the details of each method described in this chapter. Examples of incorrect usage include allowing a child out of time-out before the timer has sounded, not using a timer with time-out, spanking on impulse in anger without forewarning the child, spanking in public, yelling when trying to reason with an older child, and failing to enforce grounding as originally imposed.

Calm

Your child will react to your demeanor during discipline, so it is important to maintain a calm, calculated approach. Here are steps that will help.

1. Rehearse what you intend to say ahead of time.
2. Take a deep breath before your start.
3. Keep your voice low and controlled the entire time.
4. Take your time in responding to your child's responses.
5. Avoid lengthy verbal defenses of your request or directive.
6. Stay focused on the specific behavior. Don't get drawn into discussion of other matters. Likewise, don't bring up unrelated misbehaviors to shame your child.
7. Talk yourself through it: "I can get through this. If I stay calm she'll calm down."
8. If you feel your emotions taking over, call in another adult to help, or take a break.

Age-appropriate and Progressive

The specific method of correction you choose will vary depending upon your child's age and developmental stage. At the earliest ages, the methods will need to be more physically restraining since mental reasoning is less effective. As your child cognitively matures and is able to be persuaded by reasoning, the methods you use should progress to those of a more mental and consequential nature. For example, time out and spanking (physical methods) will be necessary in controlling behavior with a toddler or a preschooler, but they should not be primarily relied upon to teach obedience with a school-ager. Privilege removal (reasoning method) works better than spanking with an eight-year-old because restricting his play is more "painful" than a quick spanking. This progression from physical to reasoning methods makes correction more effective. It is a big mistake to rely upon reasoning alone with a young child who is cognitively immature, and an equal mistake to use physical methods with older children who have the maturity for reason. When correction methods are mismatched with child's developmental level, frustration for the parent and anger for the child occur.

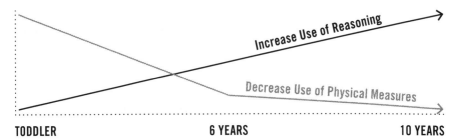

TODDLER   6 YEARS   10 YEARS

The following is a basic list of corrective measures available to parents and the stage of development when each can begin:

Methods of Behavioral Correction	
Age of Earliest Use	Corrective Measure
Infancy	Distraction
12 months	Disapproval
12 months	Logical and Natural Consequences
12 months	Time-Out (playpen)
18 months	Time-Out (chair)
18 months	Disciplinary Spanking
2 years	Basic Reasoning used with other measures
3½ years	Privilege Removal
6 years	Reasoning, alone
School-age	Grounding and Fining

At the earliest ages, the methods will need to be more physically restraining since mental reasoning is less effective. As your child cognitively matures and is able to be persuaded by reasoning, the methods you use should progress to those of a more mental and consequential nature.

Correction Reviewed

To summarize, here are some Dos and Don'ts to consider when correcting your child.

Dos

- *Discipline proactively.* Plan ahead in how you will correct specific problem behaviors. Inform your child ahead of time what the specific corrective consequence will be. Warn your child of upcoming deadlines.
  - Example: "Johnny, you are allowed 30 minutes of screen time each day. I will give you a ten-minute warning before the time is up for you to turn off the tablet. If you complain

or whine, you will not have any screen time tomorrow."
(Require that he acknowledge with eye contact.)

- *Respond quickly.* The corrective measure will have a greater effect
if imposed shortly after the disobedient act. This is especially true
with toddlers. Be willing to be inconvenienced in order to make
this happen.
- *Correct consistently.*
  ‣ Consistently punish misbehavior, using the same degree of
  correction for a given misbehavior. In other words, don't
  punish more harshly when you are in a frustrated mood or
  when you have been inconvenienced by the misbehavior.
  ‣ Be consistent in your application of correction. Don't give
  up when your child fails to respond to your initial efforts. Be
  persistent.
  ‣ Be consistent regardless of the setting, such as at home or
  in a public place. The rules of behavior stay the same, but
  the form of correction or consequence may change from
  location to location. In other words, in a public setting misbehavior may require a trip out to the car to discuss the
  matter, where at home it would result in time-out.
  ‣ Require consistency among the caregivers in your child's
  life. The standards of behavior should not differ according to
  whose home the child is in at the time.
- *Apologize.* None of us are perfect parents and we all occasionally
will fail to properly or respectfully correct. When we fail, we must
be willing to recognize it and ask forgiveness from our child. How
can we expect our children to ask forgiveness of us when we are
not modeling it to them? I believe you can maintain a position of
authority with your child and yet ask for their forgiveness. Looking back on my own parenting, I regret that I didn't humbly ask
forgiveness from my children more often. It would have strengthened our relationship even more if I had.

Don'ts

- *Discipline reactively.* Don't be caught unprepared. By not being
proactive, you will have to react, and this often leads to emotional
outbursts and poor decisions.

- *Excuse misbehavior as a "phase."* While it is true that some stages of your child's development may be more challenging than others, resist the temptation to dismiss problem behavior as a phase that will mysteriously resolve itself. If left uncorrected, the problem behavior may take on a different appearance (toddler whining turns into preschool rudeness) as your child grows older, but the heart issue will remain. Focus on teaching a respectful heart attitude by correcting the behavior, regardless of the phase.
- *Correct in anger.* Shouting or yelling will not improve your effectiveness. Your anger and frustration with your child may actually be the result of your procrastination or inconsistency in dealing with the disobedient act earlier.
- *Make empty threats.* Parents should "say what they mean and mean what they say." Most children will be willing to gamble that nothing will happen and continue the misbehavior in spite of a parent's warning. Empty threats lead to frustrated children and frustrated, explosive parents.
- *Be too harsh.* Know your child's emotional limits. Don't make the corrective consequence a personal attack. Focus on the behavior or heart issue, and use just the right measure of disappointment to persuade your child.
- *Punish yourself.* Don't choose a consequence that will indirectly punish yourself.
  - ‣ Example: You choose the consequence of not allowing your child to play outside, but that means that you are left to "entertain" your child while he's inside.
  - ‣ Example: You choose to prematurely end a shopping trip when your child is having a tantrum and refuses to settle, rather than dealing with the behavior in private without abandoning your trip.

Correction Methods

Parents have a limited number of corrective methods available to use with their children, and the younger the child, the more limited they are. This is why correct usage is so important. Your discipline will be easier and more effective if you decide in advance when and how to correct your child. Be creative and think ahead. Trying to decide what to do in the heat of the moment can be counterproductive.

Successful parents use the mildest effective method first, and are not hesitant to use more intense and unpleasant measures as their child's persistent misbehavior demands. When one approach fails to correct the behavior, move confidently to a more unpleasant approach. For some children, this may require the use of spanking early in the method selection process. For other children, removal of a privilege may actually be more unpleasant than spanking. Know your child.

A word of caution: A corrective consequence must be unpleasant to be effective. Some peace-loving parents, fearing an angry outburst from their child, will balk at imposing a punishment, and instead rely upon conversation to "convince" the child to obey. This rarely works and often prolongs the process, especially with a child under three years old. With this approach, parent-child conflict is only postponed to a later moment when the parent blows up in frustration and the child finally complies in an effort to re-establish peace between the two. This can be avoided. Be a leader. Act decisively. Avoid excessive talk and avoid excessive emotion with correction.

Now we are ready to look at how and when to use the various methods (see the table below). Many times a single method will be sufficient, and other times a combination of methods will be needed. All, however, will require your loving application within a nurturing relationship with your child.

METHODS OF CORRECTION BY AGE

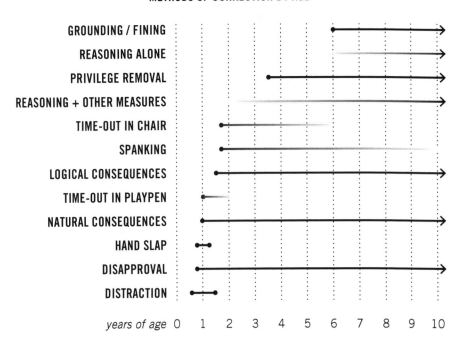

Natural and Logical Consequences

Natural Consequence

When your child suffers an unpleasant consequence that results from misbehavior or a poor choice, this is known as a *natural* consequence. No further consequence or action by the parent is usually necessary. The unpleasant consequence is often enough punishment to persuade your child not to repeat the behavior. It is, however, very appropriate to show empathy and to validate the resulting sad feelings felt by your child for making the mistake. No lecturing is typically needed. Also, allowing natural consequences to occur may at times make you (the parent) look foolish, such as the third example below. Be strong and confident in these moments and focus on your child, not on what others think of you.

Examples:
- If your child is told not to run on the sidewalk and he falls down and skins his knee, this is the natural consequence.
- If your child leaves his toy out in the rain after being told to bring it inside, and it is damaged, the consequence may be to not replace the toy.
- If your older child refuses to take your advice to wear a coat in cold weather, his consequence will be a chilly discomfort when playing outside at school.

Logical Consequence

Logical consequences are different from natural consequences in that they require the intervention and enforcement by the parent. When choosing a consequence to correct your child's behavior, consider the following:

- Consequences should logically fit the situation.
- Consequences should not be humiliating or shaming of your child.
- Consequences should always be reasonable for your child's level of development.

Examples:
- If your child makes a mess, the consequence should be to clean it up.
- If your child refuses to share a toy with his sibling, the consequence can be the loss of the toy for a day or two.

- If your older child refuses to stop playing a game on the tablet, the privilege of tablet use is suspended for a period of time.
- If your child is disrespectful in the process of choosing an article of clothing to wear, she loses the privilege to choose for a day or two.

The use of logical consequences is an excellent opportunity to teach your child how to make good decisions. Here's how it works. While the logical consequence is a form of punishment for improper behavior, your child should be forewarned of the consequence as often as it is possible. By forewarning your child, you are teaching her that proper behavior is a *choice*. Behave properly and enjoy the harmony that results; misbehave or make poor choices and suffer the consequences. The hard part for the parent is allowing the child to suffer the consequence. Teaching good decision-making requires that we allow our child to fail occasionally (when the consequences are not too severe, of course).

Teach them that proper behavior is a choice.

Note: When a child's maturity level reaches a point where the use of logical consequences is effective, it should become a parent's first choice among correction methods when it fits the situation.

Example: Dad says to his 12-year-old, "You need to stop playing around and do your homework, because when it's bedtime you will be going to bed." The child continues to play, bedtime approaches, homework is stopped, and the child receives a bad grade the next day for unfinished homework.

Reasoning

When a parent uses dialogue to persuade a child to behave, we call this *reasoning*. Reasoning appeals to a child's conscience and teaches him to understand the consequences of his behavior. Reasoning involves the following:

- Explaining the negative consequences a behavior will have upon the child (i.e., dangerous behavior)
- Explaining the negative impact a behavior will have upon others (i.e., hurtful behavior toward others)
- Explaining the rightness of helping others versus hurting others (respect for others)

- Teaching empathy by explaining how the child would not like the hurtful behavior directed toward himself (Golden Rule principle)

Reasoning, however, must not be used too early, before a child is capable of being persuaded by it. In infancy and early toddlerhood, a child's conscience and understanding of behavior are very rudimentary. Therefore, trying to talk a child into behaving at this age is typically futile. Instead, physical methods of correction, such as restraint and time-out, will be the most effective at this age. By 18–24 months of age, a child is beginning to understand the impact his behavior has upon himself and others, and is beginning to understand the concept of right and wrong (conscience). At this stage of development, brief reasoning can be paired with a negative consequence. It will take a few more years, however, before understanding and conscience reach the level of maturity sufficient to allow reasoning *alone* to be used in correction.

Examples:
- Fifteen-month-old Ricky is frequently slapping his mother, despite clearly understanding what he is doing.
  - Wrong: "Ricky, please don't slap Mommy. It hurts me and leaves a red mark every time." (using reasoning too early)
  - Right: "Ricky, No hit!" Mom says with stern look, and then places Ricky in playpen time-out for one minute. (using physical method)

- Two-year-old Sally sneaks away from Mom in the front yard and wanders into the street despite being told to never do so.
  - Wrong: Mom leads Sally back to the yard and says, "Now Sally that is the second time you have gone into the street. Don't you realize it is dangerous and that you could be hit by a car? Please don't do that again. Okay?" (using reasoning alone)
  - Right: Mom swiftly grabs Sally and goes inside where she spanks her and reviews: "Sally, I warned that you would be spanked if you went into the street again. Look at Mommy's eyes. I love you and must teach you to never do that; you could be hurt very badly." (pairing physical with reasoning)

Behavior is a Choice. Once a child is capable of reasoning, the parent can make it clear that behavior is a choice the child makes. A parent can say to the child, "Choose proper behavior, and your day will go well. Choose to misbe-have, and your day will not go well." In order for this approach to work, the parent must allow unpleasant consequences to occur when the child makes poor choices. This can be quite difficult. It is equally important to affirm the child when he makes wise choices.

It is equally important to affirm
the child when he makes wise choices.

Here's how reasoning, conscience, and logical consequences can be com-bined to correct the older child.

- Make it clear to the child that obedience is a choice.
- Allow or impose an unpleasant consequence following a poor choice.
- Appeal to the child's conscience about the wrongness of the choice.
- Express disappointment with misbehavior; explain the behavior's impact upon others.

Preschooler example: Conscience: "It is not nice to push your little brother down. See how he is crying; you hurt him." Logical Consequence: "Now, if you do this again, you will have to go to your room and not play with him for a while."

School-ager example: A fifth-grader is caught cheating on a spelling test. Conscience: "You chose to cheat on your test, so the teacher gave you a zero grade." Choice: "Your choice was to be dishonest toward your teacher and toward your classmates who studied hard to make their grade." Conscience: "I am disappointed with your decision, and I hope you now see how wrong it was."

Time-Out

Time-out is a popular and effective form of punishment that capital-izes on a child's desire for his parent's attention. When used by a parent, time-out should be a planned action (proactive), not an angry reaction (reactive). The child should be forewarned of the offenses for which time-out will be used.

When to Use Time-Out

Time-out is best used when your child is mature enough to understand the concepts of time and place. Typically by 18 months of age he is capable of sitting for a period of time in isolation and will understand the association between isolation and the misbehavior. A playpen time-out can be used as early as 12 months.

Time-out is useful when a child's behavior is inappropriate and he fails to respond to verbal warnings. For example, when a child is harassing a sibling, refuses to share the toys, or becomes illmannered at the dinner table.

Don't use time-out for *all* acts of disobedience. Overuse may make it less effective with your child. Diversify; time-out is just one tool in your corrective toolbox.

How to Use Time-Out

When the misbehavior occurs, the child is taken to a certain area of the home and required to sit in a chair for a designated period of time. Time-out locations should be dull and nonstimulating, such as the corner of the living room, dining room, or hallway. Once chosen, use the same location each time. A wooden or metal chair serves as an ideal time-out chair since it is relatively uncomfortable and durable. Use a timer to indicate the length of the time-out. The duration can be customized to the child's level of development. A good rule of thumb is one minute of time per each year of age up to a maximum of five minutes. Use of a kitchen timer holds both you and your child accountable for the exact duration of the time-out period.

Once placed in the chair, the child is told to stay seated until the timer goes off. Don't provide a lengthy rationale for the punishment or argue with your child while he is in time-out. Time-out is less effective if accompanied by a lot of attention from a parent (yelling, lecturing, or explaining). A brief discussion should only occur once your child's behavior is appropriate and the time-out is over.

Time-out is most effective if general calmness is required of the child. A couple minutes of genuine, tearful crying is certainly acceptable initially. Intentional screaming or theatrical crying, however, are weapons of rebellion directed at the parent and are not acceptable. The length of the time-out may be extended for such behavior, or the starting of the timer may be delayed until the child is quiet for several seconds. Disrespect toward a parent (name calling or sassiness) or destructive behavior (pounding on the wall) are not acceptable and may require a spanking to regain the attention of the unruly child.

When Time-Out is Over

Once the time-out period is over, frankly discuss with your child the reason for the punishment and assure him that further disobedience will be punished as well. This is not a time for further punishment or ridicule of your child, but rather a time to restore the relationship and to reemphasize the order of authority. Example: "Mommy is proud of you for staying in time-out. It was wrong for you to hit your little brother. This is why Mommy sent you to time-out. Let's find a nicer way to treat your brother next time, because if you hit him again, you will go back to time-out. Mommy loves you and always will, but your behavior was wrong. Now, let's go play with your brother."

A remorseful child should be hugged and praised for his change of attitude. After restoring the relationship, the original request must be repeated and your child's obedience required. This is essential to the success of time-out. If the original request is dropped, then your child will learn to use time-out as a way to avoid compliance.

When Your Child Refuses to Cooperate

If your child leaves the time-out chair before the time is up, return him to the chair and repeat your desire for him to stay until the alarm rings. Reset the timer. If, after two repetitions, he refuses to stay in time-out, return him to the chair and warn of a spanking if he gets out again. If he then gets down again before the timer rings, follow through with your promise. Take your child to a private location (bathroom or bedroom), spank him once on the buttocks, return him to the time-out chair and reset the timer. Tell him if he gets down again he will be spanked again.

When time-out is first instituted, most children will test their parent's seriousness. Early and consistent use of a spanking to enforce the time-out will result in greater respect for time-out. This ultimately leads to fewer spankings as a child gets older and as he comes to respect the time-out penalty.

Research has shown spanking to be one of the most effective enforcers of time-out. [7,8,9,10] It is the most practical and expedient method. Some psychologists recommend that a parent physically hold the child in time-out, or corral the child in the corner of a room. This, however, does not teach the child self-control, but merely accomplishes the child's objective of manipulating the parent and disrupting the events of the moment. Time-out should punish only the child, not the parent (although it may be inconvenient at times).

Disciplinary Spanking: The Details

Disciplinary spanking can be a useful method of correction once a child reaches an age of accountability for his behavior (18–24 months) but is too immature to respond to reasoning and explanation alone (under four to six years). At this stage of development, a parent has only a few effective methods of correction. When these milder methods (redirection, disapproval, and time-out) fail to correct a child's misbehavior, spanking can be very useful and effective if properly used.

How to Use Spanking

Like any other method of correction, disciplinary spanking will be ineffective—and counterproductive—if used improperly or on impulse. *How* a parent uses any corrective measure will often determine its effectiveness. If you choose to use spanking, the following guidelines will help you maximize its effectiveness.

- Typical ages of use and need: 18 months to 6 years, uncommon from 7 to 10 years and rarely, if ever, after 10 years. Spanking is most useful with children from 18 months to 4 years of age, when reasoning and consequences are less effective.
- The spanking should always be a planned action by the parent, not an angry reaction. Your child should be forewarned of the spanking and the reason for it. Avoid spanking on impulse or in anger.
- Always administer the spanking in private to avoid humiliating the child. The walk to the bedroom, or wherever you choose to administer the spanking, formalizes the procedure, and provides you a cooldown time if needed.
- The spanking must bring about a measured amount of pain, enough to be remembered but not enough to harm. Use a thin semi-flexible object (a light ruler) or your open hand. Never use a belt (too flexible) or heavy paddle (too rigid). Administer one to two spanks to the buttocks only. The older child may occasionally require more spanks, but physical injury should never occur.

- Always follow the spanking (or any disciplinary measure) with a verbal review of the offense, and reassurance of your unconditional love. Offer a hug and clarify your displeasure for the behavior, not your child.
- A spanking should never result in physical injury.

When to Use Spanking

Spanking should not be a parent's only method of correction. It should be one component of a total disciplinary plan and always administered in love for correction, not retaliation. The parent must be under control emotionally and always follow an established procedure for spanking. Spanking on impulse and in anger is unhealthy and less effective; a cooldown period may be required if the parent is angry. Not all children will need spankings. Some very compliant children may never need a spanking to change behavior. The particularly contrary child, however, will require more corrective measures, including spankings. Here are some scenarios where spanking can be useful:

1. When your child's misbehavior could endanger his life and the risks with repeating the behavior are high.

   Examples: A child runs into a busy street, or a toddler persists in playing with an electrical outlet or cord, despite verbal warnings to stop.

2. When your child refuses to cooperate with milder punishment, despite warnings. Spanking can serve as an effective enforcer of time-out.

   Example: A toddler refuses to stay in time-out, even after a couple of warnings. A spanking should be administered in private and the child returned to the time-out chair.

3. When your child willfully disobeys and milder forms of punishment have failed.

   Example: A toddler persistently bites or hits a sibling, despite reprimands and consequences such as time-out.

4. When your child's misbehavior is blatantly disrespectful toward the parent or deliberately destructive and milder forms of punishment have failed.

Example: A three-year-old in the midst of a temper tantrum resorts to throwing toys, pounding on the door, or sassing the parent. The child should be told to stop and warned of a spanking if the behavior continues. If the misbehavior continues, the child should be spanked. (The first approach to common temper tantrums is to ignore the behavior and allow for its ultimate extinction. See Temper Tantrums and Whining later in this chapter.)

Reasons for Spanking Failures

1. The child's misbehavior is more persistent than the parent's response. Once punished, the child repeats the misbehavior without a corrective response from the parent. Be persistent with your correction of your child. If consistent, persistent, and calm, you can avoid the mistake of increasing your anger or the severity of punishment.

2. The parent inconsistently punishes misbehavior. Sometimes the child is punished for a particular act of disobedience and other times the act is ignored. The use of spanking or any other corrective measure should not depend upon your mood, level of exasperation, or the convenience of the setting. Clearly inform your child of the rules and the consequences of disobedience, and then consistently enforce them.

3. The parent uses an improper method. A spanking should always be carefully administered according to a predetermined plan and followed by a review of the offense and a restoration of your relationship with your child. Erratic, temperamental use of spanking is improper and ineffective.

4. Spanking is suddenly initiated after months or years of permissive parenting. It will take a while before your child responds to any change in your disciplinary approach. Initially, he will test your seriousness about the change. First, explain to your child the reason for the change and then implement the plan with persistence and consistency.

5. Spanking is excessively used as the only form of discipline and the parent's attitude is negative or authoritarian. The best approach to discipline uses a variety of correction methods in a diversified fashion. If one method is always used, it will eventually lose its

effectiveness. Plus, the excessive use of spanking is overly harsh and may be an indication of a troubled parent-child relationship and a need for counseling. Praise and encouragement of the child should play a major role in any disciplinary plan.

What Research Tells Us About Spanking

Until the past decade, the use of disciplinary spanking with young children was acceptable to most parents, pediatricians, and psychologists. Lately, it has come under fire and is being questioned even by grandparents who used it with their children. Why has spanking become controversial? Has new research proven it to be ineffective or harmful to the child? Let's look and see.

Spanking opponents have misled society by presenting biased research that is based upon poor data (retrospective interviews, nonspecific uses of corporal punishment) and inaccurate methodology (guilty by association). They have promoted permissive parenting under the premise that children are basically good and don't require correction, especially not spanking. They claim that parental control of a child should loosen and that educating with reasoning is sufficient to properly train a child. Renowned research psychologist, Dr. Diana Baumrind, and other prominent scientists would disagree. Dr. Baumrind's landmark research (as detailed in chapter 2) proved that an authoritative style of parenting works the best. She concludes:

> "Authoritative parents endorse the judicious use of aversive consequences, which may include spanking, in the context of a warm, engaged rational parent-child relationship. The authoritative model of discipline is characterized by use of firm control contingently applied and justified by rational explanation."[11]

Quality prospective longitudinal studies are clear and consistent with respect to a parent's use of spanking and its effect upon the child. Here are summarized findings from a few of these studies.

After more than 10 years of study (Baumrind):[12]

> Evidence from this study "did not indicate that negative reinforcement or corporal punishment per se were harmful or ineffective procedures, but rather the *total pattern* of parental control determined the effects on the child of these procedures." (italics added)

After 10 years of study (Eron):[13]

"Upon follow-up ten years after the original data collection, we found that punishment [including physical punishment] of aggressive acts at the earlier age was no longer related to current aggression, and instead, other variables like parental nurturance and children's identification with their parents were more important in predicting later aggression."

After 3 years of focused study (Simons):[14]

"Once the effect of parental involvement was removed, corporal punishment showed no detrimental impact on adolescent aggressiveness, delinquency, or psychological well-being."

A Comprehensive Research Review

More recently, in a systematic review of the literature, research psychologist Robert Larzelere, PhD examined the child outcomes in families where parents used nonabusive, customary physical punishment (in other words, ordinary spanking).[15] Among the review's conclusions were that disciplinary spanking has "consistently beneficial outcomes when it is nonabusive and used primarily to back up milder disciplinary tactics with two- to six-year-olds by loving parents." Also, "most detrimental outcomes in causally relevant studies are due to overly frequent use of physical punishment." Evidence from the review suggested the following conditions to be more characteristic of effective spanking than of counterproductive physical punishment:

1. Use is not overly severe.
2. Used by a parent under control, not in danger of "losing it" from anger.
3. Used during ages two to six, not during the teenage years. Although conclusive evidence is scarce, spanking should be phased out as soon as possible between ages seven and twelve years.
4. Used with reasoning, preferably eliciting an intermediate rather than a high level of child distress.
5. Used privately.
6. Motivated by concern for the child, not parent-oriented concerns.
7. Used after a single warning (generalizing from Roberts' research).[16]
   Roberts showed that a single warning before time-out reduced the

necessary time-outs by 74% without sacrificing any effectiveness of the behavioral parent training.

8. Used flexibly. If spanking does not work, parents should try other approaches and other tactics rather than increasing the intensity of the spanking.

The outcome of parenting is primarily determined by the overall quality of the parent-child relationship. Optimal child development results from a parent's balanced use of firm behavioral control (which may include spanking) and a high degree of nurturance (encouragement and love). The use of disciplinary spanking during childhood in a nurturing environment does not lead to adult dysfunction.

Practical Research on the Use of Spanking

Are you still unsure about the consequences of spanking? Consider the project by Children's Hospital of Akron, Ohio, headed by clinical psychologist, Ray Guarendi, PhD, which sought to discover the secrets of highly successful families who reared outstanding children.[17] The 50 state winners of the teacher-of-the-year award were asked to name the most outstanding children they had taught over the course of their career. The teachers were not to select the highest academic achievers, but the students who exhibited the greatest self-motivation, consideration for others, morality, and general strength of character. These students' families were thoroughly studied and spanking was among the many aspects of parenting examined. The study's findings included:

- 70% of the parents employed some physical punishment with their children. Some relied upon it often and others rarely used it. "Spanking was generally considered to be one tool in a parent's discipline repertoire."
- Most began spanking between 18 and 24 months, and phased it out by ages 4–6 years.
- Spanking was neither the main method nor a last-ditch intervention.
- The occasions when spanking was used:
  - ‣ When teaching a child to avoid potentially dangerous situations.
  - ‣ When punishing for deliberate disobedience.
  - ‣ When punishing for disrespectful behavior.

- Spanking was not used for accidents, childish behavior, or impulsive acts; the parents preferred to employ other consequences for these behaviors.

The study's conclusions about spanking:

1. A majority of parents with outstanding children are willing to spank. They consider it a healthy discipline option.
2. Spanking is not child abuse. Not one of these spanking parents was a child abuser.
3. Spanking does not in and of itself lead a child to be aggressive or to approach problems with a "might-makes-right" mentality. Consistently, the youngsters in these families were identified as normally mature and sensitive.
4. One need not spank to be a good parent. A significant minority of parents chose not to spank for personal and practical reasons. They neither viewed spanking as the psychological dark side of discipline nor as an outmoded or brutal technique.

In Summary

Disciplinary spanking can be useful, effective, and harmless when properly used. Not all children will require spanking to correct misbehavior and to achieve behavior control. Spanking can be particularly useful in strengthening cooperation with milder measures, such as time-out. In so doing, the milder measure becomes more effective and spanking is less necessary as the child matures. Spanking is most needed between the ages of eighteen months and six years, when reasoning, consequences, and privilege removal are less effective. It should rarely, if ever, be used after ten years of age.

Privilege Removal

Privilege removal is a very persuasive method of correction, but is not very effective until after three to three and a half years of age. It is then when a child realizes they have privileges and will notice if they are restricted. At older ages, privilege removal can even be more effective than physical methods since its penalty is longer lasting and, to an older child, more unpleasant. Examples of removable privileges include playing with toys, clothing choices, watching TV/tablet, video gaming, playing with friends, or going to a neighbor's house.

Grounding

Grounding is the temporary removal of a social privilege, particularly prohibiting the child from leaving home. It can be especially effective with teenagers if used under the right circumstances and for the right period of time. If misused, grounding can drive a wedge between parents and teen.

Older children and teens are naturally social in their recreation, which is healthy as they become more comfortable away from home and begin the gradual transition to independent adulthood. Regulating the privilege of being away from home can be powerful disciplinary tool at this age. Ideally, the type of grounding should fit the offense. For example, if the child violates a weekend night curfew, he is grounded from being with friends for the next two weekends.

Here are some extremes to avoid when grounding your older child.

1. Don't take away all his freedom in a fit of frustration. Be selective about the restriction.
2. Don't take away a special planned event or an entire season of a special activity. Removing the child from a baseball team or ending piano lessons would be too severe for most offenses. One mother told me once that her child made her so mad that she cancelled his birthday party. This, in my opinion, was an adult tantrum and probably damaged the relationship rather than correcting the behavior.
3. Don't cut off all social contacts with friends during the grounding period. Again, be selective.
4. Don't make the grounding period too lengthy. A few days or a couple weekends is much more reasonable than weeks or months. Long periods can be overly embarrassing to the child before his friends and can be too difficult to monitor or enforce.

Temper Tantrums and Whining

All children will have a tantrum or two during their toddler years, when their communication is limited and frustration is more likely. A tantrum is a fit of ill temper (screaming, kicking, or bucking) in response to a frustrating situation or displeasing decision by the parent. Tantrums are part of the growing-up process as children struggle with communicating their desires and accepting their parent's directives and limitations. How you, as a parent, handle this behavior will largely determine whether your child will continue to throw tantrums to get her way.

When a tantrum begins, first ask yourself about the condition of your child:

- Is my child sleepy?

A sleepy toddler is often ill-tempered and prone to display poor self-control. Train your child to be a healthy sleeper. (See chapter 6 on *Meeting Your Child's Basic Needs: Sleep.*)

- Is my child hungry?

Hunger can also cause a toddler to be ill-tempered and impulsive. Train your child to be a healthy eater and serve meals and snacks on time as much as possible. (See chapter 6 on *Meeting Your Child's Basic Needs: Nutrition.*)

Next, determine how you will respond based upon the type of tantrum your child is displaying. Is this tantrum due to *frustration* with a difficult task, or *protest* over a decision you have made?

Frustration Tantrum

Sympathize and assist. Acknowledge your child's frustration and help him with the task, encouraging him to be calm. Example: A toddler trying to open a box, or reach a toy. First, name your child's emotion (e.g., "You seem very frustrated."). This will help your child begin using words to describe his emotion and eventually do less screaming. Teaching your child sign language can help with the frustration associated with his inability to communicate his needs or wants. Next, assist your child, showing him how to accomplish the task at hand.

Protest Tantrum

Sympathize without compromise. A protest temper tantrum usually begins when your mostly nonverbal toddler is denied a request or refused a desire. A simple and brief expression of disappointment from your child over your dissatisfying decision is acceptable. However, when this escalates to screaming and thrashing about in protest (a tantrum), it is no longer appropriate.

First, show some sympathy by acknowledging your child's frustration with your directive or decision. Remember, part of the reason for the tantrum is frustration over his inability to communicate his desires. Next, briefly state to your child that his behavior is inappropriate. Finally, ignore the act and look or walk away.

Think about it: What is your child's goal in having the tantrum? Answer: To persuade you to change your mind. It follows, then, that the continuation of this behavior requires an audience and occasional success in getting you to change your mind. So, don't be an audience and don't change your directive. Consistency is the key. Because, if you only change your decision one out of ten times, to the child it will be worth trying nine more times. The cure: Ignore the tantrum and don't give in.

When a Protest Temper Tantrum Persists

If the ignored tantrum goes on longer than one to two minutes, try the following:

1. Inform your child that you are not going to change your mind and that he must stop "screaming." It is important to give the tantrum behavior a name, such as screaming, yelling, or a tantrum.

2. If it continues for another one to two minutes, take him to his room and place him on the floor. Tell him that he may not come out until he has stopped "screaming." Walk away.

3. If he comes out screaming, take him back and repeat the instruction. If he comes out a second time, put him back in his room and close the door for about two to three minutes. Then, open the door. If he is quiet or sobbing in remorse, pick him up and go back to the original setting, reminding him that you are not going to change your mind about the matter. If he is protesting even louder, close the door again for two to three minutes. Repeat this process until he is remorseful.

4. If, while in the room, your child's tantrum becomes even louder or he displays aggressive behavior, like hitting the door or throwing things within the room, a spanking may be necessary to gain his attention and diffuse the situation.

Head Banging in Protest

The same approach to tantrums can be used for protesting fits of head banging. Some children will slap their head, while others will knock it against the wall or the floor in protest of your decision. Solution: Ignore it and walk away. Surprisingly, the more you intervene to stop this behavior, the more you encourage your child to repeat it. The discomfort of the act and the loss of your attention to it will eventually cause him to stop. If this behavior is common for your child, it is appropriate to move him to an area where he is less likely to hurt himself during the tantrum (e.g., on to a rug or carpeted surface). Persistent head banging should be brought to the attention of your pediatrician.

Whining in Protest

Like tantrums, whining is another immature attempt by a child to convince a parent to change a decision or to at least give more attention to a matter that should be closed. A child's whining is most effective when used in a setting that would delay or embarrass the parent, such as when in a hurry or in a public place. Also, like tantrums, the cure is not to reward the action, but to ignore the request until the child can speak in a proper tone. Say, "I don't hear you when you whine. Let's try that again." Teach him to speak in a clearer, deeper tone of voice; imitate for him the voice you desire. If the whining persists, the child should be excused to another room.

Anticipation is the Best Prevention

Anticipate situations where tantrums or whining are likely to occur and plan ahead. Before entering these situations, inform your child (get down on his level and speak eye-to-eye) of your expectations for proper behavior and of the consequences for misbehavior. Remind him of the consequences that occurred last time he misbehaved, and how proud you were when he behaved properly at other times. Tantrums and whining are most successful for a child when you are in a rush. Don't fall into the trap of giving in for temporary convenience.

Examples of putting this strategy to work:

- *Grocery store:* Before entering the store, remind your child that he is to stay in the shopping cart, that he is not to beg you to buy various foods/candy, and that if he whines or tantrums, he will be disciplined.
- *Telephone call:* Before you make that lengthy phone call, forewarn your child that she is not to interrupt you, unless there is an emergency. If she has a true need, she can quietly come to your side, place her hand on your arm, and wait for an opportunity to make a request. If she impatiently interrupts, she will be corrected.
- *Visiting friend:* Before an invited friend arrives, review the ground rules with your child. "First and best for our guests," may be a good start. Tell your child that you expect her to share generously. Put up any toys that will not be shared. Remind her that if there

is whining, the playtime will be shortened and further discipline applied, if necessary.

Self-control is Your Target

Self-control is a basic and essential character quality that should be pursued for every child at an early age. It is fundamental to acquiring other character qualities such as obedience, respect for authority, honesty, and patience. Teaching a child self-control requires that a parent model a steady temperament, praise good behavior, and calmly correct misbehavior. For children with milder temperaments, success can occur earlier and with less effort by the parent. For the more defiant child, more time, energy, and creativity will be required to produce proper behavior and correct rebellious behavior. Successfully managing temper tantrums and whining is a great start toward teaching your child self-control.

Why is My Child Misbehaving?

Now that we have described all the components of discipline and the factors affecting their use, let's apply what we have learned.

For purposes of illustration, let's say your child is being disobedient or disrespectful, and you can't figure out why your efforts to correct him aren't working. Use the following checklist to identify possible areas where your approach could be interfering with success. As you review the list, don't get overwhelmed when you see flaws or weaknesses in your approach. There are no perfect parents. Take it one step at a time, working on the areas you feel are having the greatest impact upon your child.

1. Child's Basic Needs

a) Sleep

Is my child cranky and short-tempered due to lack of sleep? Do I consistently require a designated bedtime each evening for my child?

Solution: For your toddler and preschooler, require daily napping and a healthy bedtime (7–7:30). For your school-age child, have a bedtime routine and regular bedtime (7:30–8:00). For a child to be self-controlled, he must be well rested.

b) Nutrition

How's my child's nutrition? Do I offer my child sweet drinks and snacks any time she wants them, or at times just to keep her happy? Do I offer my child only the foods she wants, even if unhealthy (chicken fingers, French fries, etc.)?

Solution: Avoid continuous snacking on unhealthy foods and unlimited sweet drinks or milk. Instead, offer water between meals. Limit snacking to healthy foods (fruits, nuts, vegetables) at designated times (mid-afternoon and mid-morning). Attempt to eat a family meal together at home as often as possible. Model healthy eating habits as a parent. Realize that nutrition can affect behavior. (For more information, see chapter 6.)

c) Exercise

Is my child having screen withdrawal? Excessive screen time is addictive and captivating, so that when it is turned off, the young child is often edgy and quick tempered.

Solution: Avoid screens with children under two years, including offering your smartphone for entertainment. Although it may seem like an innocent form of entertainment or distraction for your young child, screen time is addictive and often makes the behavior worse when the screens are turned off. Don't allow gaming screen time (video gaming or app games on the phone or tablet) after school on school day evenings (Sunday through Thursday). Instead, encourage outside play, musical instrument play or reading. It is amazing how this can improve your child's behavior.

How active is my child? Is he viewing too much TV, tablet, or video gaming?

Solution: Encourage outside play. Nurture your child's creativity with non-electronic toys, such as LEGO blocks, toy cars, dolls, coloring books, and picture books. Encourage a sport or extracurricular activity for your school-age child. Model an active lifestyle as a parent. Too little exercise will affect your child's physical, mental, and emotional health, especially as a teenager.

2. Relationship

Has life gotten crazy lately? Have I neglected my child's need for time and affection lately?

Solution: Slow down. Commit to spending regular focused time with your child. Schedule the time, even if it is just 15 minutes of one-on-one time when you get home in the evenings, or a block of 15–30 minutes after the afternoon nap each day. Examples include playing with LEGO sets, working a puzzle, going for a walk, playing a game, talking, or going on a breakfast date together.

3. Instruction

Have I not made clear my expectations for my child's behavior?

Solution: Take time during the calm moments of a day to explain to your child the rules and your expectations for his behavior.

Have I been *reactive* in my correction rather than *proactive*?

Solution: Plan ahead. Don't just react to your child's misbehavior. Prior to the event, review the rules and consequences (e.g., before entering the grocery store or restaurant). Regularly discuss your child's behavior with your spouse and strategize on how to improve your approach to her needs and misbehavior.

4. Affirmation

Is most of the attention I show my child focused on correcting him? Do I affirm him enough when he behaves correctly?

Solution: "Catch 'em being good." Look for opportunities to praise your child's good behavior. If you only notice negative behavior, your child will misbehave simply to get your attention. Your encouraging words should outnumber your words of correction.

5. Correction

Have I been inconsistent in my correction? Do I only correct when the misbehavior interferes with my personal plans?

Solution: Be consistent with your correction. "Say what you mean, and mean what you say." Follow through with your promises to correct. What is your true motivation for your child to behave? Is it to make you look good to others, or is it to build his character?

Solution: Have a plan for your correction. Don't get overwhelmed. Pick two or three behaviors that you want to correct and focus your efforts there. Talk with your spouse about being consistent in the corrective measures you both will use with your child's behavior.

Have I chosen the right corrective measure for my child's age? Am I over-using the same correction measure, rather than being creative in my correction?

Solution: Review the measures available for your child's age. Study how to use them effectively. When you are alone, practice saying your corrective phrases aloud so they will come to you during the more intense moments.

6. Parent Factors

How's my marriage? Is there unrest in our relationship that could be causing insecurity in my child or edginess in me?

Solution: Consult resources, and consider counsel from a close friend, pastor, or professional counselor.

Have I been impatient lately due to issues in my personal life or at work?

Solution: Consult resources, discuss with your spouse, and consider counsel from a close friend, pastor, or professional counselor.

If divorced: Are we parents regularly communicating about our child's needs and behavior? Am I contributing equally to our child's emotional well-being?

Solution: Don't let conflict between you and your ex-spouse interfere with communication about your child's needs. Whether your child is living in your home or not, it is your responsibility to do your part to facilitate communication with the other parent. When parents feud, their child always loses. (See chapter 19 Challenging Home Settings for more details.)

Chapter 9

PARENTING DILEMMAS

Hopefully, by now you are convinced of your child's need of your leadership and of the discipline process. As we have defined the process and identified its basic components, you have given thought to the parenting style you will adopt along with the goals you will pursue in rearing your child.

Now, before we get into specific application of discipline at certain ages, and at the risk of being a bit redundant, I'd like to highlight a few parenting dilemmas that you may experience. These are based on situations that I have noted with parents in my practice or have experienced myself.

Encourage Growing Up: Don't Interfere

Childhood isn't forever, and we shouldn't parent our children as if it were. In the early years, they need our protection and provision, but as they mature, more and more responsibility should be granted to them and expected of them. This is the natural growing process.

Many adolescents today are ill-equipped for life. They don't know how to carry out some of the basic life tasks such as balancing a bank account, running a washing machine, using a lawn mower, repairing a broken household item, or even making their bed. They have been freely given all they wanted and haven't been required to work for or manage money.

Many parents feel their mission in life is to run interference for their child by blocking disappointment at every turn, and making life fun. This child, however, grows up believing that his personal pleasure is the world's number one priority—he expects his parents to keep it that way. The final product of this approach is an adolescent who has a poor work ethic, has never taken school studies seriously, and is uncertain about what he wants to do with his life. Many will go off to college, fail to choose a productive major, continue to play, and return home to live with their parents as unskilled, unproductive young adults. This sad, but real, scenario is preventable—if you take an authoritative, intentional approach to parenting your child.

How Strict Should You Be?

Parents will occasionally ask, "How strict should I be with my children? Am I being too strict or not strict enough?" My short answer is always, "Be lovingly firm."

Be *loving* by demonstrating your affection in action and in word. Let your child know that she is very important to you, more important than your job, your pleasures, and even your own life. Demonstrating this kind of love requires giving her the time and attention she needs. If, for good reason, this time must be limited, then make it high quality. Your child will know if your attention is genuine or simply of token value. Your actions often speak louder than your words. Loving actions include hugs, kisses, tender assistance, playful wrestling, attentive conversation with eye contact, and being available. Your words and actions are a reflection of your heart.

"Be lovingly firm."

Be *firm* by being intentional with correction. As I previously stated, this means being proactive (rather than reactive), consistent, and persistent. A firm parent takes discipline seriously and seeks to be prepared in their responses to the child's actions and words. They seek to apply correction consistently and are persistent despite the child's exhausting misbehavior. Lovingly firm parents have high expectations for their children, but realize that it is okay to occasionally offer grace (not impose a punishment) when upon correction the child is clearly remorseful. To some it may seem inconsistent to ever offer grace when punishment is clearly deserved. But to the wise parent, this is an opportunity to show compassion and even vulnerability as the parent shares with the child a situation where he too committed an offense and received mercy.

In summary, to be lovingly firm is to hold your child to a high standard of behavior and heart attitude while realizing that perfection is not possible.

Be intimately involved in your child's life while remaining a strong authority figure. Love by leading your child to healthy and responsible living.

Disappointment: Dodge It or Deal with It?

Dodging It

It's easy for parents to feel that to be a good parent they must fulfill their child's every want and desire. At its extreme, they feel that their child's happiness is the chief goal of parenting and that any disappointing experiences will surely damage his self-esteem. They are sincerely driven by a desire to indulge their child, even when it goes against their better judgment. They are equally driven to protect their child from disappointment, keeping a smile on his face at all costs. Once begun, however, it is difficult to turn this train around since any effort to do otherwise is met with protest, frustration, and even panic from the child who rarely experiences disappointment and who is rarely required to submit to his parent's leadership.

This practice of "disappointment dodging" can emerge from any of the following parental perspectives.

- *Parental Uncertainty*: This parent has typically given little thought to the ideal goals of parenting and is therefore operating from the assumption that making the child happy is paramount to correction or guidance. Since denying the child his desires may lead to disappointment, this parent has fallen into a sincere but misguided pattern of indulgence and permissiveness. This parent truly fears that conflict or disappointment will harm the child. For instance, this parent ill-advisedly follows the toddler's lead in basic areas like sleep, nutrition, and personal hygiene.
- *Parental Guilt*: This parent feels guilty because of various shortcomings (working too much, being divorced, economic shortcomings etc.) and therefore tries to compensate with over indulgence in other areas. This may come in the form of bending rules, postponing correction, allowing the child to set his own schedule, showering a child with gifts, or being overly complimentary of a child's performance. For instance, parents who feel they have not given their child the time he deserves may compromise on the correction of a child's misbehavior at the end of a long day at work.

- *Parental Selfishness*: This parent simply wants to keep peace and to help his own day go more smoothly. He is not concerned for the child's overall character development or well-being. His main pursuit is good behavior for the moment without regard for the negative consequences the child may later suffer.

Disappointment dodging can begin early and without warning with a parent's hesitation to insist that the child follow directions. Knowing that insisting will result in crying or protest, the parent abandons that which is best for the child and instead gives what the child desires. Although this may be a convenient decision for the moment, it becomes a pattern where the parent is hesitant to change or retrain because of the child's expectation.

Example #1: It's time for two-year-old Johnny's nap, but he is playing with his toys and any interruption is sure to bring resistance. Besides, Johnny's play is allowing Mom to get some paperwork done at her desk in the kitchen. Because interrupting Johnny will lead to disappointment and distress, and since she can benefit as well, Mom decides to allow him to skip his nap today. By choosing to dodge a momentary disappointment, Mom has created a cranky toddler by late afternoon and the need to additionally compromise the usual rules of play, since she now feels responsible for creating Johnny's fatigue-driven misbehavior. After two days of the same compromise, Mom decides that it is time to get back on track with his naps. So, on the third day, she insists on the nap and places Johnny in his bed at the appropriate time. In frustration, he mounts a red-faced protest and cries to the point of gagging. Finally, after ten minutes of guilt and misery, Mom aborts all efforts to get him to sleep and returns Johnny to the floor of the den to resume play with his beloved toys, satisfying his obvious desire. She allowed his disappointment to influence her better judgment and to create a sleep-deprived toddler who will again throw more challenges her way with this apparent victory.

Example #2: Three-year-old Becky pitches a fit at the table when asked to stay and eat with the family, her dad lets her get down and go play. He feels this is better than making life miserable for others sitting at the table. When bedtime arrives, Becky wants to play a bit longer and therefore screams from her bed, until her dad returns to free her from the confines of her room. What is Dad doing? He is resorting to short-term solutions which will eventually lead to long-term problems of defiance and selfishness. He thinks he is doing it all in the name of harmony, alias "conflict avoidance."

Example #3: Eight-year-old Sally is ending her soccer season, and it's awards day. Her best friend gets the MVP award for her outstanding performance that season. Sally is in tears as her family drives home, complaining that she deserved the award more than her friend. Rather than tell Sally the truth about her subpar performance, her parents side with her, criticize the coach, and drive to the local sporting goods store to buy her a trophy that is even bigger than her friend's. Sadly, Sally is led to believe that she is a star player who needs no further improvement. Sally's parents are creating a narcissist and are setting her up for disheartened failure later in life.

Dealing with It

So, you might ask, what is the problem with sheltering our children from disappointment? The answer: It is not reality. Your child will experience disappointment sooner or later in life; learning how to properly handle setbacks early in life will largely define future successes. The longer this experience is delayed, the more difficult it will be for your child to recover from disappointments.

> *Learning how to properly handle setbacks early in life will largely define future successes.*

Disappointments occur early in a child's life, even in the first year. These may include halting a feeding to burp, changing a diaper, being held down for a vaccine, sitting in a car seat, being placed in a crib for naptime, or coming in from outside play. In each of these settings the child will likely cry in protest, but if the parent resists the urge to give in, the child learns valuable lessons. Allowing disappointment or occasional failure can actually strengthen a child's character. He can learn:

- Submission to his parent's lead
- That protesting does not change the directive
- To trust his parents with the outcome
- To be grateful (Occasionally denying a child a toy or desired gift teaches appreciation for what he has and even greater appreciation for that item when he eventually gets it.)
- Contentment with his possessions and his limitations (Ironically, experiencing disappointment leads to greater contentment. It has

been said, "If a person is not satisfied with what he has, he will never be fully satisfied with what he wants.")

Example #1: In sleep training, six-month-old Jack is intentionally placed in his crib wide awake at naptimes to fall asleep on his own. Initially, he cries in protest (not in pain, but disappointment) for ten minutes before falling asleep. After two days of this, Jack realizes that he really is sleepy at these naptimes, fusses for a minute or two, and then crashes into a deep, peaceful sleep. Both Jack and his parent benefit from this tolerance of disappointment.

Example #2: Ten-year-old Ricky wants a new bicycle for his birthday, even though his old one works fine and is only two years old. His best friend gets a new bike every two years. Ricky's birthday rolls around and . . . no new bike. His parents explain that his bike is in good shape and there is no need for a new one. Ricky, in turn, learns to keep his bike polished and maintained, and learns the value of contentment. His friend, on the other hand, constantly wants (and gets) accessories for his new bike, and yet he carelessly leaves it outside in the rain. He never seems content with what he has.

Fears: Protect, Petition, or Push

A common challenge for parents of toddlers or preschool children is how to handle their unreasonable or irrational fears that will occasionally arise. While fears of frightening settings such as darkness, growling dogs, or loud noises are certainly appropriate, fears of common or everyday objects or actions can be stifling to a young child. These fears would include ordinarily non-threatening situations such as petting a dog, participating in swim lessons, riding in a car through a car wash, hearing thunderstorms, or even pouring water over a child's head during a bath. Overcoming these unreasonable fears can boost a child's confidence and her boldness to take on more challenges.

So, what is a parent to do? There are three possible approaches to these fears: protect, petition, or push.

1. Protect

With this approach the parent shelters the child at the first indication of alarm and enables her to avoid any and all fear-eliciting events or settings. By never confronting the fear, this approach confirms in the child's mind the legitimacy of the fear. It subtly directs the child to deal with the fear on her own timetable, which can lead to even more unresolved and often paralyzing fears.

2. Petition

With this approach, the child is given responsibility to decide as she is always asked whether she "wants" to approach the fear-eliciting setting. Regardless of how irrational it may be, this parent always defers to the child's decision. With this sort of control comes a responsibility that can be overwhelming for the child, particularly when she is conflicted by seeing her peers approaching the setting with little to no fear. She is often helpless in these settings without her parent's direction, assurance, and even prompting.

3. Push

This approach starts with petitioning but, when the fear is unreasonable, moves into persuading and gently pushing the child to confront the fear. While persuading a child with reasoning is often unsuccessful with deeply emotional fears, it should always be attempted first. For instance, explaining to the child that the chance is low of a tornado forming in a thunderstorm will rarely alleviate her fear, but it should be stated nonetheless. Also, while pushing does cause some anxiety with the child, it is more tolerable if it is incremental. For example, when a child is fearful of dogs, the following approach can be taken:

- Parent and child stand across the street and watch the dog play in his fenced yard.
- The next week, parent and child cross the street to watch the dog play.
- The next week, parent and child walk up to the fence to pet the dog.

A parent's motivation in pushing the child should always be to build her confidence. By stepping out of her comfort zone, trusting her parent's judgment, and succeeding, the child's fears are lessened and her willingness to accept new challenges increases.

My recommendation for helping a child deal with fears: take approach #1 in dangerous settings, and take #2 followed by #3 in harmless settings.

Pushing can also be useful for social development. Take the shy three-year-old who refuses to speak to adults. It is reasonable at this age for the parent to require that the child always reply to an inquiring adult, even if it is just saying a word or two. It can start with giving eye contact and simply saying "hello" when addressed in public. Or if asked, "What's your name?" she can be required to reply, "Sally." If the child refuses to obey this simple request, then she is punished. Once accomplished, she can be required to say more words or phrases. This incremental pushing can give a child increasing social confidence, but can also prevent the manipulation that can so easily occur when a child who is allowed to snub a doting adult.

Choices: Too Many Too Early

Can there be any harm in allowing a young child the responsibility to make choices? Well, maybe. Take for example, three-year-old Megan who is allowed to choose the clothes she will wear each morning, the breakfast foods she will eat, the time she desires to spend at the dinner table, the toys she desires to play with, and the screens she wants to enjoy. In the process, however, Megan is convinced that she is pretty smart. Her mother doesn't realize it, but by allowing her to make so many decisions, Megan is being empowered beyond her cognitive abilities. In fact, Megan soon believes she should make *all* the decisions in her life. So, every night there's a battle over ending playtime to get a bath, and then with going to bed on time. Megan's mom is puzzled at her refusal to cooperate, and yet the real problem is a lack of parental guidance or *leadership*. Too many choices, too early, has definitely produced an assertive Megan, but proper submission to her parents' authority has been ignored in the process.

The recommendation for parents to indiscriminately and often allow their young children the freedom to make choices is popular among parenting experts today. The assumption is that making choices is the primary means to helping a child feel self-confident and assertive. This recommendation often emanates from an assumption that children are naturally wise and prone to make the good choices if allowed the freedom to do so. What is largely ignored is the fact that young children are naturally self-centered (egocentric) and unwise; without sufficient guidance, they will choose to please themselves with little consideration for others.

Wise decision-making does not come naturally to a young child. It is developed over time through the discipline process and acquired in stages. As privileges are granted and handled responsibly, more are entrusted to the child. If a child chooses to rebel against his parent's directives in a setting where choices have been offered, the choices are temporarily removed until responsibility is again demonstrated. For example: Two-year-old Michael is allowed to choose the color of his shirt: the red one or the blue one. He enjoys this privilege and his mother enjoys watching him choose. One day he pitches a fit because he wants to wear his dirty green shirt instead of the two offered by his mom. Michael temporarily feels he has the power to defy his mother's selection and get his way. To teach him otherwise, Mom takes away the privilege of choosing shirts for one week. Michael now realizes that life is much better if he does it Mom's way rather than his.

While a parent practicing the "early choices" approach may have sincere motives, correcting the child's overly autonomous attitude is made even more difficult if delayed. Retraining a child to submit to a parent's guidance is more difficult than teaching submission at an earlier age. Take Megan, now six years old, who regularly rejects the choices offered by her parents and instead insists on a different option that she thinks is best. When denied that option, she angrily accuses her parents of not loving her and stomps her feet insisting that she get her way. Her parents are puzzled over the selfish, ungrateful attitude that Megan often displays toward them. It's going to be tough now convincing Megan that her parents know best.

Megan's parents are also baffled by the recent trouble she is occasionally having with making decisions when asked. Megan actually displays some anxiety when placed in this position, even though she regularly demands to be the one in control. This conflict arises from pressure felt when her parents constantly rely upon her to make the *right* decision, even when it is beyond her level of development. Children actually thrive when parents rightfully *lead* them in the more challenging settings, and yet allow them to make the decisions in simpler settings.

Choices should be earned,
not simply granted.

Solution: Avoid overly empowering your child too early. Allow a few simple choices early in your child's life. As she demonstrates the responsible handling of these choices, then add more. In other words, choices should be *earned*, not simply granted.

Avoid Overindulgence, Develop Independence

It can happen before you know it. It feels good to give to our children because we love them. (My parents would tell me that they wanted me to have a better childhood than they had.) As parents, we get pleasure from seeing our children's faces light up when they receive a desired gift. But where's the balance? Is there any harm in enjoying ourselves as we sacrificially give to our children? If it makes them happy, can there really be any harm in it?

Aid workers and missionaries serving in third-world countries often speak of a common principle in ministering to native people groups. They say, "Give a man a fish and you feed him for a day. Teach a man to fish and you will feed him for a lifetime." The message is to teach skills that lead to *independence*, rather than giving only to meet their immediate needs, which leads to *dependence*. Childrearing is no different. While it is most appropriate to give to our children, it is counterproductive if it leads to dependency upon us and never learning to independently earn and do for themselves.

Parenting can be one of the most satisfying experiences in life. It can give a parent purpose and motivation for living. Healthy parenting, however, allows a child to gradually become independent by teaching him the skills needed to be a competent, self-sufficient adult. For some parents this process of transition is emotionally painful; therefore, they deliberately hinder their child's growth in order to maintain dependency. The reasons a parent may do this include:

- They view parenting as their *sole* purpose in life.
- Their children provide them with the emotional fulfillment that does not exist in their marriage relationship or through other adult relationships.
- They view their child as needy and too fragile to take on the responsibilities of the world.
- They desire to control their child's destiny and feel that only *they* know what is best.
- They fear the loss of a relationship with the child if independence is granted.

While this failure to let go of the child may sustain the parent, it delays and even jeopardizes a child's opportunity in life for a healthy transition to adulthood. As the child reaches adolescence, there is a struggle that naturally ensues between a parent's desire to hold on and the teen's desire to spread his wings. Often, because the child feels much love for, and gratefulness to, the parent for all the attention and sacrifice, he feels guilty for wanting to achieve independence. This guilt can actually be facilitated by the parent as a means of maintaining dependence.

Sadly, in its most extreme form, this unhealthy relationship can produce a young adult who fails to achieve in the working world, which further verifies the parent's conviction that he is not ready to be released. This circular trap proves to be detrimental for both parent and child.

Teach independence. Begin early and increase gradually as your child matures. Remember, your goal is to work yourself out of a job by the time your child reaches adulthood.

Part Two

LOVING BY LEADING YOUR CHILD: HOW?

Chapter 10

OPPORTUNITIES TO LEAD YOUR CHILD

We began this book by discussing the importance of parents *leading* their children rather than *following* them. We looked at *why* parents should lead. In the following chapters, I will describe *how* parents can lead their children. Under the various general headings such as Sleep, Nutrition, and Behavior, I will suggest "Opportunities to Lead" according to the age of your child. This arrangement allows you to reference the pertinent information you are looking for within your child's overall stage of development. I want to encourage you, however, to read all the general headings for your child's age since many are affected by the other. For instance, your child's behavior will be influenced by his sleep, nutrition, and exercise. So, don't just read the behavior section for your child's age; read them all for a fuller understanding of your child.

Here is the layout of the following chapters:

General topics: Encouragement, Sleep, Nutrition, Exercise, Behavior, Digital Challenges, Industriousness, and Personal Matters.

Age categories: Range from the first year to the tenth year.

Opportunities, Not Requirements

Some of the opportunities I recommend will seem obvious to some parents and revolutionary to others. To be successful does not require that you implement every one of my recommendations. I simply want to offer you opportunities to lead, and you can choose which to implement according to your situation and your child's temperament.

It's Never Too Late

Regardless of the age of your child or the obstacles you may face, I believe you can benefit from the following advice. If your child is older and you are just now recognizing your missed opportunities to lead her, please understand that it is not too late. If your financial situation does not allow you to stay at home with your young child, or if your work schedule means long hours away from your family, there are still recommendations in the following chapters that can be helpful to you. Remember, you can only do what you can do. Don't feel burdened for what you cannot do, just be diligent about what you can. In the words of the great basketball coach, John Wooden, "Do not let what you cannot do interfere with what you can do."

Chapter 11

ENCOURAGEMENT

As we learned in chapter 7, one of the three components of healthy discipline is affirmation. In affirming our children, we encourage them to continue that particular behavior or attitude. We must resist the temptation to discipline our children only through correction. They need clear instruction and generous affirmation as well. In fact, correction will be incomplete and less effective without affirmation. Consider putting into practice some of the following opportunities to lead your child through encouragement.

The First Year

- Be physical with your baby. Hold her, rock her, carry her, and kiss her.
- Smile at your baby often, especially in the first six months. Encourage siblings to do the same with the baby.
- Talk, sing, and read to your baby. She watches your facial expressions and mouth movements as she listens to your voice. This is how she learns to express herself.
- Be there for your baby, especially the newborn. Babies need to know that a parent is always available, and with this realization comes personal security. Don't be overly concerned about spoiling your newborn by too much holding or rocking.
- Dads, spend time with the baby, even in the first few months when she is less interactive and responsive. Research shows that increased engagement with fathers is associated with higher cognitive scores at two years of age. These fathers displayed more sensitivity, playfulness, and talking with the babies. A nursing mother need not be reminded to spend time

with her baby; it is naturally necessary. However, dads can be otherwise occupied and distracted.

- Choose the healthiest toys for play. Traditional, non-electronic toys are best. Electronic, screened toys have been associated with delayed language development due to poor interaction between infant and parent. Traditional toys (such as books, blocks, and puzzles) foster more interaction and more language development.[1,2] Avoid the temptation to use your phone as a toy or distraction to control your child's behavior. This will prove to be a short-term solution that leads to a long-term problem. Delay intentional exposure to screens until two years of age or older.
- Spend time outside with your baby, especially after six months when he is more aware. Go for strolls and walks.

12–18 Months

Be your child's primary teacher and make his environment conducive to learning. Here are some practical measures you can take.

- Keep your daily schedule as simple as you can. Try to be at home as often as possible to allow for family dining (healthier nutrition) and for regular sleeping (consistent napping and bedtime). Working parents, come home after work and, as much as possible, stay at home throughout the evening. Turn down entertainment opportunities outside the home and focus on your family's interests. Meeting your child's basic needs will help him be less fatigued and more self-controlled. Children are very impressionable in the first three years of life and need your attention. Invest now and enjoy the rewards later. You can never recover these years once they have passed.
- Talk with your child as you go through each day and seek opportunities to teach life lessons. For example: When you see a bird, tell of its Creator; when someone does a good deed in your presence, point it out; when another child shares with yours, acknowledge how generous he is being.
- Be physical with your toddler. Hug, kiss, wrestle, and hold hands on walks.
- Take time to play with your child, even if for a few minutes in the evening.
- Continue to read to him.
- Applaud your child with each new developmental achievement (i.e., speech, understanding, and proper behavior).
- Limit your child's screen exposure. Leave the television turned off most of the time. Having it on is like inviting a stranger into your home to

influence your child. Children under two years of age should not be encouraged to watch the television. Don't use your smart phone or tablet as an entertainment source for your child when he is bored or restless. Offer books and mechanical toys instead.

- Do things as a family: meals, singing, taking walks after supper, attending church, shopping, and vacationing.

18–24 Months

With more cognitive development comes more reasoning and observation. Remember, you are your child's number one hero. He is watching. Model proper behavior and attitudes. Show your love for him.

- Continue to demonstrate your love toward your child through active play (wrestling, tumbling, and chasing) and by often saying, "I love you." Spend individual time together like going on a Saturday breakfast date, flying a kite, playing with blocks, or just going on a walk.
- Begin the practice of the "Family Table." Eating meals together at home encourages family conversation, allows parents to demonstrate positive role modeling, and even stimulates good eating habits. (Review the details in chapter 6 under Nutrition.)
- Begin giving your child some age-appropriate choices, such as choosing between two outfits to wear or choosing which of two toys to take in the car. Limit the choices to two or three to avoid frustrating your child and yourself. (See chapter 9 for more about allowing choices.)
- Generously encourage your child's proper and obedient behavior through verbal praise ("I'm so proud of my big girl") and occasional rewards, such as new privileges or a special activity.
- Look for opportunities to "catch" your child being good, and then applaud him.
- Read to your child. This will inspire your child to value reading later in life. The story may not be as important as noticing details and asking questions about the pictures. ("Do you see the bird? What is the dog doing?") Children at this age like the same books every day. Try to read at least one familiar book daily, then read some new ones occasionally. This repetitive reading is comforting for the child and makes for fun games later when you both have the words memorized!

2 Years

While your two-year-old may be willful and quite negative at times, she longs for your encouraging remarks and attention. Make an effort to show her as much attention for her good behavior as you do for her bad.

- Demonstrate your love toward your child through active play (wrestling, tumbling, and chasing) and by often saying, "I love you."
- Spend individual time together by going on a Saturday breakfast date, flying a kite, or just going on a walk. Read a book together or tell creative stories. These will be some of the most memorable times for your child.
- Begin to encourage your child's love of learning by talking about things they notice or that interest them.
- Sing songs together. Don't be afraid of how your voice sounds; your toddler can't tell a good voice from a bad one. Find poems or songs with actions that you can do together. This is especially good for car rides or when doing something that isn't much fun, like cleaning up.
- Generously encourage your child's proper and obedient behavior through verbal praise ("I'm so proud of my big girl") and occasional rewards, such as new privileges or a special activity.

3 Years

As new skills are accomplished and privileges are earned, three-year-olds are proud and pleased with themselves. A wise parent will consistently challenge this child with responsibilities within his reach, and then applaud his accomplishments with mention of him "growing up." This child wants to grow up, but is at times uncertain of his maturity when measured by comparison with the grown-ups around him. He is longing for reassurance and feels proud when it is received.

- Show physical affection often by kissing, hugging, playing, etc.
- Go on breakfast dates.
- Talk in the car, at the dinner table, before bed, and throughout the day as you have opportunity. Answer a few of the "why" questions but maybe not all of them. Help them see that their questions are important, and it's good to ask about the world around them.
- Encourage outside play. Go on walks and to the park occasionally.

- Read together daily. Plan trips to the library to get a few books that you read throughout the week. Find a story time at a local library that is appropriate for this age and doesn't require a lot of quiet sitting.
- Encourage them in their ability to accomplish simple tasks around the house, and praise them for being so grown up. Examples are sorting clean silverware, dusting, and putting toys away.

4–5 Years

A preschooler is increasingly observant of her parents' actions and lifestyle. *Do my parents love me? Am I important to my parents? Do their actions match their talk?* Answers to these questions come in the form of time spent with a child and actions of affection shown to a child. A child will often overlook the lack of time together when a parent is busy, *if* the parent spends quality time with the child whenever possible. Words of encouragement are always beneficial, but they have less meaning when coming from a disinterested or highly distracted parent. Give eye-to-eye attention to your child during conversation. Be physically affectionate. Look for opportunities to applaud your child's abilities and maturing character.

- Read with your child daily for 10-20 minutes, if possible. Find stories that make you both laugh and think.
- Talk through difficult situations and listen to your child without trying to make them stop crying. Ask what they are feeling, and help them name the feeling if possible so they develop a feeling vocabulary for themselves.
- Do puzzles together.
- Play age-appropriate board and card games together.
- Model and teach good sportsmanship by playing outdoor sports/games together and teaching how to win well and lose well.

6–10 Years

Continue to spend time together as a family and individually with your child. Make this a priority by marking time in your weekly schedule.

- Encourage your school-age child by teaching and requiring a healthy lifestyle: regular sleep, good nutrition, and plenty of exercise. (See chapter 6 for details.)

- Show physical affection often with hugs and pats on the back.
- Look for opportunities to compliment your child, especially when she chooses to behave responsibly and displays desirable character qualities.
- Encourage your child by sharing stories of when you made mistakes and what you learned from it. It helps our children know that we fail, too.
- Be available for questions. Regularly ask your children if there have been things in their day or week that they have questions about. This will help your children see that you are available to talk about things and allow them space to think through things about life that are confusing or difficult. Don't always solve the problem for them; occasionally ask them what they think is best to do. Or offer what you have done when confronted with the same problem yourself.
- Continue to read books they enjoy together, even as a family after dinner. Allow your child to read to you for 15-20 minutes a day, even if it is the same book repeatedly.
- Find projects to do together that you both enjoy, such as woodworking, building a model kit, painting pictures, or pottery.
- Be involved with your child in organized activities, such as sports and ballet. Help your child learn how to practice the individual skills needed for the activity.
- Identify your child's strengths and weaknesses. Help him to be thankful for successes and accept responsibility for occasional failures. Teach him to work hard and bounce back from defeat.
- Children need encouragement especially during this school-age period when their interaction with peers brings much comparison and competition.
- Teach your children how to study and be a good student. Communicate with her teachers. Be involved at the school as opportunites arise. Place a high value on learning.
- Build up your family. Regularly do things together. On a daily basis, practice the Family Table, have family devotions after dinner, and pray together each evening before bedtime. On a weekly basis, attend church together, have family night on Friday or Saturday at home with favorite foods and games, take walks in the neighborhood, and enjoy Saturday breakfast together. Occasionally, go to the park, museum or zoo together; take a long weekend trip, serve at a soup kitchen together, and visit relatives so children can know their extended family.

- Take family vacations together—the cheaper the better. Camping, hiking, a night away at a hotel with a swimming pool.
- Help your children learn to accept new responsibilities and watch their confidence grow as they tackle harder projects.
- Allow your children to contribute to the family by doing chores. Begin an allowance program. (See chapter 17 Industriousness for details on how to start these.)
- Find a couple of families who share similar values and spend time with them regularly. This creates a community that your child sees regularly with different ages and life stages so that your child has an extended "family" that watches him grow and provides additional support.

Chapter 12

SLEEP

Don't we all feel better when we get a good night's sleep? Children are no different. Healthy sleep begins in infancy, and it starts with establishing good sleep habits. There is reliable research to prove that when infants are taught to sleep well, the healthy sleep habit continues into adolescence.

Let's look at leading your child to healthy sleep by age group. The first year is the longest section because of all the variables affecting an infant's sleep. Also, my Infant Sleep Training method is set apart in a special section (page 172) since it can be used anytime in the first two years of your baby's life.

The First Year: (Sleeping + Feeding)

Sleep and feeding are closely tied to each other in the first six months of a baby's life. For this reason, I will address them together for the first four months. Then, at five months of age, sleep and feeding will be addressed separately.

The first month of a newborn's life can be quite chaotic. It is naturally fraught with both excitement and exhaustion for the parents. When parents come in to my office for their newborn's first few visits, heavy on their minds is the question, "Will we ever sleep through the night again?" The answer obviously is yes, but they are especially reassured when I show them my suggested plan for their baby's first year. This is what I call, "Your Baby's Daily Schedule," and it is a graphic display of the approximate feeding and sleeping times for your baby's first year. This is simply a guide for you and your child, not a rigid schedule. I will present and explain the details of the schedule at each stage of this first year of life, so don't look too far ahead. Also, be aware that at four months I recommend you do the sleep training with your child to achieve the illustrated sleep pattern.

YOUR BABY'S DAILY SCHEDULE: BREASTFEEDING

Most infants are capable of following a predictable feeding and sleeping routine if guided by their parents. This schedule will serve as a guide for you and your baby. Closely follow the instructions detailed in this chapter. If your baby has difficulty with sleeping or feeding, consult your pediatrician.

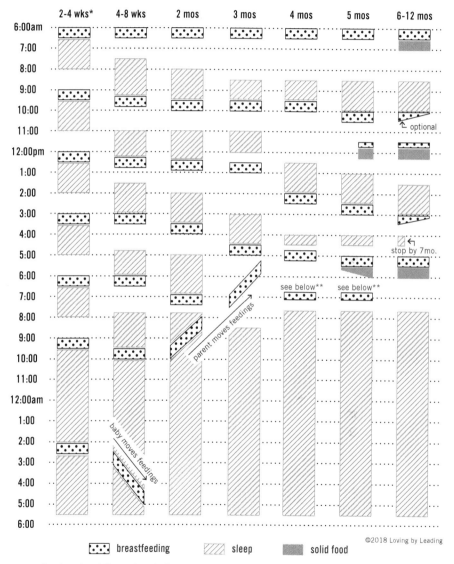

©2018 Loving by Leading

*In the first 4 weeks of life, babies will feed on demand, at least every 3 hours.
**To maintain milk supply, breastfeeding mothers need to nurse at least 5 times a day. This additional feeding can occur 45 minutes before bedtime, or mother can pump after baby goes to sleep.

This is simply a guide for you and your child, not a rigid schedule.

YOUR BABY'S DAILY SCHEDULE: BOTTLE FEEDING

Most infants are capable of following a predictable feeding and sleeping routine if guided by their parents. This schedule will serve as a guide for you and your baby. Closely follow the instructions detailed in this chapter. If your baby has difficulty with sleeping or feeding, consult your pediatrician.

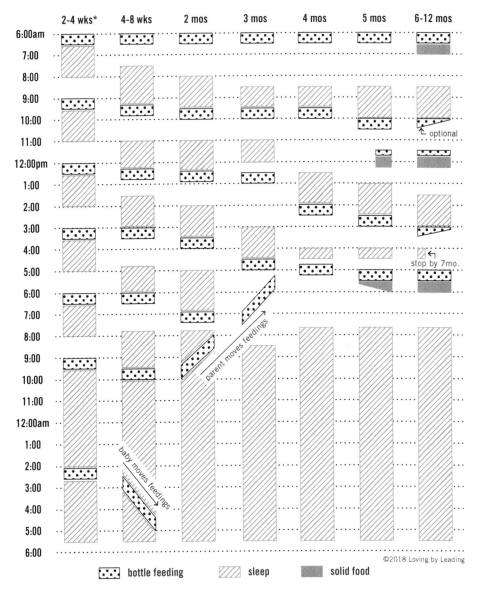

*In the first 4 weeks of life, babies will feed on demand, at least every 3 hours.

This is simply a guide for you and your child, not a rigid schedule.

Birth to 2 Weeks

Feeding

One of the earliest decisions you will make with your newborn is whether to breastfeed or formula feed. The research is clear on this matter: breastfeeding is best for you and your baby. This is an option whether you will stay at home or return to work after having the baby. Also, whether you nurse for one month or twelve months, there are health benefits for both of you. Here are a few of the benefits for mother and child.

Breastfeeding is best for you and your baby.

Benefits of Breastfeeding

For the baby:

- Greater bonding and attachment between mother and child
- Lower risk of Sudden Infant Death Syndrome (SIDS)
- Lower risk of ear infections and respiratory infections
- Lower risk of obesity as a child (longer the breastfeeding duration, the lower the risk)
- Lower risk of diabetes
- Less atopic dermatitis (eczema)
- Lower risk of asthma

For the mother:

- Closer bonding with newborn baby
- Less post-partum depression
- Faster return of uterine tone and cessation of bleeding
- Temporary suppression of ovulation
- Lower risk of breast cancer
- Lower risk of ovarian cancer
- Savings on the costs of formula

If You Are Breastfeeding

Breastfeeding can be a wonderful time of bonding for you and your baby, but it can also be a time of uncertainty for you. Questions will likely arise over your milk supply, your baby's feeding pattern (or lack of pattern), and your lack of control over your day. This is natural and is handled much better if you know what to expect.

First of all, if you have chosen to breastfeed, determine to exclusively nurse for at least the first two weeks. By refusing to offer bottles or formula, your baby will nurse with more vigor and your milk will come in more fully. Sometimes supplementation is needed, but that generally is not determined by your doctor until 10–14 days of age.

Next, you will probably have some doubts about your milk supply in the first two to three days of feeding. This is normal. Breastfeed your baby as often as she desires during the day and night (i.e., "on demand"). Feed her at least every three hours (from the start of one feeding to the start of the next), but as often as every hour. This may seem chaotic at first, but frequent feeding helps her learn the process of breastfeeding and it stimulates your body to produce more milk.

Know that the breast milk you are producing is all the milk your baby needs. This simple fact may be hard to believe when your baby is eating every hour and your breasts feel empty. The natural process for successful breast-feeding requires that your baby lose weight (fluid), becomes very hungry, and feeds more often with each passing day. Your milk supply increases with each day as well, but does not begin to fully come in until the baby's fourth or fifth day of life. Be patient, your baby will not allow you to under-feed her without protesting. You can rely upon your baby's desire to know when to feed. This is why "demand feeding" should be your approach in the first four weeks. At times, when your baby seems the hungriest, you may be tempted to offer formula. While this may seem to help at the moment, it can complicate the overall feeding process, causing your baby to feed less often and thereby causing your body to produce less milk. You will feel more confident on day four or five when your milk comes in. If you do not experience this increase in milk supply, talk with the lactation nurse at the hospital, or schedule a visit with your baby's doctor for a weight check and advice.

Here's what you can expect in the first days: On day one, your baby will probably be sluggish with his feeding since he naturally has more fluid within his body than he needs. As he loses weight with each day, he will be thirstier and feed with more interest. With each day your milk supply will increase, from minimal amounts of a thin white solution (colostrum) on the first day to more generous amounts of richer, thicker milk by the fourth to fifth day.

Just remember during this time, the milk you have is all your baby needs. As his needs increase, so will your milk supply.

If You Are Formula Feeding

Feed your baby formula as often as she desires, but at least every three hours from start to start during the day. In the first 36–48 hours of life, I recommend limiting the amount of formula you give to your baby to about 15–20 ml per feeding. Your baby's tummy is quite small in the first hours of life, and therefore if offered an unlimited amount of formula, she will often over-feed and spit up. By 48 hours of age, babies can usually take an ounce or more and not spit up. Thereafter, you can follow your baby's desires by increasing the amount you offer by 10–15 ml if she: (a) appears hungry immediately following a feeding, or (b) wants to feed earlier than expected for the next feeding.

Sleeping

Newborns sleep a total of 12–18 hours a day in a random manner with wake periods of one to three hours. They are restless sleepers as they randomly move about, twitch their arms and legs, make noises, smile, and even suckle. Many newborns will sleep more during the day and be awake more at night. In order to reverse this pattern, babies need to be stimulated more during the day and less at night. Feeding your baby at least every three hours (from start to start) during the day will cause her to be regularly stimulated and awake during the day. When feeding at night, keep the lights down low, be as quiet as you can, feed her, get a quick burp, and then put her back to bed. Also, giving a warm bath in the evening prior to the last feeding may help your baby relax and sleep more at night.

Where to Sleep

It is common for parents to want their newborn baby to sleep in their bedroom for the first few weeks. This is especially the case when a mother is demand-feeding her newborn. In order to achieve the highest quality sleep, however, I recommend you eventually transition your baby to his own room, ideally by two to four months of age. This can begin by placing him in his crib (in his bedroom) for naps during the day for a week or two, and then placing him there for the night. This will allow for a gradual transition that begins during the daytime, when you are most alert and able to tolerate him fussing a bit as he adjusts to the new setting.

Research shows that babies who sleep in their parent's room beyond four months of age have shorter sleep periods at night, lower quality sleep, and are four times more likely to end up sleeping in the parent's bed during the night.[1] Poor sleeping habits in infancy have been shown to lead to poor sleeping at later ages, which can have negative emotional and behavioral effects upon the child. This finding emphasizes the importance of developing healthy sleep habits in the first few months of life.

The chart below lists my suggestions for where your baby can sleep. If you are uneasy about moving your baby out of your bedroom, you can certainly wait. I think you will find, however, that he sleeps better if he is not in your bedroom.

Where to Sleep		
Age	Daytime	Nighttime
Birth to 4 weeks	Whatever works—bassinette, crib, blanket on floor, parent's arms	Bassinette in parent's room or crib in baby's room
By 4–8 weeks	Ideally, crib in baby's room	Bassinet or crib
By 2–4 months	Crib in baby's room	Crib in baby's room

How to Sleep

(A) *Sleep Position.* The safest way for your newborn baby to sleep is on his back on a firm mattress in a bassinet or a crib—not sleeping beside you in the same bed. Placing your baby on his back to sleep has been shown to significantly reduce the risk of Sudden Infant Death Syndrome (SIDS). Avoid using thick mattress pads, blankets, or stuffed animals in the crib that could cause suffocation. If you prefer your baby to sleep close to you, then use a co-sleeper bassinet, which sits next to your bed. Sleeping with your baby in your bed carries the risk of rolling over on your baby and causing suffocation.

(B) *Sleep Aids.* It is common to use sleep aids like a swaddle blanket, tilted cradle sleeper, or even a swing to help a baby sleep in the first few weeks at home. While these can provide a nice transition from a mother's cozy womb to a baby's crib, they can also interfere with this transition if their use is prolonged. Since I will encourage you to eventually train your baby to self-soothe without aids at bedtime, I recommend you aim to have your baby in a regular flat crib by two to four months. If you plan to use a swaddling blanket, plan to stop its use by three to four months of age. Swaddling beyond six months increases the risk for SIDS.

(C) *Sound Machines.* Background noisemakers have become very popular and are primarily used as sleep aids with newborns. As a sleep aid, I prefer a musical toy that plays a series of chimes for about twenty minutes and is started upon entering the baby's room to begin the bedtime routine. This is soothing to the baby and makes for a gradual transition from a mother's voice to silence when the chimes end.

Sound machines also produce a "white noise" which can be useful in drowning out noises from outside the baby's room. It is most useful when noise outside the baby's room is loud and unpredictable, such as with multiple siblings in the home, or when sleeping away from home in a noisy environment. A fan in the bedroom can serve the same purpose. If you decide to use a sound machine, researchers make the following recommendations:[2]

1. Place the machine as far away from the baby as possible and never in the baby's crib.
2. Play it at the lowest volume setting.
3. Use it for a short duration, such as until the baby is asleep or until the outside noise levels diminish.

I don't recommend these machines unless you need one. Babies need quietness to completely settle and relax. Quietness is becoming more and more scarce in our society as people seek to fill every waking moment with some form of stimulation—music, video, smartphone, talking. Even adults are using noisemakers to sleep at night as their stimulated minds find silence awkward. Babies and children need times of quietness to rest and relax, especially in infancy.

2–4 Weeks

YOUR BABY'S SCHEDULE: 2 - 4 WEEKS				
DAYTIME FEEDING	**NAPPING**	**IDEAL BEDTIME**	**NIGHTTIME FEEDING**	**IDEAL WAKE UP**
Breast: 2–2½ hrs *at least every 3 hrs* Formula: 2–3 hrs	Random *sleeps about 16 hrs a day*	9:30 – 10:30 pm	Every 2–4 hours	4:00 – 6:00 am

Feeding

Breastfeeding

Between 6 a.m. and 10–11 p.m., breastfeed every two and a half to three hours from start-to-start.

If this is your first experience with breastfeeding, your baby should have a weight check visit at the doctor's office sometime within the first two weeks of life. It is normal for newborns to lose as much as 10–12% of their birth weight in the first few days of life. A reasonable feeding goal for your baby is to return to her birth weight by two weeks. Once the doctor has confirmed that your breastfeeding is going well, you may begin to lengthen your baby's feeding intervals during the day to every two to two and a half hours, instead of feeding on demand. This encourages your baby to feed with more vigor with each feeding, rather than frequent snacking throughout the day. With more aggressive feeding and filling, your baby will also tend to go for longer periods between feedings at night.

After 10–11 p.m., let him sleep up to four hours between feedings.

If the feeding is going well at this point, and your milk supply is good, you can allow your baby to sleep as long as four hours between feedings at night. Feed him when he fully wakes (crying for about one minute) in the night. Allow him to rest if he is simply grunting (which is common day and night after three weeks of age) or making intermittent noises or cries. He will eventually learn to sleep longer if you allow him to fully wake before feeding in the night.

Introducing the bottle at three to four weeks. Once the nursing is going well and there are no issues with supply or latching, consider offering your baby pumped breast milk in a bottle to train her to be flexible in accepting milk from the breast or the bottle. A good time to do this is at three to four weeks of age. If you wait much later you may have difficulty getting her to accept the bottle. Here's how to do it:

Chose a convenient, calm time of the day, perhaps the second feeding (9–10 a.m.). Pump your breasts about 15 minutes before you anticipate your baby will want to eat. Start with about two ounces and offer it repeatedly over 10 minutes. Then allow her to directly nurse to complete the feeding. Do this once daily (bottle first, then breast) until she easily accepts the bottle, and then decrease the bottle offerings to every second or third day, with eventually reducing it to once a week just to keep her memory of the bottle. This will provide you an alternative feeding method for the baby in the future, if you must be away from her.

Formula feeding

Between 6 a.m. and 10–11 p.m., feed every two to three hours from start-to-start.

Formula is heavier and more filling to a baby than breast milk. For this reason, a formula-fed baby at two weeks of age may go as long as two and a half to three hours between feedings during the day. Most formula-fed babies have regained their birth weight by 10 to 14 days of age. Continue feeding your baby at this frequency during the day, and after 10 p.m. allow him to sleep for as long as four hours.

Sleeping

At two weeks of age, your baby's sleep continues to be variable, but hopefully a bit more predictable. If she sleeps for three-hour stretches at night, consider yourself fortunate. Be patient and hopeful: this period will not last forever.

4–8 Weeks

YOUR BABY'S SCHEDULE: 4 - 8 WEEKS		IDEAL BEDTIME	NIGHTTIME FEEDING	IDEAL WAKE UP
DAYTIME FEEDING	**NAPPING**			
Breast: 2½–3¼ hrs *depending on milk supply* Formula: 3–3¼ hrs	Random *If possible, keep baby awake for at least 10 min following each feeding.*	9:30 – 10:30 pm	Variable, every 4–6 hours	4:00 – 6:00 am

Feeding and Sleeping

Adjustments at 4 weeks

For babies who are thriving nutritionally at four weeks of age, I recommend parents make four adjustments to their care that will help them sleep longer at night.

1. Feeding Interval: By four weeks of age, most babies can wait three hours between feedings during the day, with the last feeding at about 10 p.m. Some breast-fed babies may still need to nurse every two and a half hours, depending on a mother's milk supply. Formula-fed babies can go three to three and a quarter hours between feedings. When parents gently guide their baby toward longer stretches of time between feedings, the baby eats with greater interest, consumes more milk, and eventually is able to sleep for longer periods. Therefore, minimizing the "snacking" during the day will in turn lead to longer sleep intervals at night.

After the 10 p.m. feeding, most babies are able to sleep until 1:30 or 2:00 a.m. before they need to feed again. This will likely be your baby's longest stretch of sleep during the night, since she will again need to feed about three hours later.

2. Wakefulness during the Day: Begin keeping your baby awake for at least ten minutes following each feeding during the day. This accomplishes two goals:

A. More wakefulness during the day leads to more sleeping at night. Keep your baby awake as much as possible during the day, then after the last feeding at about 10 p.m. let him sleep.

B. Separates your baby's feeding experience from his sleeping experience. The earliest key to developing good sleep habits is to teach your baby not to need to feed to fall asleep. Babies who consistently fall asleep during or following feedings are inadvertently trained to need to feed to fall asleep. These babies in turn need to be fed anytime they may wake during the night, as they are unable to self-soothe. So, whether you are breastfeeding or formula feeding, try to keep your baby awake for at least ten minutes following each feeding. This is not necessary following the last evening feeding when you will want your baby to sleep. This practice begins the process of teaching a baby how to fall asleep without a parent's assistance.

It is not necessary to lay your baby down for designated naps during the day. Your baby's napping pattern will vary from day to day, but if you feed him with regularity he will generally begin sleeping well at night.

3. Bedtime Routine: Begin a bedtime routine at your last feeding of the evening, around 10 p.m. This may look something like this:

- Give a warm bath.
- Turn on a musical toy that plays soft music or chime for 20–30 minutes, or a low volume sound machine. This will eventually be your baby's auditory cue that it is bedtime.
- Feed and burp him.

- Rock him for a few minutes.
- Place him in the crib on his back to sleep.

4. Nighttime Sleeping: By four weeks of age, most babies can sleep three to four hours after the last feeding of the evening. When he wakes in the night, allow him to fuss a bit (one to two minutes) before picking him up to be sure that he is fully awake and hungry. Also, when feeding in the night, keep any stimulation of your baby to a minimum to low lighting and only whispers. Between four and eight weeks of age, your baby's 2 a.m. feeding will gradually move later and later, as illustrated on the *Your Baby's Schedule* diagram. By eight weeks of age, most babies are sleeping from the 10 p.m. feeding until 3 or 4 a.m. If your baby does not do this, be patient; he will be there by 10–12 weeks of age. If you pay close attention to your baby's daytime routine, the nighttime sleep pattern will develop on its own.

If you pay close attention to your baby's daytime routine, the nighttime sleep pattern will develop on its own.

Infant Crying

One of the most difficult challenges of parenting an infant has to do with understanding why she is crying. Babies cry for a number of reasons, but regardless, it is stressful for mom and dad. While a parent's first inclination and action should be to comfort, there are situations where crying may not require an immediate response. The question arises, "When should I attend to my baby or how long should I allow him to cry?" The answer of course is, "It depends."

- *Physical Needs:* When infants cry due to a physical need, they should be comforted and the need met.
  - Hunger: If it is time, feed the baby.
  - Dirty diaper: Change the diaper.
  - Burp: Sometimes, even one hour after a feeding, a baby may need to be held upright to burp. She will then again relax.
  - Pain: If the cry appears to be a pain cry, search for the source and comfort your infant with generous holding.
- *Communication:* Crying is an infant's only means of communication. With crying, most of the time he is expressing a need. Some

of the time he is just expressing a feeling: frustration, discomfort, fatigue, or even disappointment. While a baby's true needs should always be met with promptness, sometimes it is necessary to delay attending to his cry for a few minutes to teach and allow him to self-soothe. This is a first step toward teaching a degree of independence and self-sufficiency.

- *Fighting Sleep:* Another common reason for infant crying is resistance to falling asleep when placed in a crib. If parents are following a reasonable daily schedule for the baby, then allowing some crying is necessary and appropriate in teaching healthy sleep habits. Here are some reasonable periods of time to allow a baby to cry if he is fighting sleep:

ALLOWED CRYING TIMES FOR A SLEEPY BABY

0 min.	1-3 min.	3-5 min. twice	5-8 min. twice	10 min. or more
0-2 WEEKS OLD	**2-4 WEEKS OLD**	**1 MONTH OLD***	**2 MONTHS OLD**	**4 MONTHS OLD**

*After the first 3–5 minute period, return to your baby's room. If he is softly sobbing, then soothe him for one minute with gentle strokes and words without picking him up. If he is loudly crying, pick him up to soothe, then put him back and try another 3–5 minutes.

These crying times are based on the assumption that a soothing bedtime routine is followed, and that the baby should be sleepy because of the time elapsed since the last nap. Once these crying periods have expired, the baby should be picked up, consoled, and the parent should wait 10–20 minutes before trying again.

You may ask, "Does my baby feel rejected when I let her cry?" If you have nurtured your attachment to your baby by responding to her needs promptly and sensitively, the answer is no. In the above setting, she is not crying for emotional reasons; she is crying from fatigue. Research has also verified this fact.[3]

Tummy Time

With the recommendation to always place babies on their backs to sleep, babies tend to spend all their time on their backs, even when awake. By two months, many will acquire a flattening of the back of their head. To minimize this and for overall motor or muscle development, I recommend "tummy time" beginning at four weeks of age. Most babies will not be very pleased with this position initially, but if you start slow and gradually increase their time, they will adapt. Start with five minutes twice a day, while awake, mid-morning and mid-afternoon, with you observing. Increase the time weekly to eventually reach 15–20 minutes twice a day. You may need to get down on the floor with her (face-to-face) to encourage her. Most babies come to enjoy tummy time very quickly. Don't allow sleeping on the tummy.

2–4 Months

YOUR BABY'S SCHEDULE: 2 - 4 MONTHS				
DAYTIME FEEDING	**NAPPING**	**IDEAL BEDTIME**	**NIGHTTIME FEEDING**	**IDEAL WAKE UP**
3–3½ hrs	Random _By 3 months, typically taking 3 naps per day_	10:00 pm _moves to 8:00 pm by 4 months_	2–3:00 am _moves later and disappears by 3–4 months_	4:00 am _moves to 5–6:00 am by 4 months_

Feeding

By eight weeks of age, most babies will eat every three to three and a half hours during the day and sleep from their last feeding at about 10 p.m. until 2–3 a.m. Some will still be waking at 2 a.m. to eat, but they are only two or three weeks away from sleeping consistently until 4–5 a.m. Keep the 10 p.m. feeding constant until your baby has consistently moved his nighttime feeding from 2 a.m. until 4–5 a.m. Other babies will be difficult to wake for their 10 p.m. feeding and will try to give up the 10 p.m. feeding before they give up their middle-of-the-night (2 a.m.) feeding. If you are one to go to bed shortly after your baby's earlier feeding (7 or 8 p.m.), then this alternate plan may work for you. However, if you are one who likes to stay up later, then you should persist in waking your baby at 10 p.m. to insure that you both get at least a four hour stretch of sleep before the next feeding.

Once your baby is sleeping at least six hours in the night, you may begin moving this last feeding (10 p.m.) earlier in the evening. This can be accomplished by feeding 15 minutes earlier every five to seven days. The goal is to move the last feeding of the evening to 8 p.m. by three to three and a half months of age. This is assuming the baby continues to sleep until 4 or 5 a.m. most nights.

By about 12 weeks, babies will be feeding every three and a half to four hours during the day and are able to sleep through the night (until about 5 a.m.) with bedtime shortly after the last feeding at 8 or 9 p.m. If your baby is still waking in the night and truly appears hungry, feed her briefly and lay her back down in her crib to sleep. She will eventually sleep through the night.

Breastfeeding Moms Returning to Work

Returning to work is a must for many moms. If this is your situation, I recommend waiting until eight weeks or later to return, if possible. This is an important time for recovering from your pregnancy and delivery, as well as a special time for mother-baby bonding. Here are some tips to help a breastfeeding mom transition from home to work:

- Talk with your supervisor about your plans to pump at work and make plans for how it will occur. Plan to pump three times a day at work. If you are able, nurse your baby in the morning before you leave and in the afternoon when you return home.
- Purchase the necessary equipment to collect and transport your breast milk to and from work, such as a cooler, ice packs, and plastic or glass storage containers.
- Obtain an electric breast pump, and begin pumping at about four weeks of age to build a supply of frozen breastmilk. If your milk supply is generous, you can begin pumping as often as three times a day following nursings. You may not get much milk with each pumping, but it will add up through the day.
- Begin training your baby to drink breast milk from a bottle at three to four weeks of age. As mentioned earlier, offer it once a day until your baby accepts it well, then reduce the offerings to one to two per week.
- Once at work, if you are unable to keep up with the milk demands of your baby, you can begin supplementing with infant formula. Remember: Any amount of breast milk that your baby gets is better than none at all.

You may wonder how you will accomplish the daily patterning of sleeping and feeding that I recommend for infants in the first year of life. Don't be discouraged. There will be some challenges with daycare, but it is very feasible. I will comment along the way on what to tell your baby's caregivers. You will have the evenings and weekends to train good sleep habits.

Sleeping

By 12 weeks, you will likely begin to see your baby develop a predictable pattern of three naps a day. To begin teaching your baby to self-soothe, lay him down slightly awake to fall asleep on his own for each of these naps. As you can see on the Infant Schedule (page 151), the naps will occur at roughly 8:30, 11:00, and 3:00 with the bedtime around 8:00 p.m. If at this point your baby is under the care of someone else during the day, encourage them not to rock or feed your baby to sleep. Rather, the baby should be laid down slightly awake and allowed to fuss for five minutes or so to self-soothe to sleep.

4 Months

YOUR BABY'S SCHEDULE: 4 MONTHS			
DAYTIME FEEDING	**NAPPING**	**IDEAL BEDTIME**	**IDEAL WAKE UP**
Breast: 5 feedings Formula: 4 feedings	nap 1 - 8:30 am nap 2 - 12:30 pm nap 3 - 4:00 pm *See Infant Sleep Training on page 172.*	7:00 – 8:00 pm	5:30 – 7:00 am

Four months is a tender age, which I refer to as a "honeymoon phase" for the parent and child. Babies are smiling and cooing, while parents are smiling and celebrating since they all are finally sleeping through the night. By four months, practically all babies are capable of sleeping through the night. Although many will do this naturally, most babies will need some guidance from their parents to accomplish and maintain sleeping through the night. For this reason, four months is the ideal time to do sleep training, as detailed later in this chapter.

This training is rooted in a major change in how you pattern your baby's day. For the first four months of your baby's life, I have recommended patterning his day by his feeding times. Beginning now, I recommend that you begin patterning the day by your baby's three nap times, and only feed him when he wakes. This simple change will make all the difference, so after reading the next paragraphs on Feeding and Sleeping, go to the *Infant Sleep Training* plan on page 172 and review my recommendations for your baby at this age.

Feeding

By four months of age, nighttime nutrition and even the bedtime feeding are no longer necessary to accomplish a full night of sleep. In fact, nutrition no longer plays a role in nighttime sleeping after three to four months of age. This contradicts the deeply held belief that offering cereal to the baby in the bottle or by spoon at bedtime reduces nighttime waking. Actually, giving a heavy feeding prior to laying a baby down may interfere with sleep by causing stomach bloating and even discomfort from acid reflux. Solid foods by spoon can be introduced as early as five months, but this should have little if any effect upon a baby's nighttime sleep. Sleeping through the night at this age is now dependent upon your baby's daytime routine and his ability to fall asleep unassisted. So, nighttime sleep is now more about training, less about nutrition.

Also at this age, babies require only four feedings a day, specifically upon waking in the morning and after each of the three naps. For breastfeeding moms, however, five feedings or pumpings are necessary to maintain good milk supply. There are two options for inserting the extra feeding: (1) Add a fifth nursing before bedtime (6 or 6:30 p.m.) in the family room (not bedroom) followed by 30 minutes of wakefulness before putting the baby to sleep while still awake, or (2) pump after the baby goes to sleep for the night and use the milk at selected times in the future.

Sleeping

Babies at this age are notorious for catnapping through the day, taking brief, shallow, and poor quality naps. This is a problem because they never really learn to sleep deeply whether during the day or during the night, and therefore unnecessarily wake in the night. In order to begin training your baby to sleep more deeply and for longer periods, I recommend you limit his naps to only three a day with bedtime at approximately 7:30 p.m. This approach saves up your baby's sleepiness for each of the three napping opportunities during the day and quickly trains him to sleep more deeply and soundly day and night.

The routine you are seeking here is: Sleep-Feed-Wake. The baby should be laid in the crib awake to fall asleep on his own and be fed only when he awakes. Not only does this approach help a baby sleep more soundly, it is also healthier for his GI tract by limiting any gastric reflux since his tummy is less full when you lay him down.

In order to achieve the sleep schedule outlined below, I recommend you now turn to and study the *Infant Sleep Training* section on page 172. Once you have done this five-day "Baby's Boot Camp" with your child, I believe you and she will be much happier and even healthier.

5–7 Months

YOUR BABY'S SCHEDULE: 5-7 MONTHS			
DAYTIME FEEDING	**NAPPING**	**IDEAL BEDTIME**	**IDEAL WAKE UP**
1–2 solid feedings Breast: 5 feedings Formula: 4 feedings	nap 1 - 8:30 am nap 2 - 1:00 pm nap 3 - 4:00 pm *See Infant Sleep Training on page 172.*	7:00 – 7:30 pm	5:30 – 6:30 am

Sleeping

By five months, your baby should go to sleep easily at the designated naptimes and bedtimes. It is a sign of successful sleep training when a baby only fusses briefly, and then is cooing and playful when placed in the crib for naps and at bedtime. These sweet sounds are evidence of a baby who is secure with his surroundings and who has followed the lead of his parents in teaching him to enjoy his crib.

If the sleep training was successful, your baby's routine should include three predictable naps a day and sleeping through the night.

In order to continue the success you have achieved, do your best to keep your baby from catnapping between the designated naptimes and bedtime. Your baby should not be protesting longer than five minutes each time he is laid down to sleep. If he does cry longer, ask yourself, "Did he take a catnap in the car seat just before this nap or did he fall asleep in the swing or on the floor while playing?" If so, then he probably enjoyed a "power nap" and is not sleepy enough to go down for his regular nap. When this occurs, don't sweat it; just skip the nap, modify the rest of the day, and start afresh in the morning with your baby's routine. Likewise, with vacations or stays away from home, realize that your baby is not likely to follow his routine due to interruptions during the day and to difficulty sleeping in strange locations. Remember: This sleep routine is not a strict schedule that cannot occasionally be modified. Just be consistent on most days, realizing that your baby's routine can be easily reestablished once things normalize.

> *This sleep routine is not a strict schedule*
> *that cannot occasionally be modified.*

7–9 Months

YOUR BABY'S SCHEDULE: 7-9 MONTHS		IDEAL BEDTIME	IDEAL WAKE UP
DAYTIME FEEDING	**NAPPING**		
2–3 solid feedings	nap 1 - 8:30 am	6:30 – 7:30 pm	5:30 – 7:00 am
Breast: 5 feedings	nap 2 - 1:30 pm		
Formula: 4 feedings	*See Infant Sleep Training on page 172.*		

Sleeping

By seven months of age, most babies have given up the 4 p.m. late afternoon nap and have moved their bedtime earlier, to 6:30–7:00 p.m. This results in a schedule like the one above.

Sleep Challenges

In the second half of the first year of life, babies can experience some challenges to their sleep routine. Here are proposed solutions to a couple of them:

Nighttime waking: Many babies will begin waking in the night after six months of age. The most common reasons for waking at night are:

1. *Sleep cycle change.* With development, babies will commonly break out of their deep sleeping habits at six to eight months of age; and this break is unrelated to nutritional needs. As with any nighttime waking, you should attend to your baby's crying after waiting a few

minutes to see if it will stop. Once you have established that the baby is fine, allow her to cry herself back to sleep. This may require attending to her cry a few nights in a row before you feel confident allowing her to cry for longer periods of 20 minutes or more. As you do this, she should reestablish her full night of sleeping within two to three nights.

2. *Disruption of daytime routine.* A common reason for nighttime waking is a disruption in your baby's daytime routine. This could be a change occurring at daycare, where she is being rocked to sleep or where a napping routine is being ignored; or a change in mom's daytime routine where the baby is sleeping in the car seat while driving around town; or a weekend vacation where the baby is sleeping in different settings at odd times of the day. In situations such as these, reestablish the sleep routine during the daytime first, before expecting the baby to settle herself to sleep in the night.

3. *Habitual waking.* If you find yourself attending to your child at about the same time each night, you may be part of the problem. Feeding your child or even placing a pacifier in her mouth when she wakes can create a habit of expectant waking to receive this interaction. The solution: First, be certain you are laying your baby down at bedtime to fall asleep unassisted. Next, remove the interaction that she is seeking. Over a few nights, begin decreasing the volume of milk or duration of nursing offered at this hour to the point of stopping completely. Then, when she wakes in the night, allow her to cry for a few minutes to self-soothe back to sleep.

4. *Disruption of bedtime routine.* This is where a parent or grandparent begins rocking or feeding the baby to sleep at bedtime (sleep association). It may follow an illness or be due to a temporary change in caregiver. Obviously, the solution is to eliminate the sleep association and reestablish the bedtime routine.

5. *Hunger.* While it is possible for a six- to eight-month-old to occasionally wake from hunger, it is uncommon and unlikely. If your baby is making noises in the night, don't necessarily assume it is hunger and attend to her immediately. She may be in a shallow phase of sleep and will go back to sleep if allowed to fuss for a few

minutes. This is most likely the case if, when you feed her, she eats for only a few minutes before falling back to sleep.

6. *Pain or discomfort.* Pain should always be considered as a cause for waking. Pain from an ear infection, body aches from fever, coughing with a cold, an uncomfortable temperature change in the bedroom, acid reflux, etc. can cause waking. Attend to your baby's needs and postpone any sleep training until after the problem is corrected.

Here are some of the most common false claims for waking at nights:

1. *Wet diaper:* A wet diaper is not likely to wake an infant. Babies are more likely to wake for other reasons and then wet their diaper.
2. *Teething:* There is no research evidence that infants regularly experience pain in their gums at nighttime, especially if teeth are not seen breaking through the surface of the gums.[4] If an actively erupting tooth does cause discomfort, it should be evident during the daytime as well and should not last for days on end.
3. *Growth spurt and needs to eat:* Beyond four months, infants should not need nutrition in the night. Feeding a waking baby in the night will, however, create a habit of waking to feed.

   If, after assessing this situation, you decide to let your baby cry himself back to sleep in the night, make a plan together (with spouse) before the night begins. Decide who will do what if there is crying: how long to allow the baby to cry, who will go in to console your baby, and what you will do to console (feed or not). If you decide not to feed your baby in the night, dad may be the best one to go in if the baby is breastfed. The next day, reevaluate and plan for the next night.

   Of course, any time you feel uncomfortable with your baby's waking or resistance to sleeping, consult your baby's doctor to insure that she does not have a medical problem or unique developmental challenges.

Early morning waking: As a result of a temporary disruption in sleep, such as a vacation trip, some babies will begin waking earlier than the expected 5:30–7 a.m. wake time. If fed and laid down to sleep, they will establish this time as a routine. This can occur subtly and seemingly without explanation. The solution: When she wakes, feed her, but keep her awake until the first scheduled naptime of the day (8 or 8:30) or as close to this time as you can. She will, of course, be especially ready to sleep when you finally lay her down. Continue the rest of the day according to your typical routine. Usually after three or four mornings of doing this, your baby will again sleep until 5:30 a.m. or later.

9–12 Months

YOUR BABY'S SCHEDULE: 9-12 MONTHS			
DAYTIME FEEDING	**NAPPING**	**IDEAL BEDTIME**	**IDEAL WAKE UP**
3 solid feedings Breast: 5 feedings Formula: 4 feedings	nap 1 - 8:30 am nap 2 - 1:30 pm *See Infant Sleep Training on page 172.*	7:00 – 7:30 pm	5:30 – 7:00 am

Sleeping

At this age, babies continue with two naps a day and are down for their bedtime at about 7–7:30 p.m. It is during this period that parents clearly see the benefits of sleep training for the baby and for themselves.

NOTE: There is no need to wait until your baby is acting sleepy for his naps and bedtime. This is a common mistake made by babysitters or grandparents. Just place him in the crib according to the schedule and he will go to sleep.

For instance, it is common for an infant to fail to recognize his sleepiness until his parent takes him into the bedroom and begins the bedtime routine. The sound of the musical toy along with a parent's rocking triggers a yawn and rubbing of the eyes as the baby realizes the call of fatigue and surrenders his desire to play for the opportunity to sleep. Once the baby is placed in the crib and the parent leaves the room, baby may issue a brief cry of disappointment and then play with a crib toy for a few minutes before quietly giving in to sleep. Now, this is a child who is secure with his circumstances, has learned to follow his parent's lead, and is benefiting from the whole process—a process that began six months earlier with some degree of protest from the child and some uncertainty on the part of his parents.

When nighttime waking occurs, look to the events of that day to find a possible cause.

Nighttime waking should be fairly uncommon. When it does occur, you should be able to determine how quickly to respond by the quality of your baby's cry. If the cry has no sound of urgency, allow her to cry for five to ten minutes before going to her room; many times she will return to sleep on her own. Even if she is standing in her crib, allow her the opportunity to get back down to the mattress; she will figure it out. When you do respond, try to verbally reassure her without picking her up, and then quickly leave the room. By limiting your interaction with her, you will decrease the chance of fully waking her and causing her to repeat the waking for the next few nights. Obviously if she appears to be in pain or fearful, lift her out of the crib, hold her, and rock her if necessary to calm her.

When nighttime waking occurs, look to the events of that day to find a possible cause. As mentioned above under Sleep Challenges (page 168), a change in the child's daytime routine is a common cause for waking that night. For instance, a visit from grandparents, a new daycare, a new caregiver who prefers to rock or feed the baby to sleep for naps, or simply a disruptive day in general can all affect nighttime sleep. When there appears to be no pain and there was an explainable event the previous day to cause the waking, briefly interact with your baby and then allow her to cry herself to sleep, following the scheduled routine above.

INFANT SLEEP TRAINING

You might ask, "Why is sleep training necessary? Don't all babies know how to sleep?" Yes, and some do a better job than others. Most babies, however, do not know when they should sleep, or how long they should sleep. Driven by their many impulses, infants often fight the urge to sleep until fatigue conquers, and then after a brief catnap, they do it all again. While this random pattern may be tolerable during the daytime, most untrained babies at four to six months will begin a similar pattern of shallow sleeping and frequent waking at night. If parents simply know what to expect of an infant, they can guide their baby to healthier sleep habits. Without this knowledge and guidance, parents and baby often fall into a state of chaos and exhaustion.

Your First Opportunity to Lead

Training an infant to sleep well is actually a parent's first opportunity to lead. If parents take advantage of this opportunity, it can lead not only to a healthier and happier child, but one who has learned to trust and follow his parents' lead, and will be more willing to follow that lead with future matters.

While it is normal and natural for babies to feed and sleep "on demand" for the first months, by four months of age infants can be trained to sleep deeper, longer, and more predictably. The training brings order to what can be a chaotic time of sleeplessness for baby and parents. It is based upon knowing what to expect of a baby at this age. If the parents don't know how often the baby needs to nap, or how often he needs to feed, then they are left to follow his every whim, which changes day to day. By contrast, a parent who knows what the child needs can lead him toward a healthier schedule. Don't miss this opportunity to *lead* your child.

The Benefits of Sleep Training

1. A happier and healthier baby who learns how to sleep more soundly and for longer periods during naps and through the night.
2. Better-rested parents who can think more clearly and implement their parenting plans without frequent distraction.
3. Greater success with parenting as children are less fatigued and more capable of self-control.
4. A healthier marriage as each parent is less fatigued and frustrated, and as they have more time together in the evening to communicate.
5. More orderly home life with predictable napping and bedtime.
6. Ultimately, a better-rested toddler and preschooler whose temperament is more genuine and less compromised by fatigue.
7. Better sleep habits as a school-ager and teen.

Myths About Sleep Training

- *Myth:* It may cause insecure parent-child attachment in the short-term and lead to problematic emotions and behaviors in later childhood.

  Response: While there is no research supporting these two claims, there is research refuting them.[5,6] One study concluded that "behavioral sleep treatments may help young children sleep, yet do not lead to later emotional and behavioral problems, or later parent-child insecure attachment."[7]
- *Myth:* It desensitizes parents to the cues of their baby.

Response: Sleep training is not about ignoring legitimate crying or needs of a baby. It is about realizing that not all crying is the same and doesn't require the same response. It is about distinguishing between a needy cry and a sleepy cry, and then responding accordingly. Training a baby to self-soothe ultimately benefits the child, the parent, and the relationship.

- *Myth:* It can lead parents to ignore real health issues that cause night waking, such as an earache or fever.

  Response: This criticism ignores the fact that parents acquire an "ear" for their baby's differing cries. When a baby suddenly wakes with a distressful cry, they know to respond. This criticism ignores the 90% plus other times when babies will wake due to poor sleep habits and—if allowed to cry—will go back to sleep without assistance.

Natural Obstacles to Nighttime Sleeping

One of the main goals of sleep training is to teach an infant how to fall asleep without assistance, or to self-soothe. However, there are a few natural obstacles to accomplishing this.

A) *Random napping during the day.* As mentioned earlier, the biggest obstacle to healthy sleeping during the night is random, shallow napping during the day, which most babies will do if left to their own tendencies. It's easy to assume this random sleeping is acceptable unless informed otherwise. Babies likewise will continue shallow random sleeping day and night if they are not trained or expected to sleep in a more orderly fashion.

B) *Dependency on sleep associations.* Parents commonly try various approaches to help their baby fall asleep at bedtime. These include rocking, swinging, pacifier, feeding, swaddling, and sound devices. Babies quickly begin to associate these approaches with falling asleep at bedtime (sleep associations), and therefore will require them when they wake in the night. By four months of age, it is best to eliminate most of these sleep associations in order to accomplish self-soothing. For instance, if the baby is rocked and fed to sleep in a parents arms, he will not be able to fall back to sleep without the same routine. However, if baby is not fed at bedtime and rocked only briefly before being placed in the crib awake, then he will learn to self-soothe to sleep. Teach a baby to not need sleep associations at bedtime, and he will not need them at night.

C) *Sleep regression.* As mentioned above and detailed in chapter 6, babies sleep in cycles throughout the night. With age and development, these sleep cycles change. When they do, babies commonly wake in the night, which results in a breakdown of sleep habits, called "Sleep Regression." These periods are often triggered by a change in the baby's routine, like travel on a weekend, a cold, an ear infection, or a change in caregiver or care setting. If parents know to expect this disruption in sleeping, and if the baby has been taught to self-soothe in advance of the waking, sleep regression will not become a significant problem. However, if the baby is untrained and the parents unaware, sleep regression sets in and can continue for many months.

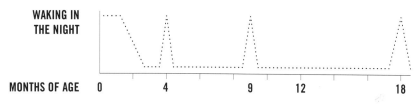

COMMON PERIODS FOR SLEEP REGRESSION

Some Crying Is Expected

A key component of sleep training is placing the baby in the crib fully awake to fall asleep on her own. This naturally leads to some degree of crying as your baby resists the change in routine and fights her urge to sleep. On the first or second day of training, these crying periods may last up to 30 minutes. Although never easy for a parent to hear, these crying spells will quickly diminish over two to three days and will never cause physical or emotional harm. With this plan, the crying is minimized by the tiredness that occurs from only allowing three designated naptimes and no catnapping. The accumulated sleepiness between naps will help her quickly fall asleep. Once trained, your baby will awake well-rested and refreshed with renewed energy to cheerfully interact with you and her environment.

Picture this: A child deprived of a nap routine is often fussy, irritable, and agitated by his unfulfilled sleep needs, often frustrated by his unrecognized fatigue as he attempts to play. A child in this miserable state will often fight sleep until exhaustion sets in. The trained sleeper, however, will often not recognize his tiredness until he is placed in his crib by his parent at the scheduled time. He may briefly protest, then with a yawn realize his fatigue, cheerfully coo or play for a few moments in the familiar setting of his crib, then surrender to his body's beckoning call, and fall asleep. Which child is happier?

The Sleep Your Baby Needs

Sleep training aims to teach infants to achieve a higher quality of sleep. This means deeper sleep and more durable sleep. Let me explain.

Deeper sleep. By three to four months of age, most babies are catnapping throughout the day and often into the night. They are often rocked, fed, or swung to sleep and therefore are usually very shallow, fragile sleepers. Their naps are random and brief, so within an hour or two of waking they are again sleepy, cranky, and in need of another short nap. By contrast, when a baby is limited to only three naps a day and is intentionally laid down awake to self-soothe, he falls into a deeper sleep, sleeps longer and wakes up much more refreshed.

Durable sleep. While most babies are sleeping through the night (five to six hours uninterrupted sleep) by three months of age, they commonly begin waking again around four months, nine months, and eighteen months of age. This waking in the night is not due to hunger, a growth spurt, or even teething, as some claim. It is due to waking between sleep cycles, which are changing at this age due to neurological developments. This sleep regression is normal. Sleep-trained babies weather these periods nicely—they have learned to self-soothe in the night because their parents have learned to allow some crying. Untrained babies have great difficulty falling back to sleep and soon become fragile sleepers.

Baby's Boot Camp: Overview

Over the past three decades I have developed a method for training babies how to sleep more healthily. I call the sleep training, "Baby's Boot Camp," but it is easier than the title implies. The parents in my practice have found it to be extremely helpful for their babies, and most claim that the benefits continue into toddlerhood, school-age, and even to adolescence.

I am aware that this method is just one of many a parent can use for sleep training. Therefore, you do not have to follow my sleep training advice with your child. I have found, however, with thousands of my patients, and with my five children, that this training can provide tremendous physical and emotional benefits during infancy and even later in life. You can do some, none, or all of the training. If you choose to do all of it, it will change your life.

Also, I want to emphasize that rigid scheduling is not my goal with sleep training. It is, instead, to provide you with some general guidelines that most healthy full-term babies are capable of following with sleeping and feeding. If your baby is premature, has special medical needs, or has particular difficulty assuming a basic feeding and sleep schedule, consult the doctor for a more customized plan.

Now, before we get started, I want to highlight some basic suppositions upon which this training is based. To be successful and truly accomplish this plan, you will need to embrace these as well. Secondly, notice that with this plan you will completely change the way you pattern your baby's day. Let me explain.

(a) The Suppositions

An understanding of the following facts about babies four months and older is necessary before implementing this sleep training:

1. Babies at four months no longer need nutrition in the night, so feedings are not necessary between 7 p.m. and 6 a.m.
2. Babies at four months only need four to five feedings in 24 hours.
3. Babies sleep deeper and more soundly if they fall asleep without assistance.
4. Random catnapping leads to poor quality, shallow sleeping. Restricting the naps to only three a day at four months of age helps babies learn to self-soothe and sleep deeper and longer.
5. Once taught how to self-soothe, babies can consistently sleep through the night at this age.

(b) Napping and Feeding Patterns

Under this plan, instead of patterning your baby's day by his feedings, you will now pattern his day by his naps. In doing this you eliminate short, shallow napping and preserve your baby's sleepiness for the designated naptimes.

Naps: Lay your baby down in the crib fully awake to fall asleep on his own at three designated naptimes.

Feedings: An equally important change in patterning the day is to feed your baby *only* when he wakes, not prior to naps. This simplifies the day by taking all the guesswork out of when to feed. It's simple: Feed him when he wakes in the morning and when he wakes from his three naps during the day. At each feeding, you should always allow your baby to nurse as long or drink as much as he desires. No feedings are needed in the night. You see, contrary to popular belief, sleeping through the night at this age is not dependent upon nutrition, but rather upon training your baby to sleep deeply.

One point of clarification: Breastfeeding moms will need to feed their baby a fifth time around 6:30 p.m. in order to maintain their milk supply. Baby, however, should be kept awake for 30–45 minutes after this feeding, then placed in his crib fully awake to self-soothe to sleep.

This training works best if you take it one step at a time. Each step builds upon the next.

Step 1: Preparation

Your baby will be more prepared for the sleep training if you have generally followed the "Your Baby's Daily Schedule" charts for feedings and naps in the first four months. In this first step of Baby's Boot Camp, I recommend parents accomplish the following:

1. Move baby to a separate room. Babies sleep best in a crib in their own room, so if you have another room for your baby, make the move. This can be done gradually by first putting your baby in a crib in his own room for naps during the daytime, and then after one to two weeks, start putting him there to sleep at nighttime. If you would rather keep your baby in your room, create a visual barrier between your bed and his crib so he cannot see you during the night.

2. Avoid using screens in the bedroom. Screens in your child's bedroom will interfere with the quality and duration of his sleep. Using the TV or a tablet as a sleep aid may seem effective in the short-term, but it will lead to long-term sleep problems.

3. Discontinue the bedtime bottle-feeding. If you are bottle-feeding your baby at bedtime (7 p.m. or later), gradually phase this feeding out by reducing the amount you feed each night over seven to ten days. Breastfed babies may continue a 7 p.m. feeding (to help maintain mom's milk supply), but that feeding should end no later than 30 minutes prior to bedtime. It is important that the baby not associate this feeding with the bedtime routine.

4. Set aside time to be at home for training. The training works best if you stay at home for five days, which makes it easier to keep baby awake between designated naps and allows you to keep to the schedule. If you only have three days, such as a long weekend, that may work just fine. If you have a job outside the home, then you can start on a Saturday morning and perhaps a grandparent or sitter can continue the training at your home on Monday.

Step 2: Daytime Training

Sleep training must first begin during the daytime, *before* you focus on any nighttime waking issues. It is a big mistake to expect a baby to be able to cry himself to sleep at night if he has not first been trained to do so during the daytime.

Begin training in the morning when your baby wakes, and then follow the schedule below. Notice three important points in this plan:

1. Baby only has three naps, so don't allow sleeping between the naps. Tricks to keeping your baby awake during or between feedings include tickling his feet, touching a wet wash cloth to his face, going outside, and listening to music.

2. Always place your baby in the crib fully awake at these naptimes and bedtime.

3. Only feed him when he wakes. Notice the feeding intervals will be determined by the length of the naps. The longer the nap, the longer the interval between his feedings and the more he feeds at that feeding. The shorter the nap, the shorter the interval and the less he will typically eat.

Here's the training schedule and routine.

DAYTIME SLEEP TRAINING: SCHEDULE & ROUTINE

WAKE-UP → 5:30–7:00 AM	The morning wake-up and nap start times may vary slightly depending upon your schedule or your baby's sleep tendencies. Allow your baby to sleep as long or as short as he will. No catnapping between these naps.
NAP 1 → 8:30–9:00 AM	
NAP 2 → 12:30–1:30 PM	
NAP 3 → 4:00–5:00 PM	
BEDTIME → 7:00–8:00 PM	

NAPTIME & BEDTIME ROUTINE

- Darken the room.
- Turn on a musical toy, fan, or sound machine for background noise.
- Rock your baby no more than 5 minutes.
- Place your baby in the crib fully awake, saying "night night" with a smile on your face.
- Allow baby to cry. See crying time options in next section.

NIGHTTIME WAKING

- Allow 3-5 minutes of crying before going into your baby's room.
- Briefly console your baby without picking him up.
- Avoid or limit any feeding in the night.
- After 3 days of Step 2 training, allow your baby to cry to sleep as described in Step 3.

Crying Time

At this point you may be wondering, "My baby will cry when I leave the room. How long should I allow him to cry?" There are two options you can take to training your baby to self-soothe. The first calls for potentially longer crying times, up to 30 minutes. For most babies, however, the crying times will be much shorter (five to ten minutes) as they quickly realize just how sleepy they are and fall asleep after a brief period of crying. Actually, the hardest part of the training for most parents is not listening to your baby crying, but rather keeping him awake between the three naps since he is accustomed to catnapping throughout the day.

OPTION A: 20 MINUTE CRYING INTERVALS

NAP 1*	NAP 2	NAP 3	BEDTIME
20 minutes	20-30 minutes, console baby, repeat	20-30 minutes, console baby, repeat	20-30 minutes, console baby, repeat

*For the first nap (8:30 am), if your baby is having great difficulty falling asleep after 20 minutes of crying, then pick him up, skip the nap, but keep him awake until the next scheduled nap at 12:30. He will certainly be sleepy by then.

OPTION B: INCREASING CRYING INTERVALS

If the previous interventions have failed, or if you would rather not allow your baby to cry for the recommended 20–30 minutes, consider this alternate plan. If your baby cries at the start of naptimes or bedtime, follow the guidelines below for crying times before entering his room. When you enter, stay only one minute, verbally console your baby, offer a pacifier, but don't pick him up or feed him. Leave the room and wait the recommended number of minutes indicated in the table before returning to the room. Continue this until he falls asleep.

Minutes to wait before briefly reentering your baby's room:*

DAY	FIRST WAIT	SECOND WAIT	THIRD WAIT	FOLLOWING WAITS
1	5 minutes	10	15	15
2	10	15	20	20
3	15	20	25	25
4	20	25	30	30
5	25	30	35	35

*Adapted from Ferber, R. *Solve Your Child's Sleep Problems*. New York: Simon & Schuster. 1985

Step 3: Nighttime Training

Nighttime sleep training should not be attempted until after at least three days of daytime sleep training (Step 2). Once you have trained your baby to self-soothe to sleep during the day, then you are ready to work on nighttime waking. You see, you cannot expect your baby to cry himself to sleep in the night if you are rocking or feeding him to sleep at naps and bedtime. However, once your baby has been trained to fall asleep unassisted during the daytime and at bedtime, then crying (self-soothing) can be allowed at night.

Take the following approach at night after at least three days of Step 2, Daytime Training.

NIGHTTIME SLEEP TRAINING: SCHEDULE & ROUTINE

NAPTIME & BEDTIME SCHEDULE: Same as Step 2: Daytime Training

NIGHTTIME WAKING:

- Allow 10 minutes of crying before going to baby's room.
- Don't turn on the light, pick baby up, change the diaper, or feed your baby.
- Console your baby with soft words, patting of the back, stroking of the head, and perhaps offering a pacifier.
- Stay only 1 minute.
- Leave the room and allow baby to cry for 20-30 minutes, checking on him at 10 minute intervals without being seen.
- If your baby is fully awake at this point, pick him up. Console and calm him while standing at the crib. Once he is quiet, place him in the crib, leave the room, and repeat the above routine.

Frequently Asked Questions

What should I do if my baby—

- *is in daycare?* Concerning sleep training, my patients occasionally tell me, "I can't march into daycare and announce that my baby needs to be on a special schedule." While this is true, this training can be still successful with daycare. Here's how: First, the parents need to take time out of their schedules to lead their baby through the three to five days of training at home. Then, once trained, they can simply ask daycare to avoid doing two things with their baby: (1) "Please don't rock or swing my baby to sleep." (2) "Please don't feed him to sleep." Typically, the next question from the daycare is, "How do we get him to go to sleep?" The parent's answer can then be, "Glad you asked. We lay him down awake to fall asleep on his own at 8:30, 12:30, and 4:00." This usually works. But, even if the daycare fails to comply with your requests, you are in charge of your baby's bedtime routine. On days you are at home with him, consistently lay him down awake at these times to self-soothe (without feeding or rocking him to sleep), and you can often overcome any poor habits from daycare.

- *sleeps longer than normal at a particular nap?* Should you wake him? No, "never wake a sleeping baby." This adage is true, even with training. He is probably making up for a late night out the day before, or for a missed nap. Keep the regular schedule even if a nap is surprisingly long.

- *misses his nap on Sunday while at church?* Don't worry about it; just make do the rest of the day and resume the schedule the next day.

- *is not hungry after a nap when he is scheduled to feed?* Just offer the feeding again in 30 minutes and let him eat according to his wants. Don't worry; he will make up for it at a future feeding.

- *continues to wake frequently in the night, or fails to settle and cries longer than expected?* Examine your approach at bedtime: Be sure your baby is fully awake when you leave his crib side at bedtime. Be sure you have not fed him within 30 minutes of bedtime. If he is nearly asleep or has a full tummy at bedtime, then he will associate this with falling asleep (sleep associations) and when he wakes in the night he will be expecting the same attention you gave at bedtime (feeding or rocking to sleep). If your approach to bedtime checks out, he could be sick or have an earache, especially if he has a fever or is excessively congested. Take your child to the doctor if any of these are present or if the waking persists.

- *cries, gags, then vomits?* This is not uncommon if you are feeding your baby to sleep and his tummy is full. To avoid this problem, be sure you have not fed your baby within 30–45 minutes of bedtime.

- *wakes from a dirty diaper?* A wet or dirty diaper will not typically wake a baby from sleep. They will, however, occasionally dirty their diaper after waking. If it is a bowel movement, change it. If simply a wet diaper, avoid changing it because the process will further wake your child and reinforce his waking on future nights. Not feeding your child at bedtime will reduce his soiling in the night.

Be Encouraged

Babies will follow their parents' lead, even in sleep. This approach to sleep training usually results in success in five days or less. If you or your baby have great difficulty with the training, simply stop and wait a couple weeks before trying again. Also, talk with your pediatrician if you have any concerns about your baby's resistance to sleeping.

Hang in there; this effort is well worth it. Take the lead, and you and your baby will be happier and healthier with the resulting uninterrupted nights of sleep.

12–18 Months

Good sleeping habits will continue as long as you stick to the routine of laying your child down at designated nap times and bedtime to fall asleep unassisted. The vast majority of babies still need two naps a day until about 15 months of age, so continue this routine even if your baby appears to not be sleepy. At this age, the start times for the naps and bedtime may need to be moved a few minutes later, (i.e., morning nap from 8:30 to 9, afternoon nap from 12:30 to 1:00, and bedtime from 7:00 to 7:30).

While the sleep start times should be consistent, the length of the naps will vary. Try to keep the following schedule for naptimes and allow your baby to sleep as long as she will.

YOUR BABY'S SCHEDULE: 12-18 MONTHS			
DAYTIME FEEDING	**NAPPING**	**IDEAL BEDTIME**	**IDEAL WAKE UP**
3 meals 2 healthy snacks 2–3 milk offerings	nap 1* - 8:30 am nap 2 - 1:30 pm *The first nap is given up between 15 and 18 months.	6:30 – 7:00 pm	5:30 – 6:30 am

Weaning to one nap. Between 15 and 17 months, toddlers begin a process of weaning from two naps a day to one. A few babies will continue to need two naps until 18 months of age. This change to one nap is usually a four to six week process, so there will be days during this time when the baby again needs two naps. The first indicators that your baby is ready for only one nap will be: (1) He plays for 20–30 minutes when laid down for the morning nap and then cries as he isn't sleepy, or (2) After a morning nap, he fights the afternoon nap showing a lack of sleepiness after several minutes in his crib. When either of these occurs on a daily basis and your baby is older than 15 months, it is probably time to move to one nap a day. Here is how the new day will look:

Skip the morning nap and keep him awake through the morning; this may be difficult for the first few days. Offer a quick lunch at about 11:15 or 11:30, and then lay him down for a nap at about 11:45 or noon. Most babies, being very fatigued at this point, will fall asleep quickly and sleep for two to two and a half hours. The bedtime on these days will probably need to occur earlier, at about 6:30, to compensate for the shorter napping.

Here is what a typical day will look like after weaned to one nap:

YOUR BABY'S SCHEDULE: AFTER 18 MONTHS		IDEAL BEDTIME	IDEAL WAKE UP
DAYTIME FEEDING	**NAPPING**		
3 meals	nap - 11:45 am	6:30 – 7:00 pm	5:30 – 7:00 am
2 healthy snacks	*This nap eventually moves to 1:30 pm by 2 years.*		
2–3 milk offerings			

Daycare: Many daycares adjust the babies' sleep schedule at 12 months of age from two naps to one nap a day. While this is about three to four months too early, babies can eventually adjust. With this change, you will be handed a very sleepy baby at the 4:00 or 5:00 pick-up who will likely fall asleep in the car seat on the way home. No problem. Allow him to sleep during the ride and after arriving at home (if he is still asleep). Make an effort to have him down for the night in his crib by 6:30 or 7:00. Also, use the weekends to make up the lost sleep by putting your baby down for two naps during the day and to bed by 6:30–7:30 at night.

Here are some basic tips to keep your baby on track with sleeping:

• Continue a bedtime routine: Turn on a musical device (one that runs for 20 minutes), briefly look at a picture book together, rock her while singing or humming, and then lay her down awake to fall asleep alone. The whole process should take ten minutes or less.

- At bedtime, always lay your child down awake to fall asleep on her own in the crib. This is critical if you are to expect your child to be able to return to sleep in the night if she awakes. Remember: If she wakes in the night, she will need at that time just what she needed at bedtime to fall asleep.
- Don't feed your child to sleep. Not only is this nutritionally unnecessary and does cause poor sleep habits, it also is unhealthy for your child's teeth and may cause gastric reflux in the night.
- Allow some crying in the night. By 12 months, your child should continue sleeping through the night with only occasional waking and returning to sleep without your assistance. When crying does occur, evaluate the quality of her cry for real distress versus waking frustration. If she seems distressed, attend to her; if not, allow her five to ten minutes of crying before going into her room. Avoid picking her up since this will cause further waking and even more crying. Once you have established that she is fine, allow her to cry herself back to sleep. This may require a couple nights of frequently attending to her before you feel confident to allow her to cry for longer periods of 20 minutes or more. As you do this, she should reestablish her full night sleeping within three to four nights.

  Causes of nighttime waking that will require a parent's assistance include discomfort from a cold or ear infection, and disturbance in the baby's daytime routine. A discussion of these and other causes can be found in the seven to nine months section on page 168.
- Continue the crib as long as you can. The crib gives you control over your child at bedtime and it gives her great security to be there. Many parents, influenced by relatives excited about little Amy growing up, will stop the crib at around 18 months and move to a toddler bed. This is often an invitation for protest. Most children will appear to be making the transition nicely for the first six to eight weeks. Then they decide, "I don't want to go to bed right now." Or "I think I will go check out mom and dad's room," in the middle of the night. Before long, chaos sets in and healthy sleep habits vanish. You will do yourself a big favor, and your child one too, if you continue the crib until she is two and a half years old or is climbing out. It's even fine if a contented child stays there until her third birthday, at which point access to a bathroom at night becomes useful if diapers are no longer being used.

2–2½ Years

Your child's sleep habits during this year will affect her attitude, behavior, and general health. A well-rested child will be happier, more self-controlled, and less likely to become sick. Attention to detail with your child's sleep will benefit both you and your child.

- Continue one nap a day. Continue to require one nap a day (1:30 p.m.) and enforce a consistent bedtime (7–7:30 p.m.). If your child doesn't sleep during this naptime, don't give it up. She still needs this time to rest in her room. Be persistent.
- Continue the crib as long as possible, ideally until two and a half years of age.
- Endure the bedtime protests. Be lovingly firm and consistent in enforcing the sleep times. With the crib this will mean listening to periods of crying after you leave the room, with intermittent returns to calm your child. When moved to a toddler bed, your child can simply climb out of the bed and walk out of the room. Repeated returns to the room may be necessary and punishment may be appropriate to maintain the routine. If your child prefers that the bedroom door be left open, you can threaten to close it as a persuasion for her to stay in bed. If she calls your bluff on this, simply close the door for a couple minutes and then promise to leave it open if she stays in her bed.
- Limit your interaction in the night. Occasional waking in the night will occur. If a need is identified, meet it. (Inappropriate needs include thirst, hunger, or wanting to be entertained.) Don't offer drinks or engage in lengthy conversation in the middle of the night. If your child is able to fall asleep at bedtime without your assistance, then she can do it in the night. Briefly announce that she is sleepy and needs to go back to sleep. Avoid taking her to your room or bed. If you do, it is likely to create a habit that will be very difficult to break.

2½–3 Years

Continue putting your child to bed for one nap a day, and keep a consistent bedtime (7–7:30 p.m.). Transition your child out of the crib into a twin or toddler bed during this time. This is especially necessary for the toilet-trained child to have access to the toilet at night. There will likely be challenges to the sleep routine at this age, so here are some tips to aid you in meeting them.

- Bedtime Routine. Continue a calming bedtime routine: bathe, brush teeth, read a story while in bed, say prayers, lie down briefly and talk a bit, then leave while your child is still awake, lights out.
- Refuses to pick up toys in bedroom and play area before bedtime. One hour before bedtime, ask all children to put items in their proper place. Set a timer for 10–15 minutes. When the timer buzzes, check the house. Move the bedtime for all children up five minutes for every item out of place.
- Delays going to bed. Give a 15-minute and then a 5-minute warning that bedtime is coming to avoid sudden disappointment. Use a crib until your child is two and a half years or older to prevent his escape from the bedroom. Place him in his crib after your bedtime routine and walk away. Don't respond to protests.
- Refusing to stay in bed at bedtime.
  - ▸ Adhere to a regular bedtime routine. Before giving your last hug, ask, "Do you need anything else?" Tell your child that he is not to come out until the morning, and then leave and don't engage in any further discussion.
  - ▸ If he yells and screams for your return, tell him you will close the bedroom door. Do it if he persists. Reopen it after five to ten minutes with the threat to close it again if he protests.
  - ▸ If he comes out of the room, take him back. If he does this repeatedly, threaten to close the bedroom door next time he comes out.
  - ▸ Alternate approach if you feel your child has legitimate needs: Give two "tickets" for requests after you leave the child's room. After those two have been used (drink of water, use the bathroom, forgot to tell you something, etc.), then punishment is imposed.
  - ▸ Possible punishments:
    - ▪ Remove a privilege tomorrow.
    - ▪ Will have to go to bed five to ten minutes earlier tomorrow night.
    - ▪ If he persists in coming out, close and lock the bedroom door from the outside (the door knob can be turned around). Open the door every five to ten minutes, telling your child that when he quiets down and returns to his bed you will

leave the door unlocked and open. Don't engage in more than a minute of dialogue.

- Talking too much between siblings in the same bed at bedtime. Separate the two by having one or both lie on the floor until you return in about ten minutes.
- Nighttime waking. Check your bedtime routine and make sure you are taking all the measures mentioned earlier in this chapter. Then, once you are convinced that your child is not waking due to illness or true fear, allow him to cry a few minutes to put himself to sleep. If your child gets out of his bed and comes to your bedroom, take him back to his own bedroom instead of letting him sleep in your bed. Lie with him briefly, and once he is again relaxed but not asleep, return to your bed, allowing him to again fall asleep on his own. Do this repeatedly if he continues to get up. Be consistent and he will eventually stop waking.

3–3½ Years

- Naptime becomes Rest Time: Most children will continue to need a daily nap until at least three and a half years of age. For older children or those who appear to not need a nap, "rest time" in the child's room is the solution. This is a time when your child is required to stay in the bedroom for one and a half hours (1:30–3:00) each afternoon. She is not required to take a nap, but she must stay in her room and in her bed until you return. Tell her, "Here is a toy and some books to look at, but don't come out of your room until I return." This routine removes the burden of determining if your child needs a nap or not, and prevents the dreaded dialogue to convince your child that she needs a nap. On most days, this routine results in the child falling asleep without resistance.
- Bedtime: Consistently enforce bedtime at 7–7:30 p.m. Follow the same routine you have already established and always leave the bedroom before he falls asleep. Be consistent and don't become slack with this time or routine.
- Nighttime waking due to fears: During this year of life many children develop nighttime fears that may not be entirely rational. This can lead to difficulty falling asleep and staying asleep in the night due to scary dreams or the fear of monsters.

  Solution: If repeatedly reassuring and returning your child to his room fails over the course of a few weeks, consider placing a pallet on the floor in your bedroom for the genuinely fearful child. The pallet can consist of an exercise mat, sheet, light blanket, and a pillow. Push it under your bed during the day and pull it out as you go to bed at night. Tell your child that if he wakes frightened and can't go back to sleep, he may come into your room and sleep on the pallet on the floor. Ask that he not wake you when he comes in (realizing that he probably will) so that his behavior is not reinforced with the satisfaction of conversation. This approach satisfies the fear factor, while avoiding the irresistible attraction of sleeping in Mom and Dad's bed. In a month or two, you will be blessed with a night when he doesn't visit your room all night. Praise him for this and point out that he is growing up since he can sleep in his bed all night long. It usually takes four to six months for the problem to vanish.

3½–4 Years

- Bedtime: Maintain a consistent bedtime of 7–7:30, assuming a morning waking time of 6–7. Children benefit from the needed sleep and parents need this time in the evenings to unwind and discuss the day's events. A consistent bedtime for your child is therefore nurturing to your marriage, which will directly and positively affect your child.
- Rest Time: By three and a half years, many children are ready to give up daily naps and begin rest time as described above. The benefits of rest time go beyond napping. It also teaches a child to be still and quiet, to play independently in his bed, to delay the gratification of playing/running around the house, and last but not least, it provides you some time alone.
- Nighttime Waking: Again, if fearfulness is the true reason for a child's repeated waking at night, institute the pallet plan as described above. Continue your usual bedtime routine and insist that your child fall asleep in her own bed without your assistance. Remember: If your child can't fall asleep on her own at bedtime, you can't expect her to go back to sleep when waking in the night. The ability to fall asleep alone must be practiced and maintained to ensure high quality sleep.

4–5 Years

Your child's target bedtime should continue to be 7–7:30. This assumes a typical waking time of 6–7 for most preschoolers. For some preschoolers who still need a nap each day, the bedtime may need to be pushed a bit later. Ideally, the nap should begin at 12:30 or 1:00, so that it will not extend beyond 3:00 or 3:30. Once the nap is given up, the bedtime should return to about 7 p.m., even 6:30 if necessary.

Read stories to your child at bedtime as often as you are able. This practice has been shown to stimulate a child's interest in reading at a later age. Don't allow TV watching or video and tablet gaming within one hour of bedtime since they tend to cause mental excitement and wakefulness. No screens allowed in the bedroom.

6–10 Years

As is detailed in chapter 6, adequate sleep is essential for optimal physical, mental, and emotional health. With your child entering grade school, sleep is even more important to allow him to be attentive and perform well in the classroom. At this age, however, extracurricular activities and increasing attractiveness of the electronic screens makes achieving a healthy bedtime even more elusive. This is an opportunity to lead your child. I recommend limiting extracurricular activities to one per season, and if participation consistently leads to late bedtimes, switch to another activity or none at all for a season. Also, limit your school-aged child's total screen time on school day evenings to one hour or less. Don't allow any video gaming or app gaming on these days. Screen time is very engaging and often causes the viewer to lose track of time, pushing homework and the bedtime later. Your child will need your guidance to achieve healthy sleep.

For details on how to create the ideal atmosphere for your child to sleep, review the sleep section in chapter 6. Here are my recommended bedtimes for your child from kindergarten to high school.

Assuming a 6:30 a.m. wake-up time, the healthiest bedtimes on school nights are:

Grade	Bedtime
Kindergarten to 6th grade:	7:30–8:00 pm
7–9th grade:	8:30–9:00 pm
10–12th grade:	9:30–10:00 pm

Chapter 13

NUTRITION

Your child will need some guidance with nutrition from birth through the teen years. This guidance will be specific as an infant and then more general as your child grows. The following opportunities to lead will help clarify your role as the parent.

Sleep and nutrition are closely tied to each other in this first year of life, so they are addressed together for the *first four months in chapter 12*. In this chapter, feeding is addressed alone, starting at five months of age. For your reference on the next page, I have created a master schedule of feeding and sleeping for the entire first year.

5–7 Months

Your baby is now five months old and you may or may not have begun introducing solid foods into his diet. At this age, your baby will continue to need four to five milk feedings a day (four formula feedings or five breast feedings) with each occurring upon waking (in the morning and from naps) and with solid feedings when begun.

Introducing Solid Foods

Introducing solids food too early is associated with obesity later in life, so it is best to delay solids until five or six months. When you do start, offer solids by spoon, not mixed in a bottle. There are many ways to introduce solid food feedings (cereal, vegetables, fruits) into your baby's diet. I generally recommend starting with an infant, iron-fortified cereal or a vegetable, and then advancing as quickly or as slowly as you desire. Here are my instructions to parents:

			IDEAL	NIGHTTIME	IDEAL
AGE	**DAYTIME FEEDING**	**NAPPING***	**IDEAL BEDTIME**	**NIGHTTIME FEEDING**	**IDEAL WAKE UP**
Birth – 2 Weeks	Breast: on demand *at least every 3 hrs* Formula: 2–3 hrs	Random *sleeps about 16 hrs a day*	9:30 – 10:30 pm	Every 2–4 hours	4:00 – 6:00 am
2 – 4 Weeks	Breast: 2–2½ hrs *at least every 3 hrs* Formula: 2–3 hrs	Random *sleeps about 16 hrs a day*	9:30 – 10:30 pm	Every 2–4 hours	4:00 – 6:00 am
4 – 8 Weeks	Breast: 2½–3¼ hrs *depending on milk supply* Formula: 3–3¼ hrs	Random *If possible, keep baby awake for at least 10 min following each feeding.*	9:30 – 10:30 pm	Variable, every 4–6 hours	4:00 – 6:00 am
2 – 4 Months	Breast: 3–3½ hrs Formula: 3–3½ hrs	Random *By 3 months, typically taking 3 naps per day*	10:00 pm *moves to 8:00 pm by 4 months*	2–3:00 am *moves later & disappears by 3–4 mos*	4:00 am *moves to 5–6:00 am by 4 mos*
4 Months	Breast: 5 feedings Formula: 4 feedings	nap1–8:30am nap2–12:30pm nap3–4:00pm	7:00 – 8:00 pm	none	5:30 – 7:00 am
5 – 7 Months	1–2 solid feedings Breast: 5 feedings Formula: 4 feedings	nap1–8:30 am nap2–1:00 pm nap3–4:00 pm	7:00 – 7:30 pm	none	5:30 – 6:30 am
7 – 9 Months	2–3 solid feedings Breast: 5 feedings Formula: 4 feedings	nap1–8:30 am nap2–1:30 pm	6:30 – 7:30 pm	none	5:30 – 7:00 am
9 – 12 Months	3 solid feedings Breast: 4–5 feedings Formula: 4 feedings	nap1–8:30 am nap2–1:30 pm	7:00 – 7:30 pm	none	5:30 – 7:00 am

YOUR BABY'S SCHEDULE: THE FIRST YEAR

The nap start times may vary slightly depending upon your daily schedule or your baby's sleep tendencies. For more information, see sleep training section in Chapter 12.

How to Introduce Solid Foods

- 5–6 months of age:

  Offer an infant cereal by spoon at suppertime, about 5:30 or 6 p.m. This may be a dry infant, iron-fortified cereal mixed with breast milk or formula, or it may be pre-mixed, jar cereal. Begin by offering one to two tablespoons and quickly increase the amount as desired by your baby. You may begin with vegetables instead of cereal. I prefer an infant cereal for the breastfeeding baby, because it provides a unique source of iron.

- 2 weeks later:

  Move the cereal feeding to lunchtime and introduce vegetables at suppertime. Start with yellow/orange vegetables, and introduce a new one every five days to allow your baby time to adjust to the new tastes. These vegetables may be pureed at home from table foods, or store-bought Stage 1 jar foods. Advance to the Stage 2 jar foods once the baby is quickly consuming the smaller jars.

- 2 weeks later:

  Move the cereal to breakfast, vegetables to lunch, and introduce fruits at suppertime. Introduce a new fruit every five days as desired. Once introduced, the cereal, vegetables, and fruits may be given alone or in combination at any of the three feedings per day.

Juices and Water

Juice drinking has minimal nutritional value, if any, and can sabotage your child's appetite. Its sweet attraction can interfere with a child's acceptance of healthy, blander foods. Therefore, I recommend delaying sweetened drinks (including juices) until after a child is two years old, and even then, not daily. If you choose to start juice sooner, offer it only in a sippy cup (not the bottle), use only 100% juice (not fruit drink with added sugar), and limit the daily amount to four ounces or less. Juice drinking from a bottle increases the risk of tooth decay.

Water can be introduced after six months from a sippy cup in small amounts as your baby is learning to drink from a cup. There is no benefit to offering water before six months and it can be harmful if over-consumed. Don't replace a baby's regular milk feeding with water.

7–9 Months

Your baby needs four or five milk offerings a day and does not need a bottle at bedtime. For breastfeeding mothers, I recommend that solid foods be offered after nursing in order to preserve baby's interest in nursing and maintain mom's milk supply. For formula-fed babies, solids should be offered before the formula is given. If a nursing mom is desiring to wean her baby, solids can be offered before breast feedings (as with a formula-fed baby) to cause the baby to drink less breast milk.

Water may be introduced (although not necessary), but I'd suggest delaying juices until two years or later. Limiting baby's fluid intake to only milk will enhance his desire for a greater variety of solid foods. Juice drinking makes vegetables look unattractive to the baby by comparison.

9–12 Months

At this stage in your baby's first year, you have two important opportunities to *lead* your child to healthy nutrition. The first comes with the introduction of table foods and the second with breast or bottle weaning.

Table Foods

Soft table foods may be offered as early as six to eight months of age. Most infants will reject these foods at first, but be persistent in offering the same new food for five to ten days, allowing your baby to adapt to the new taste and texture of the foods. It will be tempting to move toward the more tasty foods, but by persisting, your baby will come to accept a greater variety of foods in his diet.

Bottle Weaning

Bottles are not forever, but some babies seem to wish they were. It is natural for babies to become attached to their bottles. This attachment is often greater for those infants who do not use a pacifier. As a child approaches 12 months of age, she will typically increase her intake of solid foods and therefore decrease her intake (nutritional need of) of formula or breast milk. This healthy transition can be hampered if a child is offered milk too often, or if a child stays on the bottle after 12 months of age. This is another leadership opportunity for the parent.

By nine months, babies only need four offerings a day of formula or breast milk and should not receive a feeding at bedtime. Weaning from a bottle to a sippy or straw cup can begin now with the goal of discontinuing the bottle by 12 months. Breast-fed babies may continue to nurse beyond 12 months, but should also come off any bottles by one year. Here are two ways to accomplish bottle weaning:

- At nine months, begin empirically replacing one bottle feeding of formula with a sippy cup of formula every two weeks. Initially, your baby may reject the cup, but after a few days he will realize that the bottle is not appearing at that feeding and the cup is not so bad with the milk it provides. This temporary decrease in milk intake will not be harmful and the success in weaning from the bottle will be healthier in the long run.

- If the first method was unsuccessful, or just not preferred, and the one-year birthday is approaching, then another option is to fill the bottles with water instead of milk. With each feeding, the baby is offered water in the bottle and milk in a cup. It will not take long for her to choose the cup with milk and reject the bottle with water. Then, put away all the bottles.

An added incentive for parents in this weaning process is that once the 12-month-old is off the bottle, the formula can be stopped and whole milk can be introduced. To help your child make this transition, you may want to mix whole milk and formula in the cup for a few days, and then move to all whole milk.

Breast Weaning

For the breastfeeding mom, the question of when to wean arises during this age range. Although the healthiest plan is to nurse until one year of age, weaning sooner or extending beyond a year is just fine as well. Weaning is best accomplished gradually. I recommend replacing a breast feeding every two to four weeks in an alternating fashion with the morning feeding being the last to replace. For example, drop the supper feeding first, then the lunch, then the one after the afternoon nap, then the morning feeding. If your baby is under 12 months, replace the breastfeedings with a sippy cup of formula. If your baby is over 12 months, whole milk can be used as the replacement milk.

12–18 Months

Milk

By now your baby should no longer be drinking from a bottle and should be offered milk from a sippy cup or straw cup two to three times a day. These offerings can occur at either breakfast, lunch, after the afternoon nap, or supper. He does not need any drink at bedtime. Breastfeeding can certainly be continued with the same frequency or less. Milk drinking or breastfeeding should not occur in the night with waking as this leads to poor sleep habits and tooth decay.

Juice vs. Water

Delay the introduction of juices until two years of age, even diluted juice. Offer water instead. Once begun, offer the juice primarily on special occasions and limit it to four to six ounces in a day. Excessive sweet drink consumption (more than 16 ounces a day) at this age is associated with obesity at a later age, and can cause tooth decay. A sippy cup with sweet drink may appear to be the perfect "pacifier" for a restless toddler while running errands. Don't do this; take water in a sippy cup instead. While unlimited sweet drink may appear to be a nice distraction for a fussy toddler, it can become an alluring habit and foster a constant desire for pleasure by mouth; which is probably why it is associated with obesity. Some children will even drink away their appetite if given unlimited milk or sweet drink with meals. If you offer juice at a snack time, do it only once a day, and satisfy any additional thirst with offerings of water; filtered ice water (with fluoride remaining) tastes better than tap water. Also, never offer sweet drink at mealtimes. It makes bland foods (like vegetables) on your child's plate seem even less attractive to him by comparison. Offer only milk or water at these times.

Foods

Toddlers between 12 and 18 months are usually good eaters with an interest in almost any food offered. Take advantage of this stage and offer a variety of foods, especially vegetables, at the three meals each day. Start each meal with the vegetables to encourage his desire for them. Offer a heathy afternoon snack, but if it interferes with your child's appetite for supper, reduce the amount of snack.

As mentioned in chapter 6, it is important that you establish some guidelines for eating, in order to minimize distractions and formalize the mealtime process for your child. This will help nurture your child's appetite and encourage his self-control.

- Eat in a dining area. When at home, begin the practice of feeding your child only while in a high chair and only in the dining area of the home. This goes for mealtime and routine snack times. This formalizes the act of eating for your child and teaches him to take it more seriously. It will also decrease the temptation for your child to want to snack when bored, since it would mean climbing into the highchair. By limiting random snacking, you will enhance his hunger at mealtime for the foods you have chosen for him.
- Eat together as a family, whenever possible. Your modeling will greatly influence your child's desire to eat a variety of foods. As you eat your vegetables, he will be more likely to eat his.
- Offer a variety of healthy foods, especially vegetables, which may not be as desirable to him at a later age. If he rejects one food item at a meal, don't assume that he will always dislike it; try it again in a few days. His likes and dislikes should not be your primary guide in selecting his foods. He is more likely to accept the food variety you offer if he knows you will not resort to the same old foods you know he will eat.

18–24 Months

After 18 months of age, your toddler will likely be an unpredictable eater. His appetite may vary greatly from day to day and cause you to doubt whether he is getting enough food to eat. It is important to realize that he will never under-feed himself. He will always eat according to his needs, and it is not your responsibility to get him to eat. When he is sick, his needs will decline, and he will not eat his typical amount. When he is better and his nutritional needs are greater, he will eat more. Your responsibility is to only provide the right setting, the proper foods, and the right timing. It is your child's responsibility to eat according to his needs and to follow your guidance in how to eat (not how much to eat).

Preserve Your Toddler's Appetite

Preserve your toddler's appetite for mealtime. Here are some suggestions:

- Delay offering juice or sweet drink until after two years of age. If introduced sooner, only give 100% juice on special occasions, not daily.

- Don't allow unlimited snacking between meals. Offer snacks at designated times, mid-morning and mid-afternoon. Serve them in the kitchen in a highchair to formalize the practice.
- Don't allow unlimited drinking of milk or sweet drink between meals. If you allow your toddler to roam about with a sippy cup of milk or sweet drink in his hand, he will drink excessively, and the cup may become a security object. By restricting sippy cup use to the kitchen or dining area, you will reduce his desire for random drinking (and also reduce sticky messes throughout the house).
- Don't allow unlimited milk drinking during meals. Toddlers can easily drink away their appetite if allowed unlimited milk. Offer an eight-ounce cup and then water as desired.
- Don't serve dessert. Avoid using a tasty dessert to bribe your child to eat. It will only teach him to avoid the healthier foods and wait for this reward.
- Don't regularly add chocolate to the milk. This is a common tactic to get a child to drink milk, but it will haunt you for years to come. It encourages a child's craving for sweetness and can interfere with his natural hunger for more bland, yet healthy, solid foods and drink. If your child refuses milk at mealtime, offer only water as an alternative. Then, meet his calcium needs by offering cheese or yogurt at snack time, and after two years of age, calcium-fortified orange juice at breakfast. On the other hand, too much milk drinking is also unhealthy, since it too can interfere with a child's appetite for solid foods. Limit the whole milk to three offerings a day served at the table with meals, and avoid serving it in her sippy cup when away from the dinner table.

Begin the Family Table

Begin the practice of the "Family Table" as a mealtime routine for the family. The details and reasoning for this practice are detailed in chapter 6. The following guidelines will help you train your child to be a healthier eater and to harmonize mealtime for everyone:

- Eat together as a family whenever possible.
- Turn off the television and other electronic devices. TV distracts a child from the focus of eating, and it interferes with conversation among those at the table. The phone also distracts the parent from conversation with the family.

- Serve everyone the same foods. No short-order cooking. By 18 months of age, a child should be offered the same foods served to the other family members. This practice teaches a child to eat a healthier variety, but it does put pressure on the parent in two areas. First, the parents must model healthy eating. This means eating less fast food and preparing more fresh foods at home, especially vegetables and fruits. Second, the parents must resist the temptation to simply offer the child the foods he wants rather than the healthy variety he needs. To repeatedly offer mac & cheese or chicken strips is the easier path, which avoids conflict with the child. However, this is just a short-term solution that leads to a long-term problem of poor eating habits that will eventually result in even greater conflict between parent and child at an older age.

- Stop manipulative efforts to get your child to eat. This includes bribing with the promise of sweets, game playing with the spoon, and hovering over the highchair to convince him to eat. Literally look away from his highchair and allow him to eat according to his needs. If he begins to play with his food by throwing or dropping it on the floor, take it away and set it on the table in front of him as you continue to eat. If he wants it back, then verbally remind him, "No throw food," and return it to his plate. If he persists in playing with the food, he may need to be placed in a playpen time-out for a couple minutes as punishment for his actions. When you return him to his seat, remind him, "No throw food."

- Allow your child to eat according to his needs; there is no reason to attempt to force him to eat. Once he stops eating the foods you have served, resist the temptation to offer more tasty (usually less healthy) foods just to get him to eat more. Offer and re-offer the foods you have planned, and let him get down once adequate eating time has passed.

- Everyone stays at the table until everyone has finished. In addition to the routine outlined above, now is a good time to begin requiring that your child stay in the highchair until everyone has finished eating. It is common for a toddler's appetite to be finicky after 18 months of age. He simply requires less food intake to satisfy his hunger. So, when your toddler wants to get down after only five minutes into the meal, you will be challenged to determine whether it is because he is truly not hungry or if he is just bored, distracted, or wanting to get back to the play he was enjoying before dinner. Certainly, if the foods he sees on his plate are unappealing, he will want to get down and go play.

The problem: If dismissed early, when your child returns to the kitchen after the meal is over and asks for more to eat, you'll have to determine, is he truly hungry or just wanting a tasty snack?

The solution: This situation can be avoided by requiring that everyone, including parents and older siblings, remain at the dining table until everyone is finished eating. Now, if Johnny sits through the entire mealtime and barely touches his food, the parent can be safely assured that he just isn't hungry. This practice also fosters the concept of the "Family Table" where conversation and connecting occur among those at the table since everyone stays for the entire mealtime.

2–3 Years

Continue to practice the Family Table, as described above. Here are some additional pointers to consider:

- Offer breakfast daily. Breakfast provides children with cognitive benefits for learning and may help prevent obesity. Examples of healthy breakfast foods include whole grain cereal, whole grain muffins, fruit, eggs, granola cereal, yogurt, oatmeal with nuts/raisins, bagel with cream cheese, banana with peanut butter, and whole wheat pancakes or waffles.
- Be a good example. Eat your veggies, and eat breakfast.
- Only serve water or milk at mealtimes. Many children will attempt to drink away their appetite with sweet drink.
- Don't serve desserts on a regular basis as it competes with the less-tasty, healthier foods.
- Offer a mid-morning and a mid-afternoon snack. Avoid allowing your child to "graze" on snack foods throughout the day so his appetite for healthier foods is preserved.
- Restrict access to the pantry or refrigerator. Require your child to always ask permission before getting food.
- Limit sweet drinks to one to two offerings a day. Encourage water drinking. The calories are not the issue but the sweetness and a child's craving for it. Research shows that excessive drinking of sweet drinks is associated with overeating and obesity. When running errands away from home with your child, put water in his cup, not juice.

- Remember: Your responsibility is to serve healthy foods and provide the right setting. Your child's responsibility is to eat according to his needs. It is not your responsibility to get your child to eat.

3–5 Years

- Follow all the earlier advice, especially eating together as a family when possible.
- One or two bites. At this age, I believe it is reasonable to require your child to take one or two bites of each uneaten item on his plate at the end of the meal before leaving the table. In doing this, you improve the possibility that he will eventually like to eat those foods.
- Require respectful and appreciative response from your child at mealtime. She should be taught not to complain about disliking a food on her plate. You can teach, "When you come to the table and see a food on your plate that you don't like, don't say, 'I don't like that!' You can think, 'I don't like that,' but saying it hurts the feelings of the one who worked so hard to cook it." Although she doesn't have to eat all of it, she must show respect to the adult who prepared the food by remaining quiet about her preferences.
- Everyone stays. Remember to require that everyone stay at the dinner table until all have finished eating. This will provide valuable family time for conversation and help you access your child's true level of hunger.
- May I be excused? At the end of the meal, teach your child to say, "May I be excused? Thank you for the supper." This is a good habit of appreciation that hopefully will cause your child to routinely express thanks when visiting others.

6–10 Years

- Practice the Family Table, as detailed in chapter 6.
- Eat at home as often as possible. Eating out interferes with teaching healthy eating habits.
- Order at the table. Maintain a certain degree of order at mealtime. Laughter is always healthy, but too much entertainment/loudness can distract a child from eating.
- Good talk. Everyone should have respectful talk. Siblings should not be repeatedly critical of one another and the talk should be encouraging.

Resist the urge to talk with your child about situations of misbehavior that occurred earlier in the day.

- Patience. Teach your children not to speak while others are talking and to politely wait their turn to speak. This is a wonderful training ground that many parents overlook. Don't expect your child to behave differently in public than in private. Home is the best classroom.

- Punishments for disobedience at mealtime may include: time-out, early dismissal from the table before finishing the meal, or going to bed early.

- Everyone should stay at the table until all have finished eating. This opens the door for family conversation, especially with your older children. Require that your child try at least a bite or two of any foods not eaten during the meal. This practice exposes your child to healthy foods and often causes the child to eventually come to like the shunned food one day.

It has been said, "We are what we eat." Nutrition affects all aspects of our health: physical, emotional, mental, and even social. Your efforts in this area with your children will yield rewards for years to come.

Chapter 14

EXERCISE AND PLAY

As we learned in chapter 6, teaching our children to have an active lifestyle is essential for their physical and emotional health. This can start early in life with active play and continue later in life with sports and outdoor activities in general. Here I offer opportunities for you to lead your child toward active living. Remember, any success you have with your child will be greatly influenced by the lifestyle you lead.

4–12 Months

Playing with our babies begins early with smiling, talking, singing, and later with interactive games like peek-a-boo. After six months, babies need a lot of floor time to roll, scoot, crawl, and eventually walk. Make time and opportunity for this; get down on the floor with them to stimulate active play.

1–2 Years

Now that she is walking, you can engage your toddler in more active play. Make a point to play with her on the floor every day. Encourage her active play with simple, non-electronic toys and blocks. Avoid intentional screen time which encourages passive play, discourages active play, and is not recommended for children under two years.

2–3 Years

Learning how to interact with others begins at home. Playing with our children teaches them how to communicate, how to enjoy one another, how to imagine, what makes us laugh, what makes us sad, and allows them to know us better. Play among siblings and with parents also teaches a child how to resolve conflict. In our busy world it is easy to forget the importance of play to a young child. Take time to play with your child and encourage your child to play.

- Get on the floor and play games.
- Wrestle with your toddler.
- Play with mechanical (non-digital) toys, like puzzles, or building blocks. Children learn mechanical skills by using their hands and fingers to carefully manipulate and create.
- Spend time outside with your child. Encourage them to play and explore.

Parents must take the lead in managing their children's exposure to screened devices.

Physical play demonstrates and teaches our children the value of being active. The anti-active influence in the lives of all young people today is the screened device, including the TV. Parents must take the lead in managing their children's exposure to screened devices. Intentional screen time is not recommended for children under two years of age. After two years, allow limited time (one hour or less) of quality programming on the family TV or playing quality apps on a family tablet. Ideally, watch the TV or play the games with your child. See chapter 5 for more details on Digital Influences.

3–5 Years

Continue to mark out time on your schedule to play with your children. Encourage *active* play with non-electronic toys, and limit *passive* play with digital devices. The attraction of electronics will be enormous during the school years, so make every effort to keep life simple during these preschool years. In doing this, you will prompt a more active lifestyle for your child. Electronic toys/devices require sitting, watching, and typically lead to excessive snacking during their use.

- Encourage outside playing. This will lead a child to be more active and is a healthy distraction from the refrigerator and pantry.
- Encourage indoor play with building blocks, dolls, cars/trucks, puzzles, and board games. Occasionally play with your child.
- Encourage imaginary play, such as doctor/nurse, teacher, or simply dressing up in costumes or creative clothing.
- Teach simple card games. These will be especially enjoyable to children when the TV is turned off.
- Have a tea party. This is an opportunity for face-to-face conversation in a controlled moment with no distractions.
- Read books to your children often.
- Limit total screen time to less than one hour, and only on certain days of the week.
- No video game console until after eight years of age. App game playing on handheld devices can be equally addicting. If allowed, this screen time should be limited as well, and not allowed every day.
- Make playing outside attractive for your child. Have a swing set, sand box, various balls, bicycle, scooter, and even a tree house or play house.

6–10 Years

- Continue to encourage and model an active lifestyle. Do your own yard work and give your child opportunities to help. Pay him for help with extra projects.
- Individual and team sports are a fun way to keep your child regularly active. Be available to practice with your child. One sport per season is a good rule of thumb to prevent these activities from interfering with your child's and family's routine.
- Engage in active play with your child. Ride bikes together, play ball, go on walks, and, as opportunity allows, take hikes as a family at a state park.
- Get a pet for your child to walk and to play with outside.
- Build a project together (i.e., birdhouse, model car, pottery, etc.).
- Plant a garden if possible. Not only will this teach your child the origin of foods they eat, it will also stimulate her interest in eating vegetables.

Chapter 15

BEHAVIOR

Behavior is the most obvious sign of a child's state of discipline and character, and as such, it can become the primary focus of a parent's attention. This, however, is a big mistake. As was emphasized in the first chapters, a child's heart or motive should actually be our aim in disciplining our children, since it will be their guide through life. So, as you consult this section for solutions to your child's misbehaviors, don't overlook this important fact. Look beyond their actions and into their heart. Don't simply confront the *what* of their behaviors, confront the *why*.

Also, as you consult the following pages to find guidance for managing your child's behavior, please remember that correction is only one of the components of discipline. Don't overlook your responsibility to provide your child with both clear instruction and consistent affirmation within a loving relationship.

Don't overlook your responsibility to provide
your child with both clear instruction and consistent
affirmation within a loving relationship.

Finally, the guidance provided in this section is a compilation of my experiences in the office with patients, experiences with my own children, and a few helpful resources as well.[1] Some of my advice may not fit your specific situation and your specific child, so remember to customize. My primary objective is to help you *lead* your child in the manner you see fit.

The First Year

The first year can be focused on meeting your baby's basic needs while behavioral training is sidelined. The excitement of your baby's new accomplishments can distract you from this early opportunity to train. There are a few opportunities, however, for you to *lead* your child to proper behavior, even though most of an infant's behaviors are motivated by innocent exploration. The following are some common behavioral challenges most parents will face.

Boundaries and Limitations

When your baby begins to crawl, he will naturally want to explore his environment. Childproof your house as best you can.

- Put precious breakable items beyond your baby's reach.
- Coil electrical cords and put them out of sight.
- Place plastic covers over electrical outlets.
- Put safety latches on cabinet doors and drawers that are off limits.
- Remove poisonous plants.
- Close doors and gate areas that are off limits.
- Cover fireplace hearth or other hard structures that may be crawled upon.

Taking these measures will remove some irresistible temptations from your baby's path and also make his environment safer. However, it is not necessary to clear all restricted objects from his crawling area. These will provide you the opportunity to lead him to obediently avoid them. For example, certain durable items on an end table or a large potted plant that you would prefer to keep in the room for attractiveness should stay. Your baby can be taught to avoid these and in the process learn obedience.

1. **Instruct:** Instruction during this infant stage of your baby's life will consist of redirection and removal as he crawls about. As he approaches a forbidden item, first attempt to redirect him to another item in the room. If he returns, say "Uh, Uh," shake your head and remove him.

2. **Affirm:** If he properly follows your lead and avoids the item, affirm him for this good choice: "Good boy. Thank you for obeying Mommy."

3. **Correct:** If he persists in returning to touch the item, say "no," shake your head and remove him. If he stubbornly returns, do all the previous and remove him to a place of isolation, such as a playpen for about one minute. This is the earliest form of "time-out" and consists of placing him in a playpen that has no toys in it, and is set up in a quiet room. Pick him up with his face turned away from you, take him to the playpen with little talk, place him inside, and walk away. When the time is up, return, pick him up, hold him close, return to the original room, and remind him that the activity is forbidden: "No touch [item]." If the misbehavior recurs, repeat the playpen time-out for slightly longer periods of time.

For the crawler who persistently pursues and reaches for the electrical outlet or another forbidden (especially dangerous) object that cannot be removed, a slap to the back of his hand can also be useful. This attention-getter, when combined with a firm verbal and facial expression of disapproval, can end his pursuit and eliminate the need for a playpen time-out. The hand slap should mainly be used for wrongful touching of a forbidden object, so that your action (hand slap) fits with the offense (the reaching hand).

Biting and Hitting

Some babies will naturally attempt to swat at a parent or bite in a moment of frustration. Initially, it may be experimentation, but if left unchecked the behavior can escalate to intentional aggression. Here are some approaches to stop the behaviors.

1. **Instruct:** Verbally correct the baby and demonstrate the proper behavior. Rather than simply saying "No," show your baby how you want him to behave. For example, with hitting say, "No hit." Take his hand and say, "Gentle" while you softly place his hand on your shoulder. Reemphasize, "Gentle." With biting: Say, "No bite. That hurts Mommy." Gently tap his mouth indicating to him the source of the biting and show him an expression of sadness on your face. Then gently push his lips against your face and say, "Kiss mommy. No bite." Show a happy expression.

Some have claimed that babies who bite are more orally fixated and have a greater need to chew or bite on something when under stress. Therefore, offering a baby a teething ring or soft toy to bite during these moments may help reduce his biting of others.

2. **Affirm:** The next time he gets frustrated and does not hit or bite, affirm him with a hug and happy expression.

3. **Correct:** If instruction and affirmation do not resolve the problem behavior, you must correct with some form of unpleasantness toward him. Do not hit back or bite your baby; these are inappropriate and will be perceived by the baby as retaliation. Your goal is to persuade him toward proper behavior, and correction is sometimes necessary. Consider these options:

   - If you are holding your baby when he bites or hits, give the verbal instruction outlined above, put him down on the floor and walk away. After one to two minutes of rejection, return to him and restate, "No hit [or bite]." Pick him up and move on with your day.
   - If a couple minutes of rejection are unsuccessful, then a playpen time-out is in order. Give instruction, take him to the playpen (or crib), set him inside and walk away. After one to three minutes of isolation, return, pick him up, and restate the instruction.

12–18 Months

The toddler, with his newfound mobility, has seemingly endless energy and curiosity but often very poor judgment. He is innately driven to explore and attempt new physical feats, for in doing so he learns and develops. In his interaction with his environment, he learns by walking, climbing, touching, smelling, feeling, and even tasting as he goes. This interaction, however, can lead him into harm of self or others. Unlike the infant who needed mostly loving encouragement with few limits, the toddler needs some encouragement with more definite limits. Although resistant initially, a toddler will eventually feel secure and safe to act within the boundaries when they are enforced. With too much freedom and few limits, a child eventually becomes impulsive, anxious, and desperate as he searches for boundaries. With defined, predictable boundaries, however, a child is able to relax within these confines, free from fear of harm or punishment.

As discussed in chapter 7, training a child in proper behavior and to comply with a parent's instruction will involve implementing the process of discipline. This consists of (1) instructing in proper behavior, and then (2) affirming proper behavior when it occurs, and finally (3) correcting misbehavior. Following the order of each component within the process is essential to achieving success. Each builds upon the next. This is the structure I will use in offering advice for training your child toward proper behavior and ultimately in teaching him self-control and high character.

Important: Always affirm your child's proper behavior with encouraging words and actions. Then, upon discovering any misbehavior, judge your child's intent or motivation to determine your corrective action.

- If accidental, forgive and instruct.
- If an innocent mistake, express disapproval and instruct.
- If an act of intentional disobedience, express disapproval, instruct, and correct.

Managing Limitations

As mentioned in the previous chapter, you will do yourself and your child a big favor by childproofing the house. This does not mean clearing the deck of all items to make way for his reckless exploration. What it does mean is to remove those irresistible temptations from his path or reach and making the home as safe as possible. Keep those durable items on the end table or the potted plant that you would prefer to keep in the room for attractiveness. Your child can be taught to avoid these and in the process learn obedience and self-control.

1. **Instruct:** Where redirection and removal were the beginnings of instruction in the first year, verbal commands should now be used to guide. You are beginning to teach your child the foundational principle of obedience and simply redirecting his attention does not accomplish this goal. When giving instruction to your toddler, make sure you have her attention. This can be done by always stating her name first and then seeking eye contact from her. For example, "Sally, don't drop food." Instructions should be clear, simple, and brief.

2. **Affirm:** Always display your pleasure to your child when she obeys. Toddlers long to please their parents and this is a major motivator to proper behavior. Deliberately look for opportunities to affirm her regardless how small they may seem. For example: "Sally, thank you for talking softly and not screaming."

3. **Correct:** With an increase in mobility and awareness comes a toddler's increase in persistence to achieve his desires. This at times results in conflict between you and your child when his desires defy the limitations

you've set for him. Correction should first consist of your expression of disapproval and a brief explanation. If he persists in defying your direction, then unpleasantness (punishment) will be necessary to persuade him. Depending upon the setting, this may include any of the following measures:

- A playpen time-out: As used in the first year, this is the earliest form of time-out and consists of placing the baby in a playpen that has no toys in it and is set up in a quiet room. The baby is picked up with his face turned away from the parent, taken to the playpen with little talk, placed inside, and the parent departs. After one to two minutes the parent returns, picks up the baby, holds him close, returns to the original room, and reminds him that the activity is forbidden: "No touch [item]" or "Hands off!" If the misbehavior recurs, repeat the playpen time-out for slightly longer periods of time.
- A logical consequence: Removing a toy or play opportunity can be enough to correct a connected misbehavior. For example: If Johnny continues to throw a toy, it is taken away. If Sally continues to throw food, the food is temporarily removed from the tray.
- A natural consequence: This type of consequence naturally follows the misbehavior, thereby persuading the child not to do it again. For example: Falling and skinning a knee after defying a parent's command not to run. A pinch of a finger while continuing to play with a cabinet door after being told to stop.

Highchair Behavior and Food Throwing

Feeding time can be fascinating as your baby advances in her ability to accept solid foods and eventually feed herself. It can also be quite frustrating as she experiments with these slimy substances and attempts to drop and throw pieces of food from the highchair tray. It may be tempting at first to laugh and play along with chants of "Uh-Oh." However, keep in mind that this cheerleading may come back to bite you when you decide the messes are too much and you want the behavior to stop.

1. **Instruct:** From the beginning, make it clear to your baby that food dropping and throwing is not allowed. Place one food item at a time on the plate, and delay placing more on the plate if food is dropped. Remember, babies are more tempted to play with their food when their hunger is satisfied,

so if this is the case, end the meal and let her get down. This will prevent a lot of unnecessary conflict. After 18 months, you will train your baby to stay at the table with the family until everyone has finished.

2. **Affirm:** If she doesn't throw or stops throwing the food, affirm her with a pleasant comment: "That's mommy's girl. Thank you for not throwing food."

3. **Correct:** When food is dropped or thrown:

- Pick up the food and say, "We don't throw/drop food. No-no."
- If she repeats, take all the food off her highchair tray for a few minutes while everyone else continues eating. Give it back with the warning, "No throwing food, or food goes away again."
- If she repeats, take the food away again.
- If she repeats, turn the highchair around so that she is facing away from the family for one and a half to two minutes. Turn it back around with a repeat warning.
- If she disobeys again, take her out of the highchair and place her in a playpen time-out for one and a half to two minutes in another room. Return her to the highchair with food on her tray and a repeat warning.
- If she continues to disobey, end the meal and reengage next time. Repetition is your child's best teacher.
- NOTE: Your child will not willingly underfeed herself. She will eat according to her needs. If she is repeatedly throwing food, then she is obviously not hungry. Ending the meal will not cause her nutritional harm.

Biting and Hitting

Almost all toddlers will attempt to bite or hit sometime in this second year of life. In dealing with these problems, it is helpful to know when they are more likely to occur. Consider the following settings. Anticipation can be the best prevention:

- When fatigued and sleepy: Keeping your child on a consistent napping schedule can help.
- When hungry: Anticipate your child's hunger and be prepared with healthy snacks.

- When among a group of other children: When gathered together in a nursery, daycare, or playgroup, children should be closely monitored for aggressive behavior. Often times, hitting and biting are tactics of self-defense. Other times, they are tactics of aggressiveness in getting what a child wants.
- When frustrated: Although these behaviors should never be tolerated, the child may simply need your assistance with a toy or difficult situation.
- When feeling ignored: This is a tough one when considering a child in daycare or a nursery. Frustration and discouragement can set in when a child has constant competition from others for their provider's attention.

In identifying these settings, I am not making excuses for the behaviors or implying that biting or hitting should ever be ignored. I am simply helping you analyze the *why* behind the problem. Here are some approaches to stop the behaviors:

1. **Instruct:** Continue to verbally correct your child and demonstrate the proper behavior. Rather than simply saying "No," show him how you want him to behave. For example with hitting: Say, "No hit." Take his hand and say "Gentle" while you softly place his hand on your shoulder. Reemphasize, "Gentle." With biting: Say, "No bite. That hurts Mommy." Gently tap his mouth indicating to him the source of the biting, and show him an expression of sadness on your face. Then gently push his lips against your face and say, "Kiss mommy. No bite." Show a happy expression.

   Most toddlers by 15 months, and many by 12 months, know the wrongness of these actions. Once you are convinced of an intentional motive behind your child's biting or hitting, further instruction should stop and correction begin with each incident.

2. **Affirm:** Each time your child is tempted, but does not hit or bite, affirm him with hugs and happy expressions. Point out how respectful this behavior is toward others. For example: "Sally really likes it when you ask her for the toy without grabbing or hitting."

3. **Correct:** When instruction and affirmation do not resolve the problem behavior, you must correct with some form of unpleasantness.

Biting back or hitting your child will only escalate his frustration and does not model the self-control you want to teach. Your goal is to persuade him toward proper behavior and obedience with some form of correction. Consider these options:

- Squeeze the hand. To emphasize the significance of your child's action and to get his attention, squeeze his hand and say, "No hit (bite)."
- Put him down. If you are holding your baby when he bites or hits, give the verbal instruction outlined above, put him down on the floor and walk away. After one to three minutes of rejection, return to him and restate, "No hit (or bite)." Pick him up and move on with your day.
- A playpen time-out may be in order if the temporary rejection was unsuccessful. Give instruction, take him to the playpen (or crib), set him inside and walk away. After one to three minutes of isolation, return, pick him up, and restate the instruction.

Temper Tantrums

For a detailed discussion of these behaviors, see "Tantrums and Whining" in chapter 8.

Common Situations of Protest

- Resisting bedtime
- Resisting a diaper change
- Protesting sitting in the car seat
- Protesting sitting in the highchair at mealtime

Each of these situations is best handled with a brief explanation, and then making your child cooperate. Just place him in the crib, say "night-night," and walk away; physically hold him in place on the changing table while changing the diaper; place him in the car seat and snap down the harness; strap him in the highchair and continue eating. When a brief explanation doesn't persuade him to cooperate, it is best to move ahead and make the appropriate action happen. A prolonged explanation or changing your approach will typically not change your child's mind, since his primary motivation is to get his way. In time, he will realize his protests will not alter your directive and that he must submit. These are all opportunities to lead your child.

18–24 Months

With a child's increasing age should come increasing responsibility for his actions. Such is the case, even at 18 months of age. The toddler is increasingly able to link his behavior with his parent's approval or disapproval. His conscience is developing; therefore, he can be held accountable for more and more of his actions. There will be times when you wonder if your child really understands that his behavior is wrong, and it will be a judgment call on your part for sure. In general, however, your child probably knows that you know he knows. Consider the following diagram:

*If misbehavior is misread by a parent as innocent
and not corrected, the child is led to believe that
the behavior is acceptable to repeat.*

As misbehavior becomes more deliberate, correction becomes more necessary. This is an important principle. If misbehavior is misread by a parent as innocent and not corrected, the child is led to believe that the behavior is acceptable to repeat. This eventually leads to the need for "retraining," which is even more difficult than initial training. So, during the transition period of 12–18 months you must balance repeating instruction (giving your child the benefit of the doubt) with needed correction (when there is no doubt about his understanding of consequences for his actions).

Also with your child's maturing cognitive development comes the need to use additional corrective measures, such as time-out in a chair and disciplinary spanking (at 18–24 months). These measures will be needed additions to your repertoire as your child is more deliberate and persistent in his misbehavior, and as the earlier measures are less sufficient in persuading proper behavior. (See chapter 8 for a complete list of correction methods.)

As a child matures, reasoning can be added to your corrective measures to persuade proper behavior. Reasoning means "to offer an explanation to the child for why the behavior is improper and how it can impact others." In the early stages of development, reasoning is ineffective because the child is driven by his basic desire to please himself. At about 18 months, reasoning can begin to be used along with other more tangible corrective measures, such as time-out, consequences, and spanking. Research shows that reasoning alone is ineffective in disciplining children younger than four and may not work with a child until he is six years.[2] Using it too early may even be counterproductive. It has been said, "Arguing with a toddler is like wrestling with a shark." You can't win with words alone. Parents must correct first, and reason later.

Here are some common situations that will require your leadership in implementing discipline.

Defying Limitations

Defying limitations at this age not only refers to physical limits, but increasingly refers to your child's motive and attitude. Your long-term goal is to shape your child's heart and mind, not simply her behavior. At later ages, behavior will be a reflection of the child's heart. In general, when behavior is *required* early on, it will be *acquired* (heart attitude) later on. (Review the Discipline Process in chapter 7 for more details.)

1. **Instruct:** When giving instruction, make sure you have your child's attention. State her name first and then seek eye contact from her. For example, "Sally (wait for eye contact), don't bite your brother." Instructions should be clear, simple, and singular.

2. **Affirm:** Always display your pleasure to your child when she obeys. Deliberately look for opportunities to affirm her. Seek to affirm her at least twice as often as you correct her. Example: "Sally, good girl for playing nicely with Wesley."

3. **Correct:** Correction is only appropriate when your child has been previously instructed in the proper behavior. For first-time misbehavior, simply express disapproval and instruct. When your child intentionally defies your direction for her, then unpleasantness (punishment) will be necessary to persuade her. Example: "Sally, no bite

Wesley! Now I will _____." Depending upon the setting, this may include any of the following measures.

- Time-out in playpen or chair: After 18 months of age many children are capable (with training) of sitting in a chair during a time-out. Although this will require some repetitive training, it is superior to a playpen time-out as it is an opportunity to teach self-control. (See Time-Out in chapter 8 for more details.)
- Consequences, logical and natural: As previously described, consequences will be a useful corrective measure for years to come. Separating siblings for an hour can seem like torture to the offender (the biter).
- Disciplinary spanking: When milder measures of correction have failed to persuade your child to behave, properly applied spanking can restore his compliance. (See Disciplinary Spanking in chapter 8 for details.)

Controlling Impulses

As toddlers become more mobile and verbal, they naturally become more impulsive with their actions. They are often haphazardly running, curiously touching, boldly grabbing, and erratically screaming. And, while much of this is innocent exploration and gleeful expression, the toddler must be taught to slow down and think before he acts. The "think" is initially learning *what* behaviors are right or wrong, then later understanding *why* they are. The longer a parent delays in training impulse control, the harder it will be.

As mentioned in chapter 4, behavioral control or self-control is a critical element in child development that can be affected by many factors. But, don't overlook the influence that sleep has on self-control, both as a young child and as a teen. Research shows that "higher childhood sleep rhythmicity (i.e., going to bed and waking up at about the same time, absence of trouble sleeping and absence of being tired for no reasons) predicted higher adolescent self-control, which predicted a lower likelihood of having an alcohol use disorder and substance use problems (e.g., driving under the influence of alcohol, lost a job due to drinking or drug use)."[3] Here are some practical tips on how to teach impulse control.

- *Be proactive* in warning your child before the occasion of the temptations he may encounter. This is the Instruct component, where you also inform him of your expectations and the consequences if he disobeys. This is important. Don't be caught flatfooted with your child's impulsive behavior.

- *Rehearse appropriate behavior.* Role-playing is enjoyable to young children and it is effective. During a neutral moment in the evening, role play proper behavior in make-believe situations. Be funny and excited about proper behavior. Show frowns and sadness with improper behaviors.
- *Affirm.* Praise your child when his actions are appropriate and thoughtful.
- *Teach "Hands Off."* One good way to avoid constantly saying no is to develop the command, "Hands Off!" when things are impulsively touched by your toddler. Likewise, practice "Hands On" with appropriate actions, like playing with toys, and touching after permission has been granted. Role-playing works well here too.
- *Other possible commands include:*
  ‣ For screaming: "Inside voice, please."
  ‣ For running: "Walk, don't run."
- *Correct consistently.* Use the mildest form of punishment first, and if the misbehavior persists, use more unpleasant forms, like spanking.

Biting or Hitting

By 18 months a toddler clearly knows the wrongness of hitting and biting—if these behaviors have been appropriately addressed. At this point, these behaviors have moved from being innocent acts of curiosity to intentional acts of aggression. When it is clear to a parent that the behaviors are intentional, it is important that they not be excused or ignored. Punishment is likely the most effective form of correction at this point.

1. **Instruct:** Always make it clear to your child that these acts are hurtful to others and wrong. Also tell of the consequence for continuing the behavior.
2. **Affirm:** You observe your child in a tempting situation yet he resists hitting or biting, praise him. Example: You announce that it is time for a nap and pick your child up to go to the bedroom. He is obviously not pleased with your decision and briefly protests yet does not react with hitting you. Applaud him for not biting or hitting you (if he has done so in the past).
3. **Correct:** If, despite clear instruction and occasional affirmation, your child continues to hit, punishment is appropriate and necessary.

Inform him that the next time he hits he will go to time-out. When he hits, keep your promise; he goes to time-out. (See chapter 8 for details.)

Refusing to Yield to a Parent's Voice

Willingly submitting to a parent's directive does not come naturally to a toddler; especially one who is in the midst of play. Yielding to a parent's voice in these settings, however, is opportunity for learning to yield in a more serious or dangerous setting, like a busy parking lot. Your child's proper attention to your instructions will require proper delivery from you with expectations of compliance.

- *Be assertive and expectant.* Project a posture of authority, not uncertainty. Expect your child's obedience. Don't act surprised when obedience follows. Require compliance. This is largely an attitude.
- *Be deliberate.* When giving directions to your toddler, tell him, don't ask him. While it may seem more compassionate to gently ask him to comply, it gives the false impression that obedience is optional and this is confusing. "Say what you mean and mean what you say." You are the wise parent; act like one and lead your child to proper behavior and character.
- *Require attention.* As often as you can, train your child to give you eye contact when you call his name. This may initially mean walking over to your child and touching his shoulder or directing his face toward yours as you speak assertively. Also, require a verbal response of some sort. Example: Mom: "Will, do not play with the ____." Will: "Yes, Mom." Not, "Let's not play with the ____, Okay?"
- *Keep it simple.* When giving instructions, use simple words consistently, such as "stop," "no," and "do not touch." When he hears these familiar words, he is more likely to respond immediately than if he must listen to an explanation for your reasoning with each command.
- *Be persistent.* Your child must know that you will not tolerate disobedience. He must know that his disobedience will always and eventually lead to either compliance or punishment. If this is evident early in his life, he is less likely to challenge you later.

    Example: Running from a parent in a dangerous setting, like a parking lot.
    1. **Instruct:** Before entering the situation (i.e., getting out of the car), clearly instruct your child about staying close to you and about the consequences if he does not.

2. **Affirm:** Verbally commend your child if he cooperates without protest.
3. **Correct:** Firmly hold your child's hand until he promises to obey. If the running away is defiant (disregards your command to stop) and your child is at least 18 months old, a spanking may be necessary to persuade him. Administer it immediately, but in private. (See *Disciplinary Spanking* in Chapter 8 for details.)

Protesting Bedtime

When a child is taught how to go to sleep without your help in the first year of life (as presented in chapter 12), he comes to appreciate the opportunity for sleep. However, around 18 months of age, the attraction of continued play often leads a child to attempt to change his parent's mind through protest at bedtime. Convincing him of the futility of his efforts will be much easier if you continue to use the crib instead of moving him to a toddler bed. Because the crib restricts his escape, you can briefly console, put him in the crib, and walk away. Allowing 10–20 minutes of crying will usually cause him to give up and go to sleep. If you begin to give in and delay his bedtime in response to his protests, he will be tempted to protest even more at future bedtimes. Once again, your consistency is key to your child's obedience.

Temper Tantrums and Whining

Does your child often whine or have a tantrum when you tell him to do something? Review *Temper Tantrums* in chapter 8. Here are some questions to ask:

• Are you handling these behaviors correctly? (See page 120 for details.)
• Do you reward the tantrums by giving her what she wants most of the time?
• Is she often tired or fatigued from poor or insufficient sleep? This is an all too common reason for poor self-control. (Review chapters 6 and 12 on training a child to be a good sleeper.)
• Is the family too busy, leaving little time at home for napping and play?
• Is she whining to get the attention she rarely gets otherwise?

Negative Responses: "No!"

Does your child constantly say *no* to your requests of him? When your toddler says *no*, he is looking for a response from you. Your response will largely determine whether he continues to use this expression. If you respond with hesitation, then he has accomplished his goal. If you casually ignore his *no* and quickly move back to your original request, he will be less likely to continue to use this expression in the future. If he refuses to act or obey your request, physically help him obey.

Example: Mom says, "It is time to pick up your toys and put them away." Will says, "No." Mom says, "Now let's get moving. We will not have time to play outside unless you get these toys picked up." Will again says, "No." Mom says, "Pick them up right now." At this point Mom takes Will's hand and helps him pick up the toys one by one. The point: You must not allow his words of refusal to affect your request. If he continues to refuse to obey, he must be punished with an appropriate corrective measure.

2–2½ Years

Often mislabeled as the "Terrible Twos," this year of life is full of challenging transition and exciting development. In your parenting, you are laying a foundation for your child's character from which he will draw for years to come. Your goal is not to simply maintain and endure through this period, but rather to continue instructing, affirming, and correcting in an effort to influence your child's heart, not just his behavior. This period can indeed be terrible—if you ignore your responsibility to understand your child and his need of discipline. Constantly indulging a demanding child will lead him toward an insatiable desire to please himself rather than you. It may seem like an effective short-term solution when conflict arises, but it leads to a long-term problem that is increasingly difficult to reverse. Yes, there will be pushback and seemingly constant chants of *no* from your toddler as you direct him. Don't be discouraged. Have high expectations for his behavior, but also expect challenges along the way.

Your goal is not to simply maintain and endure through this period.

Occasionally, a parent of a disobeying child will ask me, "Doc, is this just a phase that my child is going through?" Most of the time, the parent wants me to answer yes so that the behavior can be excused. I call this "excuse parenting." Rather than looking for an excuse, look for answers. Invest now in the discipline of your child, and he will grow in his desire to honor you and those around him. Delay discipline, and your child's character and relationship with you will suffer.

Finally, enjoy your child and this wonderful period of life. It is tempting to long for years when your child is older and less dependent upon you. Keep in mind that every period of parenting has its challenges. Meet the challenges and the experience will be exciting and rewarding.

Applaud proper behavior and correct misbehavior. When necessary, confront your child; don't avoid conflict, even when it is tempting to do so after a busy day. The following are opportunities to *lead* your child to good behavior.

- Teach and encourage proper behavior.
- Look for opportunities to applaud proper behavior.
- Make certain the rules and expectations of your child fit his level of maturity. For instance, two-year-olds have difficulty sitting still, walking slowly, and remaining quiet for long periods of time.
- Anticipate difficult settings for your child and remind him of your expectations. For example, before entering a store, inform your child what is expected and warn him of the consequences of misbehavior or a temper tantrum in the store.
- Manage tantrums properly. Don't be worn down.
- Use role-play in neutral moments to teach the importance of sharing with others.
- Require respectful speech and behavior.
- Correct aggressive behavior: biting, hitting, deliberate pushing.
- Manage impulsivity. Begin to focus on teaching self-control. Require eye contact when talking to your child.
- Be consistent in your discipline. Inconsistency causes a child great frustration.

Tantrums and Whining

For full details, see the section on *Temper Tantrums and Whining* in chapter 8. The following are various tactics you can employ at this age with your frenzied child.

- Say, "I don't hear you when you whine. Let's try that again." Teach her to speak in a clearer, deeper tone of voice; imitate for her the voice you prefer.

- With your child's next temper tantrum, ask her, "Will you please continue that for a few minutes more? I'm going to get my camera to video your performance." It will usually stop before you return.
- If your child slams the door in a fit, make her practice opening and closing the door calmly 20 times.
- If your child stomps her feet in anger, send her outside to stomp her feet for one minute.
- If your child throws a fit, tell her to go to her room and "continue her fit." Tell her she isn't allowed to come out until she has cried for ten minutes.
- During a temper tantrum, tell your older child, "This is too disruptive for inside; let's go outside to finish your tantrum."
- If your child protests when your answer is no, then tell her that your answer will be no to any of her requests for the rest of the day.
- The next time your child begins to whine, give her a look of confusion and then say, "I am sorry. I don't understand that language. Would you like to try again?" Don't reward whining by granting her request.

At the Dinner Table

Continue to practice the Family Table as detailed in chapter 6. Turn the TV and all electronic devices off, and require that everyone stay at the table until everyone finishes eating. This prevents any anticipation by your child of leaving the table early. Tell all that disrespectful, negative comments about others at the table is not allowed. Say, "Our words must be encouraging." This also means parents will not do any reprimanding during the meal for misbehaviors that occurred earlier in the day. Serve the same foods for all at the table; no short order cooking. In the event of disruptive behavior:

- Require a child to ask forgiveness for any hurtful words said during the meal.
- Place the child in time-out (a minute for every year of age) in another room while everyone else continues to enjoy the meal.

2½–3 Years

Continue all of the behavioral advice mentioned previously. Be proactive in disciplining her behavior. Forewarn your child of upcoming events and new settings. Remind her of your expectations for her proper behavior, and of the consequences for any misbehavior. For example, before entering the grocery store, remind her of the rules. She is to stay in the shopping cart, and if she protests she will be punished. Also, remind her of previous visits when she obeyed and how proud of her you were.

- Teach her to respect your authority as her parent.
- Applaud her obedient response to your directions.
- Remind her of the benefits of obedience: safety, self-satisfaction, harmony with others, better relationships with others, etc.
- Teach and require respectful speech and eye contact.
- Teach to say "please" and "thank you."
- Teach to clearly and respectfully reply "yes" or "no."
- Teach your child to respond when spoken to by an adult. This can be a simple one or two word response. Teach the disrespectfulness of ignoring or acting shy when addressed by an adult.
- When disrespectful language or whining has occurred, teach the proper words/phrases and tone of voice. Actually stop and rehearse this with your child. By doing this, you are replacing improper language with proper language. Also, you are teaching proper behavior rather than just punishing improper behavior.

3–3½ Years

At three years of age, your child is beginning to be capable of understanding the moral reason for proper behavior. You should now begin appealing to your child's heart or motive, not simply focusing on his actions. Persuading your child to behave rightly can now include an element of reasoning, but don't stop using the more tangible methods of correction, like time-out. Relying upon reasoning alone at this age will be counterproductive. Also, begin revealing to your child your source of moral standards. (I outline the approach we took with our children in chapter 20.) Nurturing your child's conscience is more likely to produce a life-long desire to behave rightly and respect others.

Nurturing your child's conscience is more likely to produce a life-long desire to behave rightly and respect others.

- Be as consistent as possible. It is getting harder now as he is more independent and capable of arguing; it's more tempting to let some misbehavior slide. Don't become complacent. It's okay to grant grace occasionally, but it should come as a surprise to your child, not as a routine.
- Begin to use reasoning with your child. Briefly explain that the behavior is wrong and is not to be repeated. Appeal to her conscience and point out previous situations where she did the right thing and you were so proud of her. Caution: Resist relying solely upon talk to produce change in your preschooler's behavior.
- Require respectful talk. Correct disrespectful attitudes and rehearse respectful responses with your child.
- Correct all whining. Don't just tolerate or ignore it. Use the tactics mentioned earlier in this chapter.

Active Behavior

Sharing

1. **Instruct:** Explain the kindness in sharing, emphasizing how grateful we are when others share with us. Designate some toys as "share toys" and others as personal toys. Explain that it is polite to share all our personal toys, but he must share the share toys.
2. **Affirm:** Be quick to applaud him for any sharing you observe.
3. **Correct:** Remove the toy(s) for a day or two if your child refuses to share.

Appropriate Play

1. **Instruct:** Teach the importance of being respectful with our actions and our words toward one another.
2. **Affirm:** Praise your child when he treats his sibling with respect and gentleness.
3. **Correct:**
   - Use time-out for the aggressor.
   - Separate the two children by requiring they stay in separate rooms for a couple hours.
   - Forbid any talking between the siblings for an hour or two.
   - Spank the aggressor or both children if the aggression is mutual and milder measures have failed.

Behavior at Home and in Public

1. **Instruct:** Forewarn your children of the proper behavior in public. Make clear your expectations and develop a code word for reminding your children in public to control their impulses.

2. **Affirm:** At home, sometimes children need to run off their excess energy. Consider allowing her to run around the backyard for a few minutes before coming inside to settle down. Applaud your child when she does not run around recklessly in public.

3. **Correct:** At home, siblings can get very rowdy after a meal or anytime they are feeling bold or brash. When running around inside the home becomes excessive, have them crawl on all fours to release energy as they move about in the house for a few minutes. Another "penalty" can be physical exercise, such as running a lap around the yard or doing some push-ups or jumping jacks. Make it a game and participation will come easy.

In public, stop your children if they become reckless and rowdy; don't ignore it. Have them come and stand by your side for a few minutes to get their attention. Instruct them with eye-to-eye contact. If disruptive play continues after this, punish when you get home with a privilege removal or a spanking if the behavior was defiant.

Verbal Behavior

Lying

1. **Instruct:** If this behavior is ignored, it can become a major character issue. Lying must be addressed. Explain the importance of truth telling, and then impose a consequence for correction.

2. **Affirm:** Applaud your child for telling the truth, especially when the confession results in punishment.

3. **Correct:** Ask your child to admit to the lie, explain the seriousness of it, and inform about the consequence if lying occurs again.

   - Consequence: Require that your child return to the offended person, admit to lying, tell the truth, and ask for forgiveness.
   - For the older child, draw up a contract about what the penalty will be any time he tells a lie. Have each of you sign it, and then post it. This can serve as a deterrent when the temptation to lie arises.

Disrespectful Talk

1. **Instruct:** Immediately point out the inappropriate speech and require him to restate his sentence in a respectful manner. This accomplishes teaching while at the same time, a bit of punishment.
2. **Affirm:** Point out to your child when she speaks to you with respectful words and tone.
3. **Correct:**

   - Require an apology: "I am sorry for saying ___. Will you forgive me?"
   - Require no talking from that child for a period of time, such as one hour. If talking continues, lengthen the silent period. Explain that talking is a privilege in the home. This can be very painful for some child personalities.
   - For crude talk, require that the child sit in the bathroom for a period of time. Bathroom talk leads to a bathroom time-out.
   - Give a teaspoon of cider vinegar by mouth as "rude medicine."
   - Fill a waste basket with slips of paper labeled with the least desirable jobs in the home, like taking out the garbage, cleaning the garbage cans, scrubbing the toilets, sweeping the garage, cleaning the pet bowls, etc. When your child begins to speak disrespectfully toward you, send him to the basket to draw his penalty.
   - Spank for defiance when milder measures have failed.

3½–4 Years

Model a harmonious relationship in your marriage. Practice healthy conflict resolution in front of your child. Demonstrate self-control when disagreements arise. Communicate respectfully with one another. We can't expect our children to stop whining and pitching tantrums when we are practicing adult versions of each.

Applaud proper behavior. Tell your child that you have noticed that her behavior is maturing and the baby behavior is going away. Say, "I am so proud of my big girl." "You are really acting like a big girl now." "I'm so glad you are not acting like a baby anymore." Also, parents should talk openly between themselves about their child's good behavior. This is very motivating to a child.

Look for opportunities to nurture your child's desire to behave properly. Good behavior comes once a child makes the choice to please the parent, or conscientiously do the right thing, versus choosing to please himself. This maturation of a child's conscience occurs when the discipline process is properly applied.

Correct Misbehavior. Choose the proper measure for correction.

- Hooray! Finally, by three and a half years a child is more likely to be persuaded by consequences and privilege removal, and therefore the more physical forms of correction (spanking and time-out) are less needed.
- Allow natural consequences to teach. Review the details of how this works in chapter 8. When your child chooses to disobey and negative consequences occur as a result, point out to your child the cause of the consequence, and let this association be his teacher. Avoid the temptation to frequently remind your child, "I told you so," as this can cause frustration and exasperation.
- Use logical consequences of disobedience to teach proper behavior. This means linking the imposed consequence to the wrong behavior. For example, when a child refuses to pick up toys after playing, the toys are put away for the next two days.
- Restrict privileges or remove toys for disobedient behavior. For example, when a child disobediently leaves the yard to play with a neighbor, he is not allowed to visit the friend for two days.
- Use time-out for misbehavior. See previous age group for examples.
- Spank for persistent disobedience or defiant disrespectfulness.
- Be consistent and calm with your correction and punishment. Remember, being consistent in your discipline will reduce exasperation from your child, improve his obedience, and cause you to remain calmer.

4–5 Years

Continue to practice the discipline process as outlined previously.

Choices—In an effort to practice more reasoning with your child, emphasize to him that his behavior is his *choice*. If he chooses to misbehave, then he is choosing to suffer a consequence. If he wants the day to go well, he can choose to behave correctly. Tell him you hope he will make good choices.

Appeal Process—An appeal process can be introduced at about four years of age. Teach your child to request an "appeal" of your directive if he has *new* information to bring to your attention. Teach him to first state his understanding of your directive and then make his appeal. While this option may not work with all children or in every situation, parents should consider this for those children who prove to be respectfully submissive.

6–10 Years

Your school-aged child now has the cognitive ability to understand and be persuaded by the reasoning behind your directives. Therefore, reasoning should be used more in correcting and physical measure be used less. This means less time-out and spanking, and more privilege removal and consequences. This is an important transition since the latter correction measures will, in many ways, be more effective than the former.

As you encourage good behavior, be a good role model for your child, and focus more on your child's motive for his behavior rather than simply on the action. Name the improper motives behind the behaviors as you see them displayed in your child, such as selfishness, greed, cruelty, dishonesty, pride, insensitivity, or rudeness. Likewise, applaud him by naming the proper motives, such as kindness, honesty, patience, trustworthiness, self-control, respect, and humility. This will help your child understand the character issue, which is motivating the behavior.

Grant new responsibilities and privileges as your child demonstrates responsibility with his obedience and maturing judgment. Look for opportunities to discuss with your child your values and convictions about daily living. I have outlined mine in chapter 20.

Help your child grow in his independence and personal responsibility. This will at times mean allowing him to experience the negative consequences of his irresponsible actions. Here are a few pointers to consider:

- Avoid constantly reminding your child of his responsibilities. Even as your child gets older, it will be tempting to do this when he "forgets" or fails to do his part. In reminding him, you are owning the responsibility rather than giving it to him. This creates dependency upon you. Don't do it, even when it is the most expedient approach at the moment. Failure due to irresponsible behavior can be an excellent teacher and motivator. Your child must suffer from his irresponsible choices, not you.
- Allow natural and logical consequences to be your primary methods of correction to teach proper behavior. For example, if a dawdling child is slow to dress in the morning, let him be marked tardy at school, or, if

a child fails to finish her homework due to procrastination, she is not allowed to stay up past her bedtime and has her work marked incomplete.

- For particularly difficult and recurring behaviors, choose two or three offenses and draw up an agreement between parents and child:
  - ► List the rule and responsibilities.
  - ► List the consequences.
  - ► Decide together which consequences are appropriate for which misbehaviors.
  - ► Both parents and child sign it, post it, and parents enforce it.
  - ► A written agreement clarifies the issues for the child and takes the guesswork out of correction.
  - ► Emphasize that compliance is a choice and the appropriate consequences will follow.

Authority Figures

Make every attempt to support and defend the authority figures in your child's life, such as a teacher or coach. Speaking negatively to your child, or in his presence, about these adults will undermine their authority in your child's eyes. When your child is disciplined or corrected by them, he must know that you will stand with those in authority. For instance, if you speak negatively about a teacher and side with your complaining child, he will be emboldened to rebel or defy that teacher in the future. If suspicion or doubt arises over how the teacher handled a situation, go directly to the teacher before agreeing with your child's complaint about her. Getting the full story from the teacher first will allow you to make a more accurate assessment.

Untidiness

In the case of a messy bedroom, consider some of the following approaches:

- Help your child get organized by creating specific places in his room for his possessions and by teaching him how to make his bed and place folded clothes in specific drawers.
- Take away any toys left on the floor. Require a payment or extra chore to earn it back.
- Charge a fine (20 cents) for each item left on the floor after clean up. Or with ample warning, take any items left out of place to the Goodwill store or donate to the church nursery.

- Develop a chore list and an allowance system (see chapter 4 Chores and Allowance). Place on the chore list dusting room weekly, making bed daily, and placing folded clothes in drawers. Impose a fine for work not done.

Acts of Disobedience

Recurrent Misdeeds

- Fine the child for recurrent misdeeds; like paying $1 for failure to buckle a seat belt.
- Privilege removal, such as tablet play, or TV program.

Laziness with Chores

- Pay no allowance for that week and require that the chore be completed.
- Remove certain privileges, such as watching sports on TV, to "allow more time" to accomplish the chore.

Shoplifting

- If you notice shoplifting by your child while in the store, alert the clerk to search the child. If the deed is discovered after your child leaves the store, require that he return to the store and return the item, confess, and possibly pay you a fine (equal to the item's price). For the most resistant child, a session with a police officer may make a stronger impression.

Sibling Issues

When negative comments are spoken to the sibling, consider the following:

- Talk about how important their relationship is to one another, and about how they should treat each other the way they want to be treated.
- Require a verbal apology: "I am sorry. Will you forgive me?"
- Require that a fee be paid to the offended sibling out of the offender's savings or allowance.

School Issues

Misbehavior

- Remove a privilege for that day that the child enjoys doing.
- Require that the child write a sentence: "I will not do __" fifty times.

- For the older child, require that he write a 100-word essay about "Why I shouldn't do ___."
- Fine the child to pay out of her allowance or savings.

Slow to do Homework; Uncooperative

Design a healthy after-school routine: Allow your child some playtime after school (30–45 minutes outside) and a snack before starting homework. Study in a quiet place of the home with the TV off. Teach your child good study habits and organizational skills. If your child is sincerely struggling with his schoolwork, seek the advice of his teachers and even consider testing to identify any learning disability.

- For the uncooperative older child, offer to help for a limited period of time, and then the child is on her own. The consequence of a poor grade the next day should help motivate her. Shielding your child from failure creates dependency upon you and is counter-productive. Use your judgment; allow for some deserved failures.
- Remove your child from an extracurricular activity (sports, club, lessons) until she demonstrates responsible homework management and pulls the grades up.

Teen Years

These are in addition to the consequences previously mentioned.

Disobedient Behavior

Disobeying Restrictions

- If a teen fails to obey a restriction on where he is allowed to go and when he is to return home, he must be punished.
- Ground your child for a short time (few days). Do not allow travel away from home after school, or do require an earlier curfew for a couple weeks.
- Fine your child. This assumes that you have forewarned of a fine for disobedience.

General Disobedience or Disrespect

- Restrict activity. Restrict child to stay in bedroom after dinner on school days and on weekends for a few days.

- Remove electronics. Prohibit social media, video gaming, or tablet entertainment. Take away his phone for a few days. Require the demonstration of respectful behavior to earn back the privileges.
- Additional chores. Require teen to assume some of his siblings' chores for a few days, or add additional duties around the house.
- Community service. Require child to volunteer for work at church or a charitable organization.
- Write a report. Require child to write a two- to four-page "research paper" on the topic at hand or an evil in society (i.e., drug use).

Chapter 16

DIGITAL CHALLENGES

Technology is here to stay, and we all have benefited from it in many ways. As with any good thing, however, too much is not good. Your child will need your guidance in managing these very attractive, yet addictive devices. (For a detailed discussion of Digital Influences on Your Child, read chapter 5.)

Here are some of the primary concerns (listed in order from the earliest age) with personal technology or digital communication devices:

- The negative effects of digital screen viewing upon the developing brain of a young child
- The unhealthy sedentary lifestyle that these devices foster for young and old
- The potentially negative and difficult-to-monitor content accessible on the devices
- The social independence a smartphone creates that interferes with parental oversight and often harms the parent-child relationship.
- The potentially negative influences of social media on the older child
- The negative effect upon time management due to screen time

Given the risks to our children, here are my recommended time limits for screen time at various ages.

Suggested Time Limits on Total Recreational Screen Time			
Child's Age	Limit on a Weekday*	Limit on a Weekend day	Device**
Less than 2 years	Avoid all intentional viewing	Avoid all intentional viewing	All devices
2–6 years	½–1 hour	½–1 hour	All devices
6–12 years	½ hour	1–2 hours	All devices
12 years or older	½–1 hour	1–3 hours	All devices

* These weekday limits assume school attendance for at least a half-day after age six years.

** Devices include television, computer, tablet, smartphone, and video consoles.

Listed below by age are various opportunities for parents to lead their child in the avoidance or proper usage of digital technology.

Under 12 Months

- Avoid using screened devices for distraction or entertainment.
- Avoid any intentional television, tablet, or phone viewing.
- Don't use a TV in the baby's room.

12–24 Months

Without a doubt, screen watching is the great American pastime. Although entertaining and informative for adults, screen exposure for young children carries subtle but real risks. (See "Digital Influences on Your Child" in chapter 5.)

- TV watching is unhealthy to the brain development of children under 24 months. Don't intentionally encourage TV watching at this age, even of the educational variety.
- Keep the television turned off most of the time in the home. Even having it on in the background can bring unhealthy exposure and cause unintended screen attraction for your child.
- Don't allow a TV or other smaller screens (tablet or smart phone) in your child's bedroom.
- Don't use these electronic devices as sleep aids for your child. This creates a subtle dependency and leads to insomnia later.
- Avoid using screens as a "pacifier" for your toddler. Parents commonly use their smart phone as a method of occupying or

distracting their child while running errands. While effective for the moment, this can subtly lead to a craving for more and more screen time, which is known to be unhealthy for the young developing mind.

- Excessive screen exposure contributes to whining, irritability, and discontentment with your toddler.

The bottom line: Protect your child's young impressionable mind. You must, for you can be sure that the forces of society certainly will not.

2–3 Years

Limit your child's screen time, including TV, tablet, smartphone, video, and computer. Early exposure to excessive screen time poses significant risks to your child's mental and physical health, including:

- Reduces reading at later ages[1]
- Reduces levels of concentration at later ages
- Attention problems at school-age[2]
- Linked to obesity later in childhood[3]
- Reduces activity level and industriousness later in childhood
- Increases violent behavior[4]

Most families will choose to have a TV and an electronic tablet in the home, but their use should be very limited and closely monitored. Review the screen time limits in the chart at the beginning of this chapter. Here are a few more opportunities to lead your child:

- Never allow a TV in your child's bedroom, since this is associated with school dysfunction, obesity, and insomnia. Don't allow electronic tablet play in the bedroom either. Make your child's bedroom a "screen-free sanctuary" for rest and sleep.
- From ages two to five years, limit total screen time to one hour or less per day. Use this time selectively for educational programs or live video chats with a relative. Watch these programs with your child to discuss the content. Realize that, with no monitoring, it is like inviting a stranger into your home to spend one-on-one time with your child, influencing him in many ways, often contrary to your beliefs.

- Encourage your child to play with non-electronic toys to stimulate his creativity. This promotes active learning (imaginative thinking and hands-on building) versus inferior passive learning (effortless visual entertainment). See chapter 6 (page 77).
- Filter the content coming through the screens to your child. Research shows that violent TV viewing in two- to five-year-olds is associated with antisocial behavior at seven to nine years of age.

3–4 Years

- Again, limit and restrict total screen time to one hour or less a day. Have the TV turned off most of the day. Avoid having the TV on as background stimulation and entertainment. Quietness within the home nurtures calmness and stirs mental creativity. Dad, limit your TV time while the children are awake. If a sports program is really important to you, record it and watch when the children are napping or asleep for the night. Get outside and play with your children. Model an active lifestyle.
- Don't allow any screens in your child's bedroom at any age. Make the bedroom a non-digital, screen-free sanctuary for rest and sleep.

4–5 Years

From ages two to five, limit screen time to one hour or less per day. Use this time selectively for educational programs or live video chats. Watch programs with your child to discuss the content. Realize that, with no monitoring, it is like inviting a stranger into your home to spend one-on-one time with your child, influencing him in many ways, often contrary to your beliefs.

The research on screen time and children is concerning. In one study, higher amounts of screen time in four- to twelve-year-olds were associated with lower physical activity rates. Both higher screen time and lower physical activity rates were linked with higher odds of psychological distress, including emotional symptoms, conduct problems, and peer relationship problems. [5] Other studies show that daily television viewing and television viewing in bedrooms are associated with sleep disturbances.[6] Excessive screen time (TV, video, gaming, and computer) has even been shown to interfere with parent-child attachment as an adolescent.[7] Therefore, limiting your child's screen time is crucial to good health.

6–10 Years

Excessive screen time leads to several unhealthy and negative effects, including:

- Exposure to unacceptable or immoral material
- Decreased physical activity and increased weight gain
- Increased violent play
- Inattention in school
- Difficulty falling asleep; poor sleep habits
- Allows for outside influences on a child's mind

Positive effects include:

- Entertainment
- Educational benefits if properly monitored by a parent
- Opportunity for interactive play time between parent and child

Review the details in chapter 5. Here are a few of the highlights:

- Delay and limit your child's use of electronic (screened) devices. Limit screen time to half an hour on school nights, and one to two hours on weekends. Watch only quality programming on the family TV or play quality apps on a family tablet. Wait until the following ages (or later) to allow personal possession of a device:
  - ‣ Tablet—10 years
  - ‣ Cell phone—13 years
  - ‣ Smartphone—15 years
- Activate parental protection or filters on all WiFi devices. Turn on filters and limits on all devices that access WiFi.
- Manage the apps on the phone. Set up parental controls on your child's devices to restrict the downloading of apps. Periodically review the apps on your child's phone. Consult websites like CommonSenseMedia.org for reviews about age-appropriate apps, games, and programs to guide you.
- Be Internet cautious. The Internet can be a useful resource for the family, but it can also be a source of dark, degrading material for a child. Consider the following measures to protect your child:

1. Allow computer use only in the common living areas of the home where monitoring is possible.

2. Program your family computer Internet browser to block pop-ups.
3. Set parental control settings on computers, tablets, and smart-phones.
4. Install an Internet filter/monitor program. These programs allow a parent to limit a child's access to certain Internet content.

- Create a charging station. To keep screened devices out of bedrooms overnight, create a charging station in a common area of the home and require that all mobile screened devices be kept there overnight. This will allow you the opportunity to review the content and history on the devices in the evenings.
- Turn off the screens on school day evenings. For a healthier mind, encourage children to read more and watch screens less. Screen usage quickly consumes time in the evenings and leads to little exercise and late nights. Limit TV and free screen time to thirty minutes to an hour on school day nights. No video gaming on a console or tablet. Limit to one to two hours per day on weekends.
- Co-view TV programs and co-play video games with your children. This allows you to monitor and explain the content to them.

Chapter 17

INDUSTRIOUSNESS

As is detailed in chapter 4, industriousness is a very desirable character quality to instill in your child for several reasons. An ambitious, productive child is naturally confident. An industrious child is active and healthier. An industrious child is responsible and more likely a contributor to the family. And an industrious child is more likely to be a successfully employed adult.

So, how do you teach a child to be industrious? By stimulating her interest in work and the rewards that follow. Here are some specific opportunities to *lead* your child by starting the practices of chores and allowance. The suggestions listed below come from my experience with my children, with my patients, and some helpful resources.[1]

Chores

Chores provide children the opportunity to play a tangible role in the operation of the family and teaches them the enriching value of work. As mentioned in chapter 4, here are some pointers to get started:

- Start young. Begin as early as three years of age by encouraging your child to help you with household chores. These are intended to inspire your little one to feel she is a needed member of the family.
- Offer praise often. Your approval is your child's greatest reward.
- Work together. In introducing chores to your little ones, do the work together, even as a game. Then slowly ease off your involvement, giving them more ownership of the task. Also, do chores when your toddler is well-fed and well-rested to avoid unnecessary battles.

- Don't insist on perfection. You can insist on completion without demanding perfection. Gauge your expectations by your child's developmental level. Don't expect performance beyond her ability.

Below are some examples of chores for your children as they reach the respective ages through adolescence. I am not suggesting that your child should be doing every chore listed under his age group, or even be doing these every day. Pick and choose the chores you feel are most reasonable for your child in your specific home setting. For more details about the value of chores, see chapter 4.

3–3½ Years

Give your preschool child some regular "Help Me" household chores to do around the house. You can start be saying, "Johnny, it is your job to _____ every day. This will help Mommy so much." Your display of satisfaction is payment enough at this age. Post a list of chores in the kitchen. Show your child how to check off the items as they are done; this cultivates satisfaction.

- Help me set the table (start with simple tasks and add as appropriate):
  - ‣ Put the salt and pepper shakers on the table.
  - ‣ Put the cups on the dinner table.
  - ‣ Put the forks and spoons on the table.
- Help me feed the dog:
  - ‣ Fill his water bowl.
  - ‣ Fill his food bowl.
- Help me make the beds:
  - ‣ Put the blankets and pillows back on the bed each morning when you wake.
- Help me keep your room neat:
  - ‣ Before naptime and bedtime pick up your toys and put them in the toy box or on the shelf.
  - ‣ Gather dirty clothes and take to the laundry room.

4 Years

- Bedroom:
  - ‣ Make own bed: straighten bed covers, straighten pillow.
  - ‣ Pick up toys and tidy room routinely.

- ‣ Dust low furniture.
- ‣ Help fold laundry.
- Kitchen:
  - ‣ Help set dinner table: napkins, silverware, and cups.
  - ‣ Help clear table after meals.
- House:
  - ‣ Help gather dirty laundry.
  - ‣ Help fold clean laundry.
  - ‣ Empty wastebaskets.

5–6 Years

Your children are watching, so demonstrate an active lifestyle by working around the house and recreating actively. You will teach industriousness by modeling work yourself and by requiring work from your children. If you are a proverbial couch potato, why should your children be any different?

Hold everyone accountable by creating a chart to be placed on the refrigerator that details the chores each child is assigned. Monitor your child's successful completion of the chores, and teach her to take pride in doing them correctly and completely. If sloppy work is praised and approved, then the child will practice that level of performance outside the home as well. Here are some examples of chores appropriate for this age:

- Bedroom:
  - ‣ All previous tasks.
  - ‣ Put clean clothes in drawers neatly.
- Kitchen:
  - ‣ Set place mats for dinner table.
  - ‣ Help load and empty dishwasher.
  - ‣ Set and clear table.
  - ‣ Help put groceries away.
- House:
  - ‣ All previous tasks.
  - ‣ Feed and water the pet.
- Outside:
  - ‣ Help with cleanup in yard.

7–8 Years

- Bedroom:
  - All previous tasks.
  - Strip own bed for laundry.
- Kitchen:
  - All previous tasks.
  - Help with cooking: measuring cups, hand mixing, pouring ingredients.
  - Peel carrots and potatoes.
  - Make own sandwich for lunch.
  - Help wash dishes.
- House:
  - All previous tasks.
  - Water house plants.
  - Sweep floors inside and outside.
- Outside:
  - Water outdoor plants.

9–11 Years

- Bedroom:
  - All previous tasks.
  - Dust and vacuum.
- Kitchen:
  - Increase skilled work in kitchen, such as cooking hotdogs, cooking eggs, making toast, operating microwave, etc.
- House:
  - All previous tasks.
  - Fold sheets and blankets.
  - Sort clothes, load and run washer.
  - Load and run dryer.
  - Clean bathroom sink, toilet, and tub.
- Outside:
  - All previous tasks.
  - Sweep, rake, clean windows.

12–15 Years

- Bedroom:
  - ‣ All previous tasks, but with greater expectations for regularity and completeness.
- Kitchen:
  - ‣ Increase cooking tasks: baking and cooking entrées.
  - ‣ Clean kitchen completely after meals.
  - ‣ Unload dishwasher.
- House:
  - ‣ All previous tasks, but with greater expectations for regularity and completeness.
  - ‣ Clean windows.
  - ‣ Organize closet.
- Outside:
  - ‣ All previous tasks.
  - ‣ Begin mowing the lawn, depending upon your child's size and strength.
- Community Service:
  - ‣ Take a babysitting course and begin sitting for family and close friends.
  - ‣ Look for opportunities to serve at church and in community.
- Get a paying job outside the home.

16 Years & Older

- All previous tasks and responsibilities.
- Driving—with a license to drive comes:
  - ‣ Run grocery errands.
  - ‣ Begin carpooling siblings (once safe driving is verified and in accordance with the local laws).
- Community Service:
  - ‣ Seek opportunities to serve in the community.
- Definitely get a paying job outside the home, even if part-time after school.

Allowance

Begin an allowance plan at about five years of age. The allowance will be your child's source of income, given by you as a stipend and used for purchasing wanted items or saved for that big item. The allowance is not tied to a child's chores, but may be taken away as a penalty for disobediance. This is your child's first opportunity to manage his money and purchases.

Pay allowance once a week. Teach your child to divide the money received into three portions: giving (10%), spending, and saving. Labeled jars work well for this. For us, it worked to put the allowance money out on the kitchen table on Saturday night so that our children could give a portion of it as an offering in church on Sunday morning.

Start with a small amount, like 50 cents a week. Increase with each birthday. Don't be overly generous or you will defeat the purpose of the plan.

The allowance system is predicated upon your child having a *need* for money. So, begin requiring your child to pay for extra items she may want, such as concessions at a ball game, or inexpensive toys. This will create incentive to work and save. Remember: If there is no need for money, then there will be little interest in earning or receiving an allowance. (For more details on the practice of allowance, refer to chapter 4.)

Here is a list of items by age that you might require your child to purchase with her own money:

5–10 Years of Age

- A prized toy
- Souvenir items from a gift shop while on vacation
- Candy or extra concessions at the ball park

11–15 Years of Age

- All of the above
- Nonessential clothing such as extra T-shirts, theme jackets, dresses, extra shoes (School and church clothes are not included here.)
- Tickets to events with friends, such as movies or ball games
- Eating out with friends

16–22 Years of Age

- All of the above
- Gas money for their car (The percentage owed of this expense can be adjusted according to your child's opportunity to get a job and earn money.)
- Saving to buy a car of their own

Homework

Homework can be a burdensome task for child and parents. Your goal in working with your child should be twofold:

1. Help your child learn the subject matter and complete the assignments.
2. Teach your child how to work more and more independently, needing your help less and less.

Pursuing the first goal, while neglecting the second, creates a dependency which can be stifling and addictive. Resist the temptation to micromanage or to do your child's work for him. Make it your goal to be out of the homework business by seventh grade, available only as a consultant upon request by your child.

6–10 Years

- Help your child develop an organized approach to doing homework by:
  - ▸ Designating a specific place in your home for studying.
  - ▸ Creating a schedule for the evenings, indicating when homework should begin and end in order to keep a consistent bedtime—ideally 7:30 p.m.
  - ▸ Using an assignment book or online tool to track progress and deadlines.
  - ▸ Completing each assignment before moving to the next.
- Train your child to work independently as she approaches the fourth or fifth grade, with the goal of needing no reminders from parents (for homework, quizzes, and tests) by seventh grade. At this point, you should be available as a consultant if your child requests help, not as a micro-manager.
- Teach your child how to manage his time in the evenings in order to be in bed on time. Remove the temptation of screen time by limiting it to a half hour or less.
- Allow your child the independence to turn in incomplete work or do poorly on a test if he refuses to complete his homework in a reasonable amount of time. He must experience the consequences of his actions or inaction.

Chapter 18

PACI, POTTY, AND PEERS

Pacifier

The pacifier can be a lifesaver to parents of a demanding baby in the first months of life. The sucking can be soothing to a restless baby in the middle of the night and can satisfy a hungry baby as the parent attempts to lengthen the interval between feedings in an effort to achieve patterned feedings. The resulting quietness, however, can be so satisfying to a parent that the pacifier is impulsively inserted with any and all crying. Soon the baby comes to think that life is impossible without this piece of plastic between his teeth. So, when should a pacifier be offered, and when should it be stopped? Reasonable times to offer a pacifier include:

- When the baby is hungry but a feeding is not possible, or it is not time for a feeding.
- When assisting a baby to fall asleep at bedtime or after waking in the night.
- When crying does not settle after one minute. Try to develop the practice of allowing your baby at least 60 seconds to self-sooth before offering a pacifier. Many times the crying will cease without a pacifier. Resist the temptation to give it with any and all crying. Once the baby is calm again, remove the pacifier and place it out of sight.
- During the daytime, avoid leaving the pacifier in your baby's mouth after he has calmed. This will be tempting especially while travelling in the car seat or while running errands around town.

Leaving the pacifier in the mouth sends your baby a message that it is necessary in order to be settled and satisfied.

By six months of age and once solid foods have been introduced, a baby's need to suck on a pacifier for satisfaction decreases. The sleep routine is well established, and babies typically are able to fall asleep unassisted with less need of a pacifier for soothing at bedtime. Therefore, at this age, babies should not continuously keep a pacifier in their mouths during the day.

I have found the ideal time to stop a pacifier is 12–15 months of age. Beyond this time, toddlers become more attached to it, not for purposes of sucking, but just to carry it around with them. Babies allowed or encouraged to use a pacifier beyond this age are inadvertently taught that they "need" this plastic object to be in their mouth or at their side at all times and that any crisis cannot be handled without it. However, toddlers who have been taught to *need* the pacifier can also be taught to *not need* it. Once it is taken away, if the parent is confident and positive, the child will quickly embrace the idea and move on. Then, both the parent and the child are free of the vice.

Why to Take It Away

- Germs. When the pacifier falls on the floor, or when it is grabbed and sucked by another toddler, germs are unnecessarily passed.
- Teeth. Beyond about 18 months, a child's front teeth will often buck out from sucking on the pacifier. This is unnecessary and can create a dental dilemma later.
- Frustration. Keeping up with the pacifier can be maddening to a parent. You may accidently leave it at home or at daycare. It can be thrown out of the crib in the night. It can be lost or hidden by the playful toddler. Each of these times, the burden falls on the parent to retrieve the pacifier or purchase another.

When and How to Stop the Pacifier

- By 12 months, restrict pacifier use to naptime and bedtime. Leave it in the crib at all times, playfully throwing it in when the baby is taken out. By now your child is off the bottle and is regularly eating solid foods and drinking from a cup. The pacifier is left over from the first year when there was so much focus on sucking and drinking. It now becomes a crutch, used more out of habit and less out of need. If its use is restricted to bedtime and naptime, your toddler will quickly realize how little he really needs it. If you *lead* in this restriction, your child will acquire the confidence to drop the habit.

- By 15–18 months, stop the pacifier. Even for the most attached child, prolonging the inevitable removal of his pacifier will not help. Introduce your plan by telling your baby, "Paci is going bye-bye in three days." Start this on a Tuesday and remind him daily with a smile on your face. The smile is an important expression of your confidence that he can do it. If you express uncertainty, he will be uncertain as well. On Friday, during the nap or after bedtime, gather all the pacifiers in the house and throw them away. This timing will give you the weekend to endure any sleeplessness that may come from pacifier withdrawal. Each time your child asks for the pacifier, confidently say, "Paci has gone bye-bye, and you are going to be fine."

    Typically parents return to me with reports of seemingly miraculous results. "It only took two days, and he never asked for it again." "He had some trouble going to sleep the first three nights, and then all was fine." And then from those who waited until two years or later to stop it, "It was easier than I thought it would be. I wish I had done this earlier." Remember, since it was you who taught your child to "need" the pacifier, you can teach him to not "need" it. Give it a try and keep smiling. This is a leadership opportunity.

- For the really "addicted" child, the pacifier can be rendered less useful by clipping the tip off to deflate it. Some have suggested reading books to your child about giving up the pacifier. Regardless of the technique you choose, it is your expression of confidence to your child that eventually *leads* to success.

Toilet Training: When and How

Toilet training a child can be a very frustrating endeavor for a parent if approached too early, too late, or without a plan. Most children are capable of training around their second birthday. Interestingly, in the 1950s, 80% of children were potty-trained by two years of age. By the 1980s the number had dropped to less than 10%. What happened? Children certainly didn't change, but the setting in which they train did. The invention of the disposable diaper removed much of the urgency of training, since the odor and messiness were greatly reduced by their use. Today, disposable diaper use is the standard, and many daycares promote their use by requiring that a child be completely toilet trained before underwear can be worn. Unfortunately, delaying the process can make the task of training more difficult as the child adapts to the discomfort of a wet diaper, loses interest in training, and becomes a bit more skilled in manipulating the process.

So, what does a child need to successfully toilet train?

1. Developmental readiness
2. Desire to be dry

A child must be developmentally capable or the effort will lead to frustration for both parent and child. Some degree of verbal communication by the child is also necessary. Take a look at the indicators of readiness listed below. A child does not necessarily need to display all of them to be ready.

Readiness

Developmental Readiness: Physical

- Stays dry for three or more hours
- Bowel movements become regular and predictable, like first thing every morning, or after a certain meal
- Often wakes from naps dry
- Shows signs of elimination, such as has a certain look on her face, grunts with BM (bowel movement), or stands a certain way with elimination
- Has an interest in being dry and wearing big girl panties or big boy underwear
- Expresses discomfort with messy diapers
- Can follow simple instructions
- Has a vocabulary for the bladder and bowel movements (pee-pee, poop, BM, stinky)

Developmental Readiness: Behavioral

If the toddler is not willing, the process will be more difficult. Also, if he is generally non-compliant in other areas of behavior, he will probably view this process as an opportunity to manipulate the parent. If this describes your child, it may be best to achieve compliance in the other areas of his life before tackling toilet training. (Review chapter 15 on *Behavior* for age-specific ideas.)

Parent Readiness

- Once convinced of your child's readiness, you must be willing to see the training through to completion. It may take one to two weeks and may be quite messy or inconvenient, but the payoff is worth it—no more changing or paying for diapers, and an opportunity to *lead* your child to a major accomplishment.
- Your child will take her cues from your level of confidence.

Desire to be Dry

Toddlers are often uncomfortable with wetness as early as 18 months. So, if developmentally ready, training can begin. If this discomfort is ignored by parents, the child often becomes numb to the sensation and will eventually accept walking around with a bulging diaper between his legs as routine. This child will need a rekindling of this desire to toilet train. The first step is to stop the disposal diapers and replace with cotton underwear. Now, when wetness happens (running down his legs), the child becomes desperate for relief and ripe for teaching. By contrast, attempting to train a child wearing absorbent disposable diapers often leads to manipulation by the child, lengthening of the process, and frustration of the parents. A diapered child is given complete control of the training process, choosing to participate—or not—since he is never inconvenienced by wet diapers. Underwear creates a *need* in the child to learn to use the toilet.

The Procedure

- At about 18 months, get a potty chair. Tell your child that this is his special chair, and allow him to sit on it in his bedroom with clothes on and in other rooms of the house before eventually placing it in the bathroom.
- Next, encourage your child to imitate you when sitting on the toilet in the bathroom.
- Talk about, and give names to, the two forms of elimination, such as "pee-pee" and "poopy."
- Explain that pee-pee and poop belong in the potty.

- Consider purchasing a children's picture book on toilet training to encourage his interest and understanding.
- Now, try to catch him accidentally urinating.
  - When he looks like he has a full bladder (grabbing himself between the legs, bouncing repeatedly, bent over trying to hold it), take him to the bathroom and place him on the potty chair.
  - If your child wakes up dry after a nap, take him to the bathroom and allow him to sit for a few minutes on the potty chair as you run some water from the faucet in the sink to stimulate the urge.
  - While filling the tub with water for a bath, place your child in the tub (feet in the water), and if he begins to urinate, move him to the potty chair. Do this so that he will "accidentally" urinate in the potty. When he does, show him what has happened, and praise him for doing it.
- Once your child has accidentally or intentionally urinated five or six times on the toilet, and you are convinced of his understanding of the process, begin the following training plan. Commit to doing the plan for one to two weeks; success usually takes a few days. Ideally, this process should occur on a weekend while at home under your supervision, but don't hesitate to involve daycare in the process. Send a couple changes of clothes with your child, and ask the caregivers to work with you on the plan. It will probably get messy before it gets good.
  - *Stop all diapers and pull-ups.* Stop using the diapers and place your child in underwear. Diapers may be continued during the naps and throughout the night. The greatest motivator for the child is the discomfort of the urine in the underwear and down the leg. Diapers eliminate this and interfere with the process of training. A plastic liner may be worn around the cloth underwear to help prevent wetting of your child's clothing.

    Keep in mind: Where there is no need, there is no desire. Using underwear that fails to absorb the flow of urine creates a *need* and therefore a *desire* to use the toilet to stay dry. Disposable diapers prevent this helpful process from occurring.

- ▸ *Set up a reward system.* Offer a unique treat when your child successfully urinates or has a bowel movement on the toilet. This can be a sticker or a piece of candy. Make it a very special reward by telling him that he only gets a treat if he uses the potty. He gets one if he urinates and two if he has a bowel movement. Continue rewarding until your child has demonstrated success for about four to six weeks. By the way, one way to involve siblings in the process is to also give them a treat each time your child succeeds.

- ▸ *Be expectant.* Let your child know that you really believe he can do it and that you expect him to succeed. Some recommend that you take your child to the toilet every hour to prompt him to use the toilet. This is fine for a couple days, but I have found it to become an opportunity for your child to rebel against the process and even manipulate the situation. I prefer placing the responsibility for going to the toilet on the child and allowing the urgency of a full bladder and the messiness of the urine to be his prompter.

- ▸ *Sit and wait.* At this point, you sit back and let the positive force (the reward offer) and the negative force (discomfort of the urine or stool) do your work for you. In taking this approach you are *leading* your child to success rather than acting upon his random desires to go, and, therefore, following him in the process. This approach eliminates the interaction between child and parent that often results in conflict and frustration. Using the "repeatedly-take-your-child-to-the-bathroom" approach, parents can feel beguiled as they act upon the child's every whim of interest in going. Many children will see this as an opportunity to control the situation.

- ▸ *No reminders.* If you see your child straining to have a BM in the corner or bouncing around the room to try and hold the urine in, don't say a word. Simply ignore these behaviors and wait for a distraught child to return with wet underwear and urine running down the legs, or with soiled underwear.

- ▸ *Responding to accidents.* When your child returns with wet or soiled underwear on, respond with sympathy: "Oh, honey, I'm so sorry you are all wet. That must be very uncomfortable. You know pee-pee belongs in the potty. I'll help you in a minute." Delay for a minute or two before changing the underwear. Then, while changing the underwear, remind her of the reward she could have had if she used the potty. Don't shame or criticize your child at this time, but once clean simply walk away.

- ▸ *Responding to success.* When your child successfully uses the toilet, offer the reward and praise her for being so grown up. Tell her that you knew she could do it and that you are proud of her. Affirm her by saying, "This is what big girls do."

Dealing with Failure

Sometimes even the best of efforts fail to convince a child to toilet train. If you are convinced of your child's capability to train, yet a couple weeks of efforts have failed, consider the following approaches:

- *Continue Underwear.* Give the process a little more time. Place your child in underwear, and re-emphasize the reward that is available for any successful use of the potty.
- *Wash It Away.* Each time your child wets or poops in her panties, tell her that you must get her cleaned up. Take her to the bathroom, remove her clothes, and place her in the bathtub. Run slightly cool water over her legs and bottom to wash off the urine and to "wash away" her interest in doing this again. This is not presented as a punishment, but rather a simple necessity to get clean again. The cool water may quickly convince her to keep her panties dry.
- *Penalty.* If the discomfort of soiled underwear has not been persuasive, then you must move to the next step. Impose a "penalty" (negative consequence) for any wetting or pooping in your child's underwear. Calmly say to your child that you know he is capable of potty training, but he seems to forget from time to time. So, to help him remember to always use the potty, you will take away his ___ (a special item of play) and he will not be allowed to play with it for the rest of the day. Tell him this will help him remember to always use the potty. Notice I didn't say this was a "punishment." This is to be imposed upon the child as though you are doing him a favor, not punishing him. Therefore, your expression must be one of sympathy as you impose the penalty. No yelling or shaming

of him over the accident. However, you must firmly impose the penalty with no room for negotiation. Once penalized, tell him that tomorrow he will be able to again play with his ___.

The next morning when he wakes, tell him with excitement in your voice that today is going to be a good day, because he will get to play with ___ all day long since he is not going to have an accident today. Then walk away and don't mention it again. If he comes to you with wet underwear later in the day, act sad for him, take away his ___, and offer to change him in a few minutes (letting the discomfort of the wetness linger for a while). Continue this approach for at least one to two weeks. If the special toy becomes less desirable to your child, you may need to choose a different one as your penalty. Again, act unconcerned about the dilemma he is in, since he is to bear the responsibility for his actions, not you. This is yet another opportunity to *lead* your child, rather than follow.

- *Accidents can recur.* If your fully-trained child begins having accidents, evaluate his environment for changes and any distressing events in his life, such as daycare change, death of a family member, family move, new sibling in home, etc. Be patient with him. Talk about his concerns and ask why the accidents are occurring. Re-emphasize that he is a big boy, that he needs to run to the bathroom with the first feelings of urgency, and that you are confident he can correct the problem.
- *Stool holding.* If while training your child begins resisting or holding back bowel movements, this can temporarily result in constipation that can be a major setback to the training process. Don't ignore this; talk with your child's doctor about how to handle it.

After Toilet Training

Most toddlers are toilet trained during the day by three years of age. Some are even dry at nights, but most are wetting their diapers most nights. You can *lead* your child to eventual dryness at nights by doing two things:

1. Only offer water to drink after supper each night; no juice or milk. This decreases the incentive to drink for pleasure.
2. Always encourage your child to attempt urinating on the toilet at bedtime.

Then, just wait for his bladder to mature resulting in more dry nights. Once your child is consistently dry more than 50% of the mornings, stop the diapers and put him in underwear at night. Cover the mattress with a plastic liner, and allow any wetness at night to wake your child. This discomfort will be his tutor to eventual dryness at night. Be patient; some children are not completely dry at night until four to six years of age.

Friendships

Friendships become increasingly important and formative to our children as they grow up. Their influence upon children can be quite significant, especially when a child's relationship with his own family and parents is unstable. Here are a few thoughts to consider in helping your children develop healthy friendships:

- Get to know your child's friends and their parents, even during the preschool years.
- Seek out children from families with similar standards to your own, especially if your child visits their home often. Try to know the:
  - ‣ Screen time limits for their children.
  - ‣ Limits to and monitoring of content seen by their children on the television/tablet.
  - ‣ Filters on devices with Internet access.
  - ‣ Channels accessible on their television, if cable or satellite based. Any adult channels?
  - ‣ Speech used in the family, especially by parents or teens in the home. Any cursing or foul talk?
- Steer your children toward relationships with other children who are respectful and responsible. Invite those children over to your home to play with your child, in order to get to know them and foster a stronger friendship.
- Friends will even influence your child's level of physical activity. In one study, children ages five to ten years constantly made adjustments to their level of activity to match that of their peers in afterschool play.[1]
- Teach your children the strong influence their friends will have upon them. They need to understand the principle, "Bad company corrupts good character," which is found in the Bible.[2]

- Teach your child the characteristics that make for a healthy friendship:
  - Trustworthy
  - Caring and loving
  - Honest
  - Respectful of others
  - Positive outlook
  - Has common interests
  - Faithful over time
- Teach your child the signs of an unhealthy friendship:
  - Puts down other friends
  - Puts you down
  - Engages in gossip
  - Encourages secrecy among peers
  - Is disloyal in the relationship and willing to turn on you
  - Criticizes and discourages family time
  - Disrespects parents
  - Enjoys disobedient behaviors and illicit activities

Dress

As adults, we deal with our choice of clothing style every day. As parents, we influence our children's tastes in dress as they mature. Our dress decisions can have subtle, seemingly imperceptible effects upon our children. They also need our leadership to guide them in appropriate dress.

4–5 Years

Contentment. Parents can actually teach contentment by the way they dress their children. If the child's dress is modest and simple, a child will likely place a lower priority on the appearance of her clothes. If a parent is constantly scrutinizing or changing a child's dress, then it will draw the child's attention to the clothes and even to the body. Dress your child to look like a child, not like an adult. Keep it simple. Avoid the temptation to compare your child's wardrobe with that of her friends. She will notice this in you and adopt the same tendency.

Modesty. If you want to teach your child to prefer modest attire, then be a good model of the same. Girls want to be like and look like their moms, and boys want to mimic their dads. Again, your actions speak louder than your words.

6 Years and Above

Teach your child the value of dressing modestly. This encourages a more humble, respectful and less provocative personality. Talk about clothing styles and what is too tight, too short, or too low-cut. Teach your child to not judge her self-worth by what she wears, but rather by who she is. Also, don't forget that your child is watching, so dress modestly yourself.

Responsibility. Allow your child more responsibility in choosing her clothing styles. Commend him when he makes wise choices. Begin to talk about a clothing budget and teach how to be frugal with these purchases.

Frugality. By 12–14 years of age, I recommend requiring your teen use his own money to purchase non-essential, non-school clothing. This will do wonders for your teen's spending habits. Once he realizes that he must save to purchase the clothes, your teen will be slower to buy, give the purchase more contemplation, and often decide that the clothes they currently own are not so bad after all. We recommended that when our children saw a desirable article of clothing in the store that they leave it on the rack, come home, and think about it for a day. Then go back and buy it if it still held its appeal. It amazed us how responsible they suddenly became when the money spent was their own.

Chapter 19

CHALLENGING HOME SETTINGS

Although the ideal setting for children is to be reared by their married biological parents in a loving home, disruptive events happen (death, divorce, unwed motherhood) that can present greater challenges for parents and child. With remarriage, adoption, or dedicated single parenting, children can certainly thrive.

The information and advice provided in the preceding chapters can apply to parents in any setting. Listed below, however, are some specific suggestions for the single parent and parents of blended families.

The Single Parent[1]

Establish Healthy Habits to Help Your Children Thrive

- Try to stick to consistent routines with mealtimes, bedtimes, chores, and other family functions. This will help your children feel secure and know what to expect. (See chapter 6 for more details on sleep, nutrition, and exercise.)

Be Consistent With Discipline and Boundaries

- Having high expectations for your children's behavior is a powerful motivator for them. (Review chapters 6, 7, and 8 for more details.)

Make Family Mealtime a Priority

- Practice the "Family Table" as detailed in chapter 6. Being consistent with family meals is often more challenging for the single parent, but this will help your children see that you value your family unit. This can be a very special time to promote family connectedness.

Avoid "Parentification"

- With the absence of a partner, it can be tempting to treat one of your children like a surrogate spouse or peer and go to her for emotional support or even counsel on adult matters. However, a child does not have the emotional or intellectual capacity to substitute for an adult partner, and this is an inappropriate burden to place on a child.
- Seek support from adult friends, family, or your religious group. Despite your busyness, don't isolate yourself. Model for your children a connectedness with others.
- Help your children develop individual identities that are independent of you by resisting the temptation to involve them deeply in your personal issues. Strive to have a balance—meet their needs for affection without smothering them.

Build a Support Structure

- Don't try to handle everything alone. Create a network of trusted friends or family members to help with responsibilities like childcare and carpooling.
- Consider connecting with other single parents and even trading babysitting responsibilities with them to save money.

Help Your Children Work Through Their Emotions

- Children in single parent homes have often experienced loss. The pain of the past often leads children to be guarded and may cause a fear of the future. These painful emotions from the past should be dealt with so that your children can grow to trust and move on.
- When your children ask about changes in the family or about the absence of the other parent, answer in an honest and age-appropriate way. Avoid making negative, malicious comments about the other parent. Your children's identity is linked to their relationship with each parent.
- Try to think of positive things to say about the other parent, as this is typically pleasing for children to hear. Avoid putting the other parent down in front of your child and encourage your child to respect the other parent.

- If the other parent is involved in your child's life, do what you can to encourage a healthy relationship. Show your children by your words and actions that you want them to have good experiences with the other parent. Don't compete with the other parent for your child's affection, particularly by buying them things or easing up your discipline, household rules, and expectations.
- Parents need to work through their own painful emotions so they don't communicate anger and unforgiveness to their children, and so they can help their children resolve their own struggles. Remember that your children are innocent parties in the midst of this conflict and it is unhealthy for them to be exposed to parental hostility or bitterness.

Cooperate With the Other Parent

- If children travel between households, it is crucial to strive for excellent communication with the other parent. Good cooperation between households typically results in children being better adjusted and better behaved. This will also help decrease the potential for your children to manipulate and try to play you against each other.
- Put your differences aside and focus on being good communicators for your children's sake.
- Remember that you cannot control what happens at the other house; you can only control your own actions and words toward your child. Make them count.
- If your child gives an account of abusive activities at the other parent's house, first go to the parent in a non-accusatory way by politely relaying to them what the child is reporting to you. If this fails to correct the situation, then go to the authorities.
- If you and the other parent have significant problems working together, then consider co-parenting counseling.

Be Good Role Models

- If your child's father or mother is absent, seek out positive, responsible adult of that sex who might serve as a role model for your child.

- When your child is nearing puberty, it may be helpful to ask a trusted relative of the same sex as your child to assist you in addressing the subject of sexuality. Consider going through a quality sex education program, such as Passport2Purity˚ (available through FamilyLife.com) with your child.

The Blended Family[2]

Have Realistic Expectations

- The average blended family needs five to seven years to form a family identity. In movies, love between adults and bonding with children happens quickly; in real life, it happens gradually.
- Be patient with yourself, your marriage, and the children as family members find their fit. Simmer your blended family in a slow cooker, not forcibly in a blender.
- If still dating, slow down on a decision to marry. Kids need more time than adults to adjust to the idea of a wedding.

The Marriage Relationship is the Most Important Relationship

- Express to your children that your marriage is the new foundation of the family and strive to balance nurturing your marriage with a strong commitment of time and energy to your children.
- Marriage is hard work and the average remarried couple has about three times as much stress as married couples of non-blended families. You cannot afford to just have better-than-last-time intentions while you guard yourself from being hurt again; have an "all-in" commitment for making your new marriage successful.
- Become a "ghostbuster." Identify and deal with any painful ghosts from a previous marriage so that they don't affect trust in this relationship. Try to prevent your fears from determining your actions.
- There is a honeymoon for couples in stepfamilies, but it often comes at the end of the journey, not the beginning.

Work Together As a Parental Team

- Conflicts will arise over discipline and other aspects of childrearing in blended families. Therefore, parents need to regularly communicate and review their approaches to parenting.

- Early on, biological parents should continue to be the primary disciplinarians to their children while stepparents build relationship, trust, and respect with stepchildren.
- As stepparents transition toward having more authority, they need backup from the biological parent. Biological parents should avoid making critical remarks about the stepparent in front of the children or reversing the stepparent's decisions (as this impairs their authority).
- Be proactive. Don't wait until problems occur to discuss behavioral expectations, methods of punishment, consequences to be enforced, and the values you wish to instill in the children. Talk as a couple about your expectations for your children.
- When in doubt about what to do in a parenting situation, tell the children that you will get back with them after discussing with your spouse. This response communicates to the kids that you seek, respect, and honor each other's input in parenting decisions, and it will speak volumes about your unity as a couple.

Help Your Children With Their Emotions

- Common difficult emotions for children in blended families include grief, anger, separation, loss, disappointment, rejection, and feelings of uprootedness. Children also often struggle with divided loyalties between biological parents and stepparents.
- Children in blended families have experienced loss. The pain of the past often leads children to be guarded and untrusting and may cause a fear of the future. Painful emotions from the past should be dealt with so that children can grow to trust and move on.
- Especially during the early years, it can be very stabilizing for the children if biological parents regularly spends time with their biological children, apart from the stepsiblings.
- Parents need to work through their own painful emotions so they can help their children resolve their thoughts and feelings.

Cooperate With Ex-spouses

- If children travel between households, it is crucial to strive toward good communication with your ex-spouse. Good cooperation between households typically results in better-disciplined and better-adjusted children.

- Ex-spouses who communicate well and cooperate on behalf of the children will make success more likely for the new blended family.
- Put your differences aside, and focus on being good communicators for your children's sake.

Chapter 20

SHARING YOUR CONVICTIONS

Why I Do What I Do

At some point, your children will likely wonder where you get your instructions and convictions for life. They might even ask how you can be certain that your directives for them are correct. Assuming your primary motivation is their well-being and character-development, they are essentially asking about your personal convictions—your moral foundation. *Why* you do what you do? From where does it come?

Everyone operates from a basic worldview, which is generally informed by one's personal life experiences. For many, their convictions arise from their religious faith. In my practice, I have parents of many faiths including Hindu, Islam, Buddhist, Jewish, and Christian, and some who are atheist. For my wife and me, our convictions are rooted in the Christian Bible. It has been our source of instruction, encouragement, and hope in life. I consider the Bible to be our "Owner's Manual for Life"—written by the Creator to instruct us in how to live and how to troubleshoot when problems arise.

If you don't have a standard for your convictions or morals, I suggest you consider starting with the "Ten Commandments" from the Bible. This divine moral code teaches us to first acknowledge and honor our creator God, and then instructs us in character-building behaviors that promote consideration for others. Christianity is unique among faiths in that it offers real forgiveness when we fail to perfectly keep the commandments.

Take a look and see how they can apply to you and your child:

Respect for a Higher Authority[1]

1. You shall have no other gods before me.
2. You shall not make for yourself an image in the form of anything in heaven above or on the earth beneath or in the waters below.
3. You shall not misuse the name of the Lord your God, for the Lord will not hold anyone guiltless who misuses his name.
4. Remember the Sabbath day by keeping it holy.

Respect for Others

5. Honor your father and your mother, so that you may live long in the land the Lord your God is giving you.
6. You shall not murder.
7. You shall not commit adultery.
8. You shall not steal.
9. You shall not give false testimony against your neighbor.
10. You shall not covet your neighbor's house. You shall not covet your neighbor's wife, or his male or female servant, his ox or donkey, or anything that belongs to your neighbor.

The Bible is full of wise advice for living. Here are a few verses that we have used in teaching our children about character development and wise living.

Verses to Live By

Obedience

Children, obey your parents in the Lord, for this is right. Honor your father and mother, that it may go well with you and that you may enjoy long life on the earth. (Ephesians 6:1-3)

Have confidence in your leaders and submit to their authority. (Hebrews 13:17)

Discipline

No discipline seems pleasant at the time, but painful. Later on, however, it produces a harvest of righteousness and peace for those who have been trained by it. (Hebrews 12:11)

Love Others

Dear friends, since God so loved us, we also ought to love one another. (1 John 4:11)

Humility

Do nothing out of selfish ambition or vain conceit. Rather, in humility value others above yourselves, not looking to your own interests but each of you to the interests of the others. (Philippians 2:3-4)

Patience

Bear with each other and forgive one another if any of you has a grievance against someone. Forgive as the Lord forgave you. (Colossians 3:13)

Kindness

Be kind and compassionate to one another, forgiving each other, just as in Christ God forgave you. (Ephesians 4:32)

Peace

Do not repay anyone evil for evil. Be careful to do what is right in the eyes of everyone. If it is possible, as far as it depends on you, live at peace with everyone. (Romans 12:17-18)

Anger

My dear brothers and sisters, take note of this: Everyone should be quick to listen, slow to speak and slow to become angry, because human anger does not produce the righteousness that God desires. (James 1:19-20)

Harsh Word

A gentle answer turns away wrath, but a harsh word stirs up anger. (Proverbs 15:1)

Hurtful Talk

Do not let any unwholesome talk come out of your mouths, but only what is helpful for building others up according to their needs, that it may benefit those who listen. (Ephesians 4:29)

Lying

Whoever of you loves life and desires to see many good days, keep your tongue from evil and your lips from telling lies. (Psalm 34:12-13)

Murmuring

Do everything without grumbling or arguing. (Philippians 2:14)

Friendships

Walk with the wise and become wise, for a companion of fools suffers harm. (Proverbs 13:20)

Do not be misled: "Bad company corrupts good character." (1 Corinthians 15:33)

Do not make friends with a hot-tempered person, do not associate with one easily angered, or you may learn their ways and get yourself ensnared. (Proverbs 22:24-25)

A gossip betrays a confidence; so avoid anyone who talks too much. (Proverbs 20:19)

Do not envy the wicked, do not desire their company; for their hearts plot violence, and their lips talk about making trouble. (Proverbs 24:1-2)

Work

Those who work their land will have abundant food, but those who chase fantasies will have their fill of poverty. (Proverbs 28:19)

Those who work their land will have abundant food, but those who chase fantasies have no sense. (Proverbs 12:11)

The craving of a sluggard will be the death of him, because his hands refuse to work. All day long he craves for more, but the righteous give without sparing. (Proverbs 21:25-26)

A sluggard's appetite is never filled, but the desires of the diligent are fully satisfied. (Proverbs 13:4)

Whoever loves pleasure will become poor; whoever loves wine and olive oil will never be rich. (Proverbs 21:17)

Whatever you do, work at it with all your heart, as working for the Lord, not for human masters (Colossians 3:23)

Go to the ant, you sluggard; consider its ways and be wise! It has no commander, no overseer or ruler, yet it stores its provisions in summer and gathers its food at harvest. How long will you lie there, you sluggard? When will you get up from your sleep? A little sleep, a little slumber, a little folding of the hands to rest—and poverty will come on you like a thief and scarcity like an armed man. (Proverbs 6:6-11)

Contentment

Be joyful always; pray continually; give thanks in all circumstances, for this is God's will for you in Christ Jesus. (1 Thessalonians 5:16-18)

A heart at peace gives life to the body, but envy rots the bones. (Proverbs 14:30)

Chapter 21

IN CLOSING

Reviewing the High Points

In closing, I want to review some high points of opportunities for you to lead your child to good health in the first five years. These are fairly simple recommendations that if followed will make your parenting experience more enjoyable and more productive. Almost every one of these will help prevent problems later. More detail of each of these points is found in the preceding chapters. If I had only a brief opportunity to offer advice to parents, it would be the following practical points.

First Year
- You can't spoil your newborn. Hold her often.
- Breastfeed as long as you can, even if it means offering formula supplementation if your breast milk supply is low.
- Avoid daycare as long as you can. Home is the healthiest place for your infant.
- Talk to her often. She will begin to talk back (coo) at about three to four months.
- Do the Sleep Training at four months of age to teach deep, sound sleeping.
- Give your baby daily "floor time;" start as early as one month.
- Delay starting juices or sweet drink until after two years of age.
- Stop the bottle by 12 months and move to a sippy or straw cup.
- Avoid screens. Don't intentionally place your baby before the television or use tablets or smart phones to entertain or distract. Hold firm to this commitment especially in the first three years.

- Stroll outside with your baby often; she needs outside time.
- Show physical affection often.

Second Year (One-year-old)

- Continue the two-nap schedule until 15–17 months.
- At mealtimes, offer only milk or water to drink, not juice or sweet drink.
- Practice the "Family Table" starting at 18 months.
- Preserve your child's appetite by limiting snacking and avoiding juice or sweet drink until after two years of age. Offer water instead.
- Encourage play with mechanical toys; avoid electronic toys/devices altogether.
- Avoid screens. No television in the bedroom, ever.
- Go outside with your child often.
- Show physical affection often: kissing, hugging, playing, etc.
- Be "lovingly firm" in applying the discipline process (instruction, affirmation, correction). Be consistent since inconsistency leads to great frustration in a child.

Third Year (Two-year-old)

- Don't stress over eating; it's not your responsibility to get your child to eat, only to offer healthy foods at regular mealtimes. Practice the "Family Table."
- Keep bedtime at 7–7:30 p.m. He still needs a daily nap.
- You can begin allowing limited screen time (one hour or less per day). Watch quality programs with your child, when possible, so that screen time is not isolation time.
- Continue to encourage play with mechanical toys.
- Go outside with your child often.
- Show physical affection often.

Fourth Year (Three-year-old)

- Continue to encourage outside play.
- Most children will give up regular napping at about age three and a half years. Start afternoon "Rest Time" daily (i.e., a quiet time in their bed, playing with a couple of toys and often napping). Bedtime at 7–7:30.

- Encourage learning through parent-child conversation, playing with mechanical toys, identifying the alphabet, and looking at books.
- Begin enouraging simple chores around the house.
- Insist upon eye contact from your child when having conversation with parents and other adults.
- Continue to be lovingly firm in your discipline.
- Show physical affection often.

Fifth Year (Four-year-old)

- Introduce an allowance system at age five and begin teaching about personal spending.
- Assign chores in the home.
- Be available to talk, play, and show affection, especially as your child enters kindergarten.
- Keep bedtime at 7:30 through sixth grade.
- Allow sufficient down time at home for simple play and imagination. Limit organized activities outside the home.
- Show physical affection and look for opportunities to verbally affirm your child's proper behavior and attitude.

You made it. Hopefully, by now, you have read both sections of this book; the first to understand *why* children need their parents' leadership, and the second to see *how* to lead a child to good health and high character. Now it's time for you to apply and customize what you have learned to your own children. Not all of what you have read will apply to your child or your specific family setting. Take what fits and use it to enrich your relationship with your child and to nurture your child's development. As I said earlier, if you invest in your children while they are young, you will enjoy the fruits of your labor when they are grown. May the Lord bless your family as you seek to lead them in a loving manner.

TOPICAL TABLE OF CONTENTS

As I mentioned in the Introduction, this book is divided into two parts. In the first part I explain *why* children need parents to lead them to good health. Then, in the second part I make specific suggestions as to *how* parents can lead their child. The following is a more detailed Table of Contents to allow you to search for specific topics and age groups.

NOTES

Chapter One

1. Sax L. *The Collapse of Parenting: How We Hurt Our Kids When We Treat Them Like Grown-ups.* 2016. Basic Books. pp 131.

Chapter Two

1. Hebrews 12:11, New International Version of the Bible. Biblica.com/bible/.
2. Baumrind D. The development of instrumental competence through socialization. *Minnesota Symp Child Psych.* 1973;7:3-46.
3. Maccoby, E. E., & Martin, J. A. (1983). Socialization in the Context of the Family: Parent–child Interaction. In P. H. Mussen & E. M. Hetherington (Eds.), *Handbook of Child Psychology*: Vol. 4. Socialization, Personality, and Social Development (4th ed., pp. 1-101). New York: John Wiley.
4. Hoffman M. Parental Discipline and Child's Moral Development. *J Pers Soc Psychol.* 1967;5:45-57.
5. Coopersmith S. *The Antecedents of Self-Esteem.* 1967. New York. WH Freeman and Company.
6. Baumrind D. Rearing Competent Children, In Damon W (Ed.), *Child Development Today and Tomorrow.* 1989; pp. 349-378. San Francisco, CA: Jossey-Bass.
7. Regnerus M. How Different Are the Adult Children of Parents Who Have Same-sex Relationships? Findings from the New Family Structures Study. *Social Science Research.* 2012; 41(4): 752-770.
8. Cretella M, Trumbull DA. *Homosexual parenting: Is It Time for Change?* America College of Pediatricians website. July 2017. www.acpeds.org/the-college-speaks/position-statements/parenting-issues/homosexual-parenting-is-it-time-for-change? Accessed on June 21, 2018.
9. Byrd D. Gender Complementarity and Child-rearing: Where Tradition and Science Agree. *Journal of Law & Family Studies*, University of Utah. 6(2): 213, 2004.
10. Paquette D, Bigras M, The Risky Situation: A Procedure for Assessing the Father-Child Activation Relationship, *Early Childhood Development & Care.* 2010; (1&2) 33.
11. Regnerus MD, Luchies LB. The Parent-Child Relationship and Opportunities for Adolescents' First Sex. *J Family Issues.* 2006;27(2):159–183
12. Silva RN, Bongardt D, Looij-Jansen P. Mother– and Father–Adolescent Relationships and Early Sexual Intercourse. *Pediatrics*; Dec 2016, 138 (6) e20160782; DOI: 10.1542/peds.2016-0782
13. Shulman S, Klein MM. Distinctive Role of the Father in Adolescent Separation – Individuation. *New Directions for Child & Adolescent Development.* 1993; 41-57.

14. Powers TG. Compliance and Self-Assertion: Young Children's Responses to Mothers Versus Fathers. *Developmental Psychology*. 1994; 30: 980-989.
15. Pruett KD, Pruett MK. *Partnership Parenting: How Men and Women Parent Differently— Why It Helps Your Kids and Can Strengthen Your Marriage*. 2009; pp18-19. Da Capo Lifelong Books.
16. Hofferth SL, Pleck J. The Demography of Fathers: What Fathers Do, in *Handbook of Father Involvement: Multidisciplinary Perspectives*. 2002; pp 81 (Catherine Tamis-Lamonda and Natasha Cabrera eds.); Coltrane, S. *Family Man: Fatherhood, Housework, and Gender Equity*. 1997. pp 54. Oxford: Oxford University Press.
17. Maccoby E. The Two Sexes: Growing Up Apart, Coming Together. *The Family and Public Policy*. 1999. pp 273. Cambridge, MA: Harvard University Press.
18. Denham SA, Workman E, Cole PM. Prediction of Externalizing Behavior Problems from Early to Middle Childhood: The Role of Parental Socialization and Emotion Expression. *Development and Psychopathology*. 2000. 12(1): 23-45.
19. Amato, Paul. More than Money? Men's Contributions to Their Children's Lives. in *Men in Families, When Do They Get Involved? What Difference Does It Make?* Psychology Press. 1998. pp 267 (Alan Booth and Ann C. Crouter, eds.).

Chapter Three

1. *Random House Unabridged Dictionary*. 2018. Retrieved from www.dictionary.com on May 10, 2018.
2. Garrett N, Lazarro SC, Ariely D, Sharot, T. The Brain Adapts to Dishonesty. *Nature Neuroscience*. 19:1727-1732. 2016.
3. Lickona, T. The power of Modeling in Children's Character Development. Edited by Streight, D. *Parenting for Character: Five Experts, Five Practices*. Council for Spiritual and Ethical Education. Pp 32-47. 2008.
4. Blum NJ, et al. Disciplining Young Children: The Role of Verbal Instructions and Reasoning. *Pediatrics*. 1995;96 (2):336-341.

Chapter Four

1. Baumrind D. Authoritative Parenting for Character and Competence. Edited by Streight, D. *Parenting for Character: Five Experts, Five Practices*. Council for Spiritual and Ethical Education. Pp 17-30. 2008.
2. Baumrind D. The Discipline Controversy Revisited. *Family Relations*. Oct 1996; 45(4):405-414.
3. Duckworth AL. The significance of self-control. Proceedings of the National Academy of Sciences of the United States of America. 2011;108(7):2639-2640. doi:10.1073/pnas .1019725108. Accessed on June 21, 2018.
4. Miller GE, Yu T, Chen E, Brody GH. Self-control forecasts better psychosocial outcomes but faster epigenetic aging in low-SES youth. Proceedings of the National Academy of Sciences Aug 2015, 112 (33) 10325-10330; DOI: 10.1073/pnas.1505063112. Accessed on June 21, 2018.
5. Moffitt TE, et al. A Gradient of Childhood Self-control Predicts Health, Wealth, and Public Safety. *Proc. Natl. Acad. Sci.* 2011. 108: 2693–2698.

6. Tao T, Wang L, Fan C, et al. Development of Self-control in Children Aged 3 to 9 Years: Perspective from a Dual-systems Model. *Scientific Reports*. 2014; 4:7272. DOI:10.1038 /srep07272.

Chapter Five

1. Webster N. *A Manual of Useful Studies*. New Haven: S. Babcock. 1839. pp. 77-78.
2. Resnick MD, et al. Protecting Adolescents From Harm. *JAMA*. Sept 1997. 278:10:823-832.
3. Koolstra C, Van der Voort T. Longitudinal Effects of Television on Children's Leisure Time Teading: A Test of Three Explanatory Models. *Hum Commun Res*. 1996;23:4–35.
4. Falbe J, Davidson K, Franckle R, Ganter C. Sleep Duration, Restfulness, and Screens in the Sleep Environment. *Pediatrics*. Volume 135, number 2, February 2015.
5. Owens J, Maxim R, McGuinn M, Nobile C. Television-viewing Habits and Sleep Disturbance in School Children. *Pediatrics* Volume 104, number 3, September 1999.
6. Christakis DA, Zimmerman FJ, DiGiuseppe DL, McCarty CA. Early Television Exposure and Subsequent Attentional Problems in Children. *Pediatrics* 2004;113:708–713.
7. Swing EL, Gentile DA. Television and Video Game Exposure and the Development of Attention Problems. *Pediatrics*. 2010;126:214-221.
8. Robinson TN, Hammer LD, Killen JD, et al. Does Television Viewing Increase Obesity and Reduce Physical Activity? Cross-sectional and Longitudinal Analyses Among Adolescent Girls. *Pediatrics*. 1993;91:273–280.
9. Robinson TN, Wilde ML, Navracruz LC, Haydel KF, Varady A. Effects of Reducing Children's Television and Video Game use on Aggressive Behavior: A Randomized Controlled Trial. *Arch Pediatr Adolesc Med*. 2001; 155:17–23.
10. Robertson LA, McAnally HM, Hancox RJ. Childhood and Adolescent Television Viewing and Antisocial Behavior in Early Adulthood. *Pediatrics* 2013;131;439.
11. Komisar E. *Being There: Why Prioritizing Motherhood in the First Three Years Matters*. 2017. Tarcher Perigee, New York, New York.
12. NICDH Study of Early Child Care and Youth Development: Findings for Children up to 4 ½ Years Old. National Institutes of Health. 2006. https://www1.nichd.nih.gov/publications/pubs/documents/seccyd_06.pdf. Accessed on June 21, 2018.
13. Huston AC, Bobbit AC, Bently A. Time Spent in Child Care: How and Why Does it Affect Social Development? *Developmental Psychology*. Vol 51(5) May 2015. 621-634.
14. Caldwell BM. Impact of Daycare on the Child. *Pediatrics* 1993; 91:1 225-228.
15. These tips were gathered from testimonies of working moms and should be customized to your specific situation.

Chapter Six

1. Sivertsen B, Harvey AG, et al. Later Emotional and Behavioral Problems Associated with Sleep Problems in Toddlers. *JAMA Pediatr*. 2015;169(6):575-582. "Short sleep duration and frequent awakenings in 1033 children at 18 months significantly predicted both concurrent and later incidence of emotional and behavioral problems at 5 years."
2. Owens JA, Mindell, JA. *Take Charge of Your Child's Sleep*. 2005. Marlowe & Company. pp11-13.

3. Anderson J, Trumbull DA. *The Benefits of the Family Table.* The American College of Pediatricians website. May 2014. www.acpeds.org/the-college-speaks/position-statements/parenting-issues/the-benefits-of-the-family-table. Accessed on June 21, 2018.

4. Eisenberg ME, Olson RE, Neumark-Sztainer D, Story M, Bearinger LH. Correlations between Family Meals and Psychosocial Well-being among Adolescents. *Archives of Pediatric and Adolescent Medicine.* 2004;158:792-6.

5. Share the Table: The Barilla Family Dinner Project. http://www.sharethetable.com/docs/BenefitsofTheFamilyDinnerWhitePaper.pdf. Accessed on June 21, 2018.

6. Hofferth, S. L. "Changes in American Children's Time, 1981-1997." University of Michigan's Institute for Social Research, Center Survey, January 1999. National probability samples of American families with children ages 0-12, using time diary data from 1981 and 1997. Findings on how time use is associated with children's well-being are reported in Hofferth, S. L. How American Children Spend Their Time. *Journal of Marriage and the Family.* 2001; 63: 295-308.

7. Gillman MW, Rifas-Shiman SL, Frazier AL, et al. Family Dinners and Diet Quality among Older Children and Adolescents. *Archives of Family Medicine.* 2000; 9:235-240.

8. Anderson SC, Whitaker RC. Household Routines and Obesity in US Preschool-Aged Children. *Pediatrics* 2010;125:420–428.

9. Neumark-Sztainer D, Eisenberg ME, et al. Family Meals and Disordered Eating in Adolescents. *Arch. Ped. Adolesc Med.* 2008; 162 (1): 17-21.

10. Elgar FJ, Napoletano A. Cyberbullying Victimization and Mental Health in Adolescents and the Moderating Role of Family Dinners. *JAMA Pediatrics.* September 1, 2014. DOI:10.1001/jamapediatrics.2014.1223. Accessed on June 21, 2018.

11. National Center on Addiction and Substance Abuse at Columbia University. The Importance of Family Dinners VIII, September 2012. Based on nationally representative surveys of teenagers. www.centeronaddiction.org/addiction-research/reports/importance-of-family-dinners-2012. Accessed on June 21, 2018.

12. Coon KA, Goldberg J, Rogers BL, Tucker KL. Relationships between Use of Television during Meals and Children's Food Consumption Patterns. *Pediatrics* 2001;107(1) p e7. January.

13. Office of Disease Prevention and Health Promotion. Physical activity guidelines. 2008. https://health.gov/paguidelines/second-edition. Accessed on June 21, 2018.

14. Hesketh KR, Goodfellow L. Activity Levels in Mothers and Their Preschool Children. *Pediatrics.* 2014. 133;4: e973-980.

Chapter Seven

1. *The American Heritage Dictionary of the English Language*, Fourth Edition. 2000. Houghton Mifflin Company.

2. Bowlby J. *Attachment and Loss.* Volume 1: Attachment, 2nd edn. New York: Basic Books, 1982.

3. Komisar E. *Being There: Why Prioritizing Motherhood in the First Three Years Matters.* 2017. Tarcher Perigee, New York, New York.

4. Baumrind D. Authoritative Parenting for Character and Competence. Edited by Streight, D. *Parenting for Character: Five Experts, Five Practices.* Council for Spiritual and Ethical Education. Pp 17-30. 2008.

5. Adapted from material found in Bruce Johnston's The Journey of Transition. Outback America 2005.

Chapter Eight

1. Larzelere RE, Gunnoe ML, Roberts MW & Ferguson CJ. Children and Parents Deserve Better Parental Discipline Research: Critiquing the Evidence for Exclusively "Positive" Parenting. *Marriage & Family Review*. 2017; 53:1, 24-35. DOI:10.1080/01494929.2016.11 45613

2. Straus MA. *Beating the Devil Out of Them: Corporal Punishment in American Families and Its Effects on Children*. 1994. New York: Lexington Books.

3. American Academy of Pediatrics. Guidance for Effective Discipline. *Pediatrics*. 1998.101;4:723-728.

4. Patterson G.R. *Punishment for Aggression*. Chapter 6 in Coercive Family Process. 1982. Vol. 3, p118. Castalia Publishing Company.

5. Parke RD. Punishment Revisited: Science, Values, and the Right Question. Comment on Gershoff (2002). *Psychological Bulletin*. 2002;128(4):596-601.

6. Behrman RE, Vaughan VC. *Nelson Textbook of Pediatrics*, Thirteenth Edition. 1987; pp 39-42. WB Saunders.

7. Roberts MW, Powers SW. Adjusting Chair Time-out Enforcement Procedures for Oppositional Children. *Behavioral Therapy*. 1990;21:257-271.

8. Bean AW, Roberts MW. The Effect of Time-out Release Contingencies on Changes in Child Noncompliance. *J Abn Child Psych*. 1981;9:95-105.

9. Day DE, Roberts MW. An Analysis of the Physical Punishment Component of a Parent Training Program. *J Abn Child Psychol*. 1983;11:141-152.

10. Forehand RL, McMahon RJ. *Helping the Noncompliant Child*. 1981;pp 79-80. New York: Guilford Press.9-42. WB Saunders.

11. Baumrind, D. The Discipline Encounter: Contemporary issues. *Aggression and Violent Behavior*, Vol. 2, No. 4, pp. 321-335, 1997.

12. Baumrind, D. The Development of Instrumental Competence Through Socialization. *Minnesota Symp Child Psych*. 1973;7:3-46.

13. Eron LD. Theories of Aggression: From Drives to Cognitions. in Huesmann LR (ed). Aggressive Behavior, *Current Perspectives*. 1994;pp 3-11. New York: Plenum Press.

14. Simons RL, Johnson C, Conger RD. Harsh Corporal Punishment Versus Quality of Parental Involvement as an Explanation of Adolescent Maladjustment. *J Marriage and Family*. 1994; 56:591-607.

15. Larzelere RE. Child Outcomes of Nonabusive and Customary Physical Punishment by Parents: An Update Literature Review. *Clinical Child and Family Psychology Review*. 2000;3:199-221.

16. Roberts MW. The Effects of Warned Versus Unwarned Time-out Procedures on Child Noncompliance. *Child & Family Behavioral Therapy*. 1982;4:37-53.

17. Guarendi R. *Back to the Family*. 1990;215-222. New York: Simon & Schuster.

Chapter Eleven

1. Association of the Type of Toy Used During Play with the Quality and Quantity of Parent-child Interaction. *JAMA Pediatr*.2016;170(2):132-137 DOI:10.1001/jamapediatrics.2015.3753.

2. Christakis DA, Zimmerman FJ, Garrison MM. Effect of Block Play on Language Acquisition and Attention in Toddlers: A Pilot Randomized Controlled Trial. *Arch Pediatr Adolesc Med.* 2007;161(10):967-971.

Chapter Twelve

1. Paul IM, Hohman EE, Loken E, et al. Mother-Infant Room-Sharing and Sleep Outcomes in the INSIGHT Study. *Pediatrics.* 2017;140(1): e20170122.
2. Hugh SC, Wolter NE, Propost EJ, et al. Infant Sleep Machines and Hazardous Sound Pressure Levels. *Pediatrics* 2014. Apr 1; 133:677.
3. Gradisar M, Jackson K, et al. Behavioral Interventions for Infant Sleep Problems: A Randomized Controlled Trial. *Pediatrics.* Vol 137: 6. June 2016. e 20151486.
4. Wake M, Hesketh K, Lucas J. Teething and Tooth Eruption in Infants: A Cohort Study. *Pediatrics.* 2000;106(6):1374–1379.
5. Price AH, Wake M, Ukoumunne OC, Hiscock H. Five Year Follow-up of Harms and Benefits of Behavioral Infant Sleep Intervention. *Pediatrics.* Vol 30: 4. pp 643-651. October 2012.
6. Benoit D. Infant-parent Attachment: Definition, Types, Antecedents, Measurement and Outcome. *Paediatr Child Health.* 2004 Oct; 9(8): 541–545.
7. Gradisar M, Jackson K, et al. Behavioral Interventions for Infant Sleep Problems: A Randomized Controlled Trial. *Pediatrics.* Vol 137: 6. June 2016. e 20151486

Chapter Fifteen

1. Adapted from the following resources: *Creative Correction* by Lisa Whelchel. (Tyndale House Publishers) is an excellent resource. Focus on the Family *Helping Families Thrive* magazine and their website are full of useful advice on parenting.
2. Blum NJ, et al. Disciplining Young Children: The Role of Verbal Instruction and Reasoning. *Pediatrics.* 1995;96(2):336-341.
3. Wong MM, Putler LI, et al. Sleep and Behavioral Control in Earlier Life Predicted Resilience in Young Adulthood: A Prospective Study of Children of Alcoholics and Controls. *Addictive Behavior.* July 2018; 86:65-71.

Chapter Sixteen

1. Koolstra C, Van der Voort T. Longitudinal effects of television on children's leisure time reading: a test of three explanatory models. *Hum Commun Res.* 1996;23: 4–35
2. Christakis DA, Zimmerman FJ, DiGiuseppe DL, McCarty CA. Early Television Exposure and Subsequent Attentional Problems in Children. *Pediatrics* 2004;113:708–713
3. Robinson TN, Hammer LD, Killen JD, et al. Does Television Viewing Increase Obesity and Reduce Physical Activity? Cross-sectional and Longitudinal Analyses Among Adolescent Girls. *Pediatrics.* 1993;91:273–280.
4. Robinson TN, Wilde ML, Navracruz LC, Haydel KF, Varady A. Effects of Reducing Children's Television and Video Game Use on Aggressive Behavior: A Randomized Controlled Trial. *Arch Pediatr Adolesc Med.* 2001; 155:17–23.
5. Hamer M, Stamatakis E, Mishra G. Psychological Distress, Television Viewing, and Physical Activity in Children Aged 4 to 12 Years. *Pediatrics.* May 2009; 123 (5) 1263-1268; DOI:10.1542/peds.2008-1523.

6. Owens J, Maxim R, McGuinn M, et al. Television-viewing Habits and Sleep Disturbance in School Children. *Pediatrics*. Sep 1999; 104 (3) e27; DOI: 10.1542/peds.104.3.e27.
7. Richards R, McGee R, Williams S, et al. Adolescent Screen Time and Attachment to Parents and Peers. *Arch Pediatr Adolesc Med*. 2010;164(3):258-262. DOI:10.1001/archpediatrics.2009.280.

Chapter Seventeen

1. Some concepts in this section were obtained from Martin, Gail. *What Every Child Should Know Along the Way*. 1998. pp. 100-116. Parent-Wise Solutions.

Chapter Eighteen

1. Gesell SB, Tesdahl E, Ruchman E. The Distribution of Physical Activity in an After-school Friendship Network. *Pediatrics*. Jun 2012; 129 (6) 1064-1071; DOI: 10.1542/peds.2011-2567.
2. 1 Corinthians 15:33. *New International Version of Bible*. Biblica.com/bible/

Chapter Nineteen

1. Huizen, R. *Tips for Single Parents*. American College of Pediatricians. 2015. www.acpeds.org/wordpress/wp-content/uploads/Tips-for-Single-Parents-2015.pdf. Accessed on June 21, 2018. Used with permission 2018.
2. Deal, R. *Tips for Step-Family Success*. American College of Pediatricians. Adapted from The Smart Stepfamily, Revised & Expanded Edition (2014) by Ron L. Deal, Bethany House Publishers, a division of Baker Publishing Group. Used with permission. All rights to this material are reserved. 2014. www.acpeds.org/wordpress/wp-content/uploads/Stepfamily-tips-handout-final-11-2014-1.pdf. Accessed on June 21, 2018.

Chapter Twenty

1. All Bible verses cited in this chapter are from the New International Version (NIV) of Bible. The International Bible Society. www.biblica.com.

ABOUT THE AUTHOR

Den A. Trumbull, MD is a board-certified pediatrician in practice for over thirty years. He earned a BS degree in Chemistry from the University of Florida, a MD from the University of Miami Miller School of Medicine and completed his pediatric residency at the University of Alabama Children's Hospital. Dr. Trumbull has had a special interest in behavioral pediatrics for decades, and has written and spoken nationally on the topic of parenting. Much of his work can be viewed on his website, GoodParent.org. His appearances, interviews, and writings include *Parenting Magazine*, *Parade Magazine*, CBS *48 Hours*, *Time Magazine*, Fox News, CNN News, NPR, *Washington Times, Family Life Today*, and *World Magazine*. Dr. Trumbull and his wife, Nancy, live in Montgomery, Alabama. They enjoy the outdoors and spending time with their five adult children and two grandchildren.